The Quest of the Sparrows

Kartik Sharma is an alumnus of IIT Delhi (2009) and IIM Ahmedabad (2011). With experience in investment banking and strategy consulting, he now works as a public health professional. The idea of choices and where they take individuals fascinates him. He finds inspiration in optimism and hope in those who choose not to be cynical.

Website: www.kartiksharma.co.in

Facebook: www.facebook.com/Daredreamersnovel/

Twitter: https://twitter.com/sykartik

Instagram: https://www.instagram.com/sykartik/

Ravi 'Nirmal' Sharma is an alumnus of Delhi College of Engineering (1982). He works as a creative conceptualizer, after being a serial entrepreneur for more than two decades.

Website: www.ravinirmalsharma.com

Twitter: https://twitter.com/Araviz

Instagram: https://www.instagram.com/ravie61

The father-son duo is Delhi based. They are passionate about telling stories that bring joy to the readers while being thought-provoking. This is their first novel, first published in 2011 to critical acclaim. Their second novel, *DareDreamers: A Start-up of Superheroes* was published in 2018 and continues to receive a lot of praise from across the world.

Also by the authors

DareDreamers: A Start-up of Superheroes

The Quest *of the* Sparrows

'Explore the joy of freedom'

Kartik Sharma
Ravi 'Nirmal' Sharma

RUPA

Published by
Rupa Publications India Pvt. Ltd 2011
7/16, Ansari Road, Daryaganj
New Delhi 110002

Sales Centres:

Allahabad Bengaluru Chennai
Hyderabad Jaipur Kathmandu
Kolkata Mumbai

ISBN: 978-81-291-1865-3

Eleventh impression 2022

15 14 13 12 11

Printed in India

Contents

Part Three: Partibhan's story

Part Four

Acknowledgements

To the Divine Mother for being the source
To Neeru for her invaluable and loving support
To Kamakshi for her human touch
To Rajeev for showing us the light
To Ankita for her innocence that inspires
To Anushree for raising questions that made us think
To Rigveda for her critical insights and companionship
To Rama Devi Nina for her editorial support
And to the sparrow in all of us....

Prologue

He knew he was dying.

Through his failing vision, he saw the trophies he'd been so proud of, adorning the walls of his room. Now, in his last moments, he felt their worthlessness. The desire he had long suppressed of becoming an artist, a painter, confronted him.

Long ago, the plight of his struggling artist friends and the complete insecurity of his future had made him lose his nerve. He fled the art scene and took up a comfortable desk job.

But the ghost of the artist never left him in peace, despite his affluence. It held him responsible for its murder. How would life have turned out if he had remained steadfast to his first love?

'Better! Would have absolved my existence. Changed me into a greater human being. All my life's work amounts to nothing!'

Tears of regret spilled from his eyes.

From the bed, he saw the sparrow he fed everyday land on the windowsill. Ironically, the sparrow never worried about tomorrow, but lived every day joyously. Unlike him; he had spent all his life securing his tomorrows. Now, all of a sudden, there was no tomorrow.

'If I get another chance ...' he murmured, before he died with the wish on his lips.

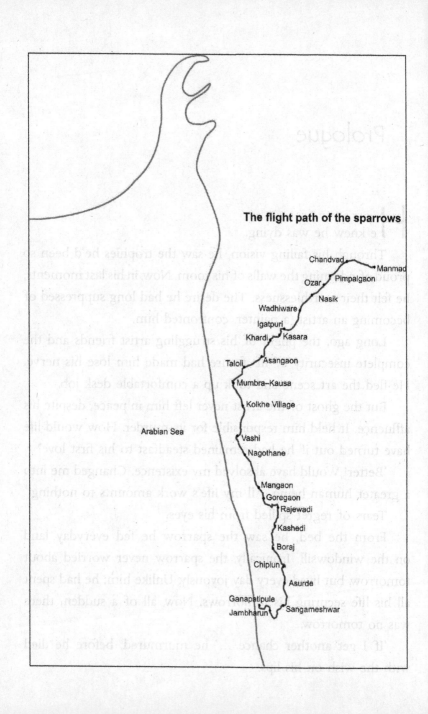

The flight path of the sparrows

Manmad
Chandvad
Pimpalgaon
Ozar
Nasik
Wadhiware
Igatpuri
Khardi Kasara
Taloli Asangaon
Mumbra–Kausa
Kolkhe Village
Arabian Sea
Vashi
Nagothane
Mangaon
Goregaon
Rajewadi
Kashedi
Boraj
Chiplun
Asurde
Ganapatipule
Jambharun Sangameshwar

1 | A Method behind the Madness

Beep ... beep ... beep ... beep ... . The oscilloscope sent out its tired signals, the waves losing their highs as they ran out of energy.

Had she been conscious, she would have brought her hands to her ears and screamed; the shrill tone would have driven her crazy. But she was beyond caring, edging past the twilight zone between darkness and light. She had suffered enough. For her sake, he wanted her to cross the thin line between life and death.

Beep ...

The sound died. The wave flattened into a straight line. With it, the three-month-old battle ended. She became another statistical figure, another coma victim.

It was drizzling when the ambulance arrived and the ward boys heaved the body into the back with a practised ease that was almost obscene. Their indifference stripped death of its dignity and reduced it to a routine, mechanical procedure. As he tried to climb into the ambulance, he felt a hand on his left shoulder.

He turned and his mouth went dry.

Three men had him cornered. Their plastic hats and raincoats looked ominous. The hand dug deeper into the flesh of his shoulder and he cried out in pain.

'Where's the money?'

'I couldn't get it today ... .' His face went pale.

Am I bleeding?

'You didn't learn any new sentences in the weeks we gave you.'

'I ... I will pay. Promise.'

'The same bullshit. Let me put your vocabulary on the fast track. Hold him, you two, or are you just going to keep standing?' he shouted at the other two menacing figures. They sprang into action. One of them held him from the back and the other grabbed his left arm.

'Stretch his forefinger ... .'

'What are you doing?' His eyes dilated in fear.

'Taking a small part of you. In my experience, the slow learners get into the act quickly if we take a tiny bit of them.'

'No!' His body stiffened when he saw the gleam of the knife as it reflected the lighting.

'Won't hurt as much as you imagine. Just enough to ensure you remember our next meeting. Trust me,' he laughed mockingly.

The man struck the knife at the root of the finger.

He screamed, but his scream stuck in his throat as the man grabbed him by his hair.

'Don't search for this finger.' The man dangled it in front of his face. 'We will feed it to a dog. Get some first-aid; we don't want you to die of sepsis.'

He moaned in agony, trying to control his pain, knowing shouting would invite more wrath.

'Cremate your mother. But remember, we will be back in ten days. If you don't pay, we will take two of your fingers next time. Understand?'

He nodded between his moans. The man shoved him as he walked away. He hit the door of the ambulance and fell on the ground with a thud.

Through his hazy vision, he saw them returning to their car as their shoes squished over the water-clogged road.

He saw his blood mix with the rainwater swirling around him before he lost consciousness.

PART ONE

Nikhil's story

2 | Confusion is the First Step Towards Understanding

I watched Susan's body, a lissome silhouette against the sunbeams flooding into my office. The weakness disgusted me. Sex and food share a striking parallel – they appear undesirable, but only after extensive splurging.

She must have experienced a synchronous thought because her lips, too, curled into a frown.

'I'm leaving,' she said as she pressed her lips together and peeked into her vanity mirror. I sensed she was not just leaving the office for the day.

'I'm getting a divorce soon.'

She looked up sharply. 'I can't marry you.'

'Then why this – this relationship?'

She was silent for a while, then:

'I'm serious. I've decided. I'm leaving the city forever.'

Exactly what I had feared.

'You can't do this to me.'

She started emptying her drawers with a nervousness suggesting the seriousness of her intent. 'I came here for old times' sake.'

'Please. Don't go. You know I like you ... .'

'See?' She looked up sharply. 'Like, not love. You and I are unable to love anyone because we don't love ourselves. That was another reason I came. To tell you why you and I ended there ...' she said, her gaze travelling to the couch.

'What does all this mean? I don't get it.'

She picked up her handbag and walked towards me. 'I don't know about you, but I drifted into this relationship because I was bored, not doing anything that made me happy. Now I've found my cure – I'm going to work with an NGO. You have to find yours.'

'You can't be serious. Is this how it ends for us?' I called out as she reached for the door. I knew if she crossed it, I would lose her forever.

'For our good, yes.'

'We can marry immediately – it won't count as cheating. You can't leave me.'

'My decision is final ...'

'But ...'

I used all the arguments I could think of, but none of them worked. My personal secretary left me that evening, ending our sixteen-year-old association.

My phone's invasive ringtone did not allow me to linger over my loss. It was the call I feared, from the detective.

'I've photographs of your wife.'

'Give them to me tomorrow morning and collect your cheque. That will be enough for now.'

On reaching home, I hadn't even connected with its warmth when the spectacle of my daughter packing her bags transformed the misery of that rainy night into worry.

'What's going on?' I asked.

'I'm leaving,' Anuradha's shoulders stiffened as she turned to face me.

'Where are you going?' The hostility in the atmosphere was so intense, I felt unwelcome in my own home.

'America. With Shridhar.'

'America? With whose permission?'

'I don't need *your* permission. In case you haven't noticed, I'm an adult now.'

I knew then that this confrontation was going to be much worse than the many we had regularly.

'Are you going to marry him?'

'No. I'm moving in with him for now.'

'What!' I took a step back, stung by the shock. 'You know what everyone will say over here! They'll laugh at me!'

'Your drug-addict wife is sleeping with someone young enough to be her son and you're worried about what they'll say about me?' Her acerbic words matched her anger.

I slapped her before I could check the impulse.

She smiled in defiance, the pink imprint glaring on her milk-white cheek.

'Do that again and you'll have to answer to the authorities.'

She could call the cops; last year she had. They let me off with a reprimand, though I had to sign many papers.

I tried to reason with her.

'That man's no good. He'll dump you for another woman ...'

'So? You dumped my mother for your factory. She survived. Your second wife dumped you for another man. You survive. If you all can survive without love ...' her voice trailed off and her face became emotionless – as cold as the steel parts I manufacture. It made her even more unreachable.

'Anu – don't go. Please.'

'I never belonged here, dad. So don't bother wasting your energies on me now. The factory needs you more than me.' Anuradha snapped her bags shut. 'Bye dad, wish me luck.'

'What luck can I wish when you're hell-bent on your destruction?'

'Thank God life doesn't run by your rules!'

A car honked outside.

'He's waiting, wanna meet him?'

'If you want me to kill him. You told your mother you're leaving?'

'Stepmother. Don't you tell her about this either.'

'Why not?'

'She'll surprise me if she asks about me even one month after I've left. She's too busy with her boyfriend to notice one person less in her world.' She wheeled her bag.

'Don't go. You know I love you ...'

'It's too late, dad.'

She shut the door behind her.

Gone!

☙

My head was throbbing when I got up the next morning. I reached for the desperately needed coffee steaming at my bedside when my gaze fell on an advertisement. The newspaper, lying at a curious angle on the table, seemed to highlight it uncannily.

> When a helpless sparrow can enjoy this world without a care, why can't you?
> Everyone seeks peace and happiness but few find it. Most humans carry some burden or the other on their shoulders. They are always sighing, always wishing for something out of their reach. They are rarely happy, if at all.

Curious, I reached for the paper and held it closer to read the rest of the advertisement.

> Ever looked at the sparrows? Why is it that they always seem happy? We pride ourselves as the most intelligent species in the world, then why is happiness so difficult for us to achieve, yet so simple for them?
> Discover happiness and change the way you view life. From just surviving one day after another, why not make your existence sublime?
> Call 91-11-9810646700 today and see life from a different perspective.

The advertisement addressed exactly my state of mind. Was there a purpose to it, a design? If not, then why should I see it just when my world was collapsing?

You find your cure. My secretary's voice echoed in my mind.

On an impulse, I decided.

3 | Coordinates Reset

I felt a bit dizzy and disoriented when I woke up and screwed my eyes to see my watch. It flashed an indifferent 3.00. Was it day or night? I didn't know. Then I remembered the night before, and stepped out of my 'still-in-London' inertia.

I was in Swami Parmanand's ashram, because of the pull of the advertisement. It was the only straw I was clutching on to, to preserve my sanity. I still didn't know if it was a sane decision or just something to hang on to.

I sauntered sleepily into the bathroom, brushed, bathed and shaved, my mind blank. I got ready leisurely and when I stepped out, my watch showed 5.00. The light of the evening greeted me as it seeped through the corridors. I was having a hard time fighting thoughts of pizzas with soups.

Still looking like a lost space traveller without physical coordinates, I followed the directions towards the canteen. When I reached there, I was surprised by what I saw. Small water fountains and a stream cascaded over steps made of rocks. Frolicking in this stream of water were beautiful and rare fish. Acrylic sheets covered the canteen's roof from which the sky stole in.

I took in the beauty of the bright green creepers hugging the pillars. Banana and bamboo trees, lemon shrubs, cacti and flowers added masterful brushstrokes to the place. Bamboo sticks spelled out the canteen's name, Ecosystem. The letters stood out beautifully against the fluorescent grass which grew on the wall. The entire place resonated with nature and I felt I had arrived not at a canteen, but at an oasis. I asked what was available, unsure if they would serve me anything at that hour. Thank God. They were still open!

The menu brought back memories of long-forgotten dishes that my mother used to cook for me. I ordered *dal makhani*, my favourite. Priya, my first wife, also arrived in the train of memories which the menu signalled. She was a Briton by birth but of Indian origin – much like my father – and valued companionship over material gains. Yet, perhaps because of the genes I had inherited from my ambitious mother, I constantly frustrated her need to slow the pace of our lives. To me, going slow meant stepping down from the roller-coaster that was life.

The artwork on the walls reminded me of her paintings. She wanted me to spend time with her, amidst nature. But the huge opportunities I saw in my rapidly expanding business made me feel such luxuries could wait.

The spicy dish I ate absentmindedly nearly caused a blackout. I hadn't reckoned what twenty years of eating bland food could do to me.

'Mix some curd with the rice,' the waiter suggested.

I tested his theory but found the mix too bland. I then poured three spoons of dal on it and tasted the result. This was better! The repressed love for Indian food was awakening in me.

The waiter gestured a thumbs-up. 'Cheers!' I said, lifting my spoonful, ready with a glass of water just in case.

Sneha appeared just then. She had welcomed me the previous night, on my arrival, with a hot cup of coffee. Her face glowed with a geniality no one could miss.

'Sneha, what a pleasure it is to see you again.'

'I must say you've recovered admirably.'

'Have coffee with me, I owe you one.'

'Not now. You carry on! Enjoyed your food?'

'You bet! Together, my friend here and I brewed a heavenly dish!'

'Good for you,' she said. 'After you are through with your food experiments, join us for meditation. In the evening, Swami Partibhan will deliver his first talk.'

'Swami Partibhan? I thought it was Swami Parmanand!'

'Don't you know? Swami Parmanand took samadhi recently.'

'Samadhi? You mean he's dead?'

'No. Samadhi isn't death. His was a willing renunciation of the body. Swami Partibhan has taken up from where Swami Parmanand left.'

Serves me right. I came all the way to India just to find what I could easily have known from a phone call.

I cursed the spontaneous streak in me. What do I do now? Pack my bags and go? My extensive research on Swami Parmanand had thrown up good reviews. I didn't know anything about Swami Partibhan.

'Don't worry,' Sneha said, sensing my uneasiness. 'You'll get what you came searching for. And maybe this change will work for the better.'

4 | Close Encounters of the Spiritual Kind

The lecture hall was a spacious room with a high ceiling. Lights and speaker systems hung on the steel trusses supporting the roof. No one could miss the carpets because there were no chairs to hide them. The acoustics of the hall amplified even the quietest whisper; this automatically induced silence. The beautiful landscape outside walked in through the huge windows.

Swami Partibhan arrived at seven. Despite the tranquility of the place, his youthful appearance made me uneasy; it looked as if he'd sauntered into the ashram straight out of college. Everyone stared at him as he strode up to the dais. Swami Partibhan ignored the unwanted attention, appearing unconscious of his youthfulness. What could he possibly have learned at such a young age to be able to teach us? Before I could elaborate on my worries, he started speaking.

'Sermonising or preaching is medieval. I sympathise with you.'

People giggled as he smiled at his own joke.

'I will try to find more innovative ways as we go along. Till then, please bear my sermons.' He paused to take a deep breath, betraying his nervousness. 'There are times when our work, our

relations, and our health trouble us. We need a new perspective –'
He reached for the glass of water, his forehead breaking into
beads of sweat.

'We live in times when media is king. It's only interested in
financial figures, records and achievements. Spirituality isn't an
object of desire, or even in the headlines; still, you are here. I
bow to your spirit, which believes in what no one has seen and
marches to a destination that appears to be even harder to achieve
than the biggest material goal.

'Most human beings search for eternal happiness. Yet, why
is it elusive? Most people fail to achieve it by following idealism,
spiritualism, capitalism, materialism, socialism or other-isms. Why
do they meet disillusionment?

'Why does a sparrow, which knows no "-isms", live without the
worries which accompany human beings? What is it we manage
throughout our complex lives? Merely survival. Hey, something
is wrong – because the bird does the same, effortlessly. So what's
the big difference between us and the helpless sparrow? Don't
you think we're missing something? What is it?

'Forget the sparrow for a moment. Think of all the people
in this world. They go to their workplaces in the morning and
then return in the evening, like swinging pendulums. But does a
pendulum swing aimlessly away and towards the centre? Or does
it personify something more, like time? That depends on what you
associate yourself with: its ball or the pendulum as a whole. How
do we associate with life? Is it aimless or does it have a higher
purpose? Like a pendulum, it swings between two states – birth
and death. What gives it meaning? Can anyone answer?'

'The Divine,' someone said.

'That's a lofty ideal for us beginners. Think of something more practical. Look around you; is everything the same as it was a century ago? What has happened in all these years?'

'Evolution,' someone else said.

'Yes. Between birth and death we are evolving. That's the higher meaning of our lives. But what do most people do? They achieve, lose, feel happy or sad, celebrate and mourn. They merely move to and fro like the ball of a pendulum, with hardly any peace. Even among believers, everyone is religious but very few are truly spiritual. Is it all linked or unrelated? Think over it. Find the connection, and I think we will be able to solve the riddle of life.'

Swamiji became quiet. The talk ended.

'So how do we improve?' someone asked.

He smiled. 'Soon. At a suitable time,' he said enigmatically.

While other people began to leave, I sat thinking. The sermon was jumbled and far from perfect. It raised a lot of questions, but answered none. Parts of it I had heard or read somewhere or the other. Some of the thoughts were even scattered. But the sparrow analogy and the evolution connect was so powerful in its impact that I was afraid that if I got up, I would lose the glimpse of a powerful insight I felt was almost within my reach.

Swami Partibhan did not seem to be someone of conventional ideas because right at the start, in his very first lecture, he spoke of innovative methods to attain self-awareness. He discounted preaching and steered clear of any reference to mythology or scriptures. He talked of evolution in a way that touched a chord in me. I had an eerie feeling that the lecture was addressed specially to me and related to my life in every way.

Maybe there was something here.

Would this kid be able to give shape to the raw brilliance of his first thoughts?

It was easy to talk, but to walk the talk was the damnedest hard thing to do. Would this twenty-eight-something of a guru be able to practise what he was preaching?

Only time would tell.

5 | First Connection with the Self

It was some time before I realised that I was the only person sitting in the hall. I recalled all those turning points in my life where I ignored the real opportunity to evolve. Instead of pursuing research in India, I opted for a manufacturing job abroad. I didn't even stop to think that I was merely following my mother's dream to earn more money. I was one of the brightest students in my college, but chose money over evolution, and today I found myself in the same predicament Swami Partibhan had described – without joy and without a real friend in the world.

My lack of peace came from not doing what I was passionate about. I had ignored my passion to develop an indigenous Indian hybrid car. Ten years later, I owned a factory which could have made the hybrid car, but a backlog of orders to make original equipment for cars left me with no time. I was trapped in self-created circumstances.

'What are you thinking?'

I turned to see Sneha.

'Looking for connections that made me what I am: a rich but unhappy person. Swami Partibhan seems good. And to think he is so young!'

'Age and experience aren't relevant. When the mind's eye opens, we see eternity.'

'You're referring to the third eye?'

'Yes, the inner eye of knowledge.'

'Can I say something to you?' I arched an eyebrow.

'Yes'

'You're usually so serious, but when you smile, you look beautiful.'

She blushed, which heightened her beauty.

'Yet, and I don't know why, you convey a deep-rooted sadness through your eyes.'

'Grief or unhappiness pushes most people towards spirituality. But some people are born seekers. They're the lucky ones.'

She turned away and left me standing where I was. I felt as if I had hurt her feelings, or reminded her of the past; one she wished to forget.

As I went out of the hall, I saw some people singing. Spontaneously, this group broke into a melodious bhajan. The singers seemed blissfully happy. Transfixed, I watched a man playing the guitar, his fingers moving deftly over the strings. He sensed my stare, even with his eyes closed.

'You wish to play this guitar?' He smiled.

I watched him hesitantly as he stood up to give me his place. 'I don't know,' I said uncertainly. 'Long time no use,' I grinned, moving my fingers in the air.

'If you want to play for the Divine, all the skills will return.'

I ran my fingers over the strings tentatively, trying to match the rhythm of the song, and found that I could play it!

I felt one with the group as they sang and danced. Then I realised I was playing the guitar even after the voices had died down. As I came out of the intense experience, I heard the music and it surprised me. I became aware of the people around me and stopped out of sheer embarrassment.

'Wow!' Rahul, who had lent me the guitar, clapped. 'I must take lessons from you one day. Too bad I have to leave right away.'

'You have an unusual talent,' Ramanujam said. He was a spiritual guide, like Sneha, and was of medium build and height, with copious curly hair.

'I used to play it a long while ago. I've never played so well before.'

'Then this guitar belongs to you,' Rahul came up to me.

His gesture left me speechless. 'I can't possibly take this from you.'

'Why? I think it was made especially for you.' He pushed it forcibly into my hands. 'Have to leave. My taxi is waiting.'

Before him, I had met many people who claimed to be spiritual, but failed to get over the pettiness in their natures. However, Rahul's generosity made me wonder if some places and people could transform human beings more than others.

∞

The next day, we assembled for meditation at 5.00 a.m. It was still dark, but soon the sky turned a charcoal grey and then acquired a steely brilliance, with a gentle breeze flapping our clothes. Sneha and Ramanujam guided the session. Sneha told us not to struggle with our posture but to be comfortable and relaxed. Ramanujam asked us to watch and regulate our breathing and to slow it to a rhythmic pattern. After a while, it became easy for me to meditate.

'Don't try to suppress your thoughts; they're like springs. Push them down and they recoil. Simply watch them. Negate them by saying "*Neti, neti*", which means "I'm not this thought nor that". When thoughts leave us, what remains is thoughtless awareness. In this domain you connect with your self.' After these instructions, they offered prayers.

We meditated on these prayers and sang devotional songs. The exercise calmed me. I went deeper and deeper into meditation and felt peace within.

When told to open our eyes, I saw the splendor of the sky as it turned to a golden red. The sun's rays showering through the clouds on the distant horizon looked spectacular. Our small group of fifty-or-so people made a tranquil silhouette against the quiet horizon.

I wondered why some people who went in search of peace returned empty-handed from India. They were bitterly critical of Indian spirituality and the greediness of Indian gurus. Whereas I could see only beauty and patience. Was I just lucky?

6 | Time to Wake Up!

Two weeks after his first lecture, Swami Partibhan started taking problem-solving sessions. He held them twice a week and they were of great help. After a brief talk, he would inquire about our problems and offer his perspectives on them.

'All matter is transient and our lives are ephemeral. Only the Supreme Spirit that resides within each one of us is eternal; everything else has a shelf-life. This Supreme Spirit is our higher self, one that seeks evolution and is much more capable than the physical self that is selfish and limiting. It is so powerful that the things it can do appear to be miracles. But our physical self tells us it's a myth, it's non-existent. And the result? We conclude we are ordinary. Incapable of being Supreme. Which is why we are content leading a mediocre life. In my perception, this higher self is the Divine, God, the Eternal Force which everyone talks about but few achieve. When we connect to the Divine within us, we transcend our worldly lives. From a bubble, which forms and explodes without meaning, we evolve beyond what we can even begin to imagine.

'Just like we have a physical side that coexists with our higher self, this universe too exists at a gross level and at a higher level. It has a material side as well as a force behind it that seems to defy the logic of the very physical world it creates. When we achieve the connection between our divine selves and this force that runs the universe, we achieve the ultimate resonance – the highest awareness about ourselves and the universe. In this resonance, the positions become interchangeable – we become at once the higher self and the very universe. But for a beginner, it is wiser and simpler to connect to the higher self first. I invite you to begin this journey with me.' Swamiji bowed to the assembly after he ended the lecture.

For me, this was a new way of looking at God. I had dismissed His existence because I believed it was a myth. It would remain so until, like Partibhan just said, we started looking for Him within us. He was no one else but our higher, more capable and wiser self.

With each session, Partibhan's confidence increased as he found his groove.

The turmoil I'd felt in London subsided and I calmed down. My daughter's desertion, from a spiritual viewpoint, seemed to be her journey of self-exploration. If she could somehow find a connection with the divine, she would evolve. If not, then at worst, she would be like me.

ஓ

Life cruised along ideally at the ashram, until one day, when a major fire broke out on the third floor. Thick smoke clouded the sky, and I could hear screams for help.

'Fire!' Someone came rushing down. 'People are trapped; they need help!'

A man standing next to me dialled the fire services.

People rushed out of the building with their belongings. The smoke nearly blacked out the sky.

I quickly discarded the thought of recovering my belongings from my room. Not worth the risk. In ten minutes, most of the inmates had left their rooms and gathered in the lawns. I glanced at my watch, wondering how long it would take for the firefighters to arrive.

In what seemed an age but was less than twenty minutes, the smoke died down and we saw volunteers descending the stairs.

'What happened?'

'Is anyone injured?'

'What about the fire?'

'The fire has been doused. There are no casualties,' Sneha said.

'Any damages?' I asked.

'Only one room. Thankfully, no one was injured.'

When we settled, it was three o' clock.

'Will Swami Partibhan resume his Q&A sessions?' I asked Ramanujam.

'Yes, after lunch,' he said and hurried away.

We finished lunch late in the evening. Then it was time to attend the evening discourse.

The fire incident was still fresh in our minds when we approached the lecture hall. I wondered how we could have a session after such turmoil. But Swamiji appeared unruffled by the incident. He took his chair and didn't even mention the fire.

'Today, I'm not going give any spiritual discourse. Instead, I'll just discuss your problems.'

That was unusual of him. He always gave a talk before he went into a Q&A session. Maybe he too was upset because of the fire.

A hand went up. A few people asked questions. I was still thinking about the fire when a young man asked an unexpected question. 'Why does God not solve all our problems if he's so powerful?'

Swamiji did not reply to the question immediately, but smiled. 'Answer a few of my questions, before I answer yours.'

His response was surprising.

'Okay,' said the young man.

'Before you came to this lecture hall, did you hear about the fire?'

So the fire was on his mind, despite his apparent indifference.

'Yes.'

'Were you aware of some people trapped in the blaze?'

'Yes.'

'Did you hear the shouts and the screams?'

'Yes.'

'Were you told the fire engines would take an hour to reach?'
He looked amused, which appeared odd to me.

'Yes.'

'Tell me, what did you do?'

The man remained quiet.

'Please answer me.'

'I rushed outside to safety, with my belongings.'

'You didn't think of helping those caught in the blaze?'

'I was – '

'You thought only of your safety.'

'I am not a firefighter, Swamiji.' The man blinked his eyes rapidly and licked his lips. I looked at the floor, unable to meet Swamiji's gaze.

'Only six people tried to help. They were not trained in fighting fire. The intent to help was all they were equipped with.'

Complete silence prevailed in the hall as Swamiji looked at us, still amused.

'Tell me, what would you have done if it was your daughter or your wife trapped in the fire? Would you still have been indifferent?'

The man remained silent. His shoulders slouched.

'Answer me honestly. Would you have thought then, whether you were a firefighter or not?'

'No. I would have tried to help them.'

'Can you see your error? All of you! Was it right to secure your belongings while ignoring people who might be dying?'

'I see it as a failure on my part.'

'Not only yours, but the entire collective's!' Swamiji said. 'None of you came out to help. And this is supposed to be a spiritual place.'

I felt stunned.

'What happened today is a sad reflection of society. Everyone's selfishly living for themselves. The habit has become so universal that we routinely neglect others, even when it is in our power to lessen their suffering. The society is a mirror us as individuals. What we do to others is what we do to ourselves. We do nothing when our higher self screams for help. We do not take the risk of freeing it from the traps we have imposed on it. We believe it is not our job and remain as insensitive to its yearning for freedom as we are to the helpless cries of the needy.

'How many of us throw our leftover food in the garbage instead of giving it to someone who might not have had a day's meal? Have you ever comforted a weeping child? Or treated an injured animal? We rarely notice other people's pain.'

No one said a word. An uneasy quiet settled within the room.

'Such situations place us in a position of power. If we help, we will create a miracle for the sufferers. For those people, we can be gods. Similarly, if we listen to our inner, higher being, we will create a miracle in our lives too. We can make our wishes and dreams come true. Yet, what do we choose to do?'

I watched the rays of the evening sun as they filtered through the ventilators and fell on the corridors. I wanted to be anywhere else but here, forced as I was to face myself. My cheeks burned with shame and guilt. I yearned for change within me but how was it going to take place?

'So what do you have to say, Mr Nikhil Bamba? Any ideas?'

I didn't say anything but dug myself deeper into my seat. Any other time, I would have been proud he knew my name. Now, it merely increased my shame.

'If you feel sorry for what's happened today, then enroll for a spiritual workshop.'

Everyone looked at him intently.

'I'll hold a practical workshop. Would it interest you?' he asked.

'What's it about?' One disciple couldn't hide his curiosity. 'Will it improve us?'

'Yes. We have to feel as free and secure as a sparrow before we can evolve. I will even call it "Operation Free Bird". Attend it to be inspired to live the special role the Divine, the higher being in each one of you, expects of you. If we're lucky, we will discover new strengths in us to become powerful yet benign human beings.'

People turned to one another and talked in muted whispers. Everyone looked excited at the prospect.

'Tomorrow morning, we'll start a journey to Ganapatipule in Ratnagiri. On foot.'

'On foot!'

'The conditions for this free workshop are: you'll carry no baggage – no suitcases, no water bottles, no bedding. Carry a thin towel and a spare set of clothes and undergarments. Stuff these in your pockets or tie them on your waist, with any medicines you may need. No excess baggage!'

Murmurs of protest flew. 'A long journey without belongings? How will we sustain ourselves?'

'I haven't finished. You will carry no money with you either, or credit cards or cell phones. We will have no advance supplies of food or shelter. We'll have to find them on our own, without organised help.'

Pandemonium broke loose. The mango we thought we were going to relish turned out to be a lemon! The gathering protested audibly, almost accusing Swamiji of madness.

'What will we eat?'

'Where will we sleep?'

'Such a long journey without money? Inconceivable!'

Several questions flew across the air.

'Now, let me see how many of you wish to enroll for this practical spiritual workshop.' Swamiji asked. He pretended not to hear the protests.

'But how can anyone undertake such a journey?'

'Why not?'

'How will we survive without the necessary belongings?' An anxious woman raised her voice.

'How does a sparrow survive all its life?' countered Swamiji. 'What does it take from its nest? Money, water, food? Nothing at all! Yet, it survives everyday. Can't you try to live like a sparrow for just a few days? Shed your unnecessary anxieties. Explore the joy of freedom.'

'But –'

'In our worries, we have forgotten why we have evolved differently from a sparrow. All the material possessions that we have created over the ages have enslaved us, and we seem incapable of going through a single day without our laptops and mobile phones. They distract us. One of the purposes of this journey is to prove to ourselves that we are not slaves of our possessions. Given this realisation, we would be able to focus better on our innate qualities – which separate man from all other creatures.'

I watched and heard this man in fascination.

'What's the big idea behind living like a sparrow? Even if we manage to complete this journey, what would it prove? Survival isn't something that commands so much importance.'

Swamiji smiled. 'You answered it yourself. Survival is no big deal, yet we spend our entire lives finding ways to do just that. We manipulate, cheat and hurt others to have our own way, and forget the Divine's way. If we see that survival is not a problem, we will begin to enjoy the freedom we're born with and achieve our true potential.'

'You mean we'll know what we're supposed to do, on completing this journey?'

'Not specific answers, but yes, I hope we'll have a higher perspective and the discretion to exercise our freedom. We'll align with our higher selves and bring out our latent abilities. Abilities far more powerful than what we create when we live insecurely.'

'Sounds great!' I said.

'How many of you are interested in this practical spirituality workshop?'

No one raised their hands. They merely exchanged looks – for some signal or reassurance that they were sane and Swamiji was mad!

'How long is the journey?' someone asked.

'About six hundred kilometres.'

I was dismayed. I thought it would be a small journey. Still, I was the first to raise my hand because I was desperate to change.

'Listening to talks won't substitute for the experience of this journey. We need to evolve and mature. We have to detach from all that we cling to.'

Some more people raised their hands. I counted them – about fifty out of the eight hundred people present in the hall.

'I'm a doctor. Can I carry medicines and thermometer?' A woman raised her voice.

'Yes you can. What's your name?'

'I'm Dr Piyushi.'

'Everyone, give Dr Piyushi a big hand for joining us on this journey.' Swamiji began to clap for her. Everyone else clapped too.

Dr Piyushi blushed. She was short, slightly overweight and wore thick rimless spectacles which gave her a scholarly look.

'We'll begin tomorrow then, at five o' clock. You can drop out of the journey any time you wish. You have about twelve hours to persuade yourselves, your wives, husbands, parents, or children.'

He was indirectly reminding us of the challenges we would face. If I was going to learn practical spiritual lessons from this journey, then it would be worth every hardship.

I waited for the morning with eagerness.

7 | First Grains for the Sparrows

At three in the afternoon I felt hungry. We had walked for eight hours, with two intervals of rest. By now, every muscle of my body ached, yet my enthusiasm remained undiluted. We didn't know how and where to get our first meal. I tried keeping my mind off the worry slowly beginning to grow on me. The sight of the mustard fields which had uplifted my mood earlier, failed to distract me from my hunger now. In this stretch, I drank water from sources I would never have considered earlier, and expected a major attack of dysentery.

'Swamiji, I need to eat,' said Piyushi.

'Any suggestions?' Swamiji turned to face the group.

'Don't *you* have a clue?' Vibha asked, pushing away her hair. She was an architect. She and her husband Subhir were the only married couple in the group.

'The spirit of surrender is all I have. And the belief that the Divine will provide what we need. Let's walk a little further.'

We walked for another hour before we saw a dhaba.

'Let's try our luck,' Swami Partibhan gave voice to what was on my mind.

Normally, I wouldn't even have considered eating in this dhaba, because of its shabby construction and lack of hygiene –

or class. But the places I normally patronised would never have entertained the request we were about to make – they would have thrown us out.

The aroma of spices and vegetables simmering in cauldrons stirred by the cooks outside the dhaba was maddening. I could smell capsicum, cauliflower, onions, tomatoes and garlic frying. I had knots in my stomach. But how would we get our meal?

Swamiji approached the cook. 'We are pilgrims on a spiritual journey with no money. Can you spare some food? We'll repay you with any chore you might want us to do.'

'The owner has gone to the city to buy groceries. He's about to arrive –'

'Then we'll wait,' he said.

An hour passed, but we saw no sign of the owner. We weren't sure, either, if he would agree to feed us on his return.

'Let's leave,' Swamiji said.

Two seekers from our group dropped out, after seeing our difficulty in getting the first meal. But I walked on with grim determination, tackling the haunting doubts within. We had barely walked for about fifteen minutes when a motorcyclist stopped close to Swami Partibhan.

'Forgive me, Swamiji, I was stuck in the city. You can't leave without your lunch.'

'Who are you?' Swamiji asked.

'I'm a follower of yours. When you stopped at my dhaba, my cook didn't recognise you. You left before I returned. Please come back.'

Our faces lit up with the brightest of smiles. We were going to get a meal after we had lost all hope of getting one.

We ate roti, daal, *subzi* and rice heartily. The dhaba owner was happy that God had given him an opportunity to serve his guru. He insisted we have tea, so we drank our first cup since morning – mixed with ginger, cloves and cardamom. The warmth and taste of it felt divine.

Diwakar, the dhaba owner, touched Swami Partibhan's feet and folded his hands when we prepared to leave.

'Thank you for your timely help. Tell us what we can do to repay you?'

'I don't need anything, Swamiji. The fact that you agreed to come back and visit my hotel is more than enough.'

'In trying to live like a sparrow, which is a scavenger and an important link in the food chain, we need to do our bit in return for what we get. You gave us something and we wish to repay you, with anything you may ask of us.'

'If you wish, then please sing a bhajan for me.'

We did as he wished and Diwakar too joined us.

I played my guitar while the group sang. I was glad I had sought permission to bring it along with me on the journey.

When the bhajan was over, we took leave from Diwakar and resumed our journey. It was an unexpected turn of events, from hunger and despair to warm and full.

The sun had lost its brightness and evening had crept in.

We were still far from Pimpalgaon, where we had planned our overnight stay.

8 | The Vision to See Through the Illusion

At 9.00 p.m., we reached a cluster of houses. Since it was already dark, we started looking for a suitable shelter. When we spotted a farm with a big *kuchha* house, Swamiji knocked on its gate. A young man emerged, his gaze sizing up the group.

'We're pilgrims on a journey to Ganapatipule and need shelter for the night.'

'I'm just a servant. The master is out of station.'

'Oh ...'

'Wait,' said the man as we turned, disappointed. 'You can do no harm by staying here for the night. Come in.'

'Are you sure you won't get into trouble for this?'

'I don't think so. Even if my master scolds me, it'll be one person suffering instead of so many.'

୧୭

An hour later, Madhoo, the servant, turned up as we prepared to settle for the night.

'Will you have rice or roti for your dinner?'

The offer came as a surprise for us. We had presumed that he wasn't authorised to serve guests without permission.

Swamiji looked at Madhoo. 'You've already taken so much trouble –'

'Do you want me to sin by leaving you hungry while my family eats?'

'Then please give us whatever you're having.'

'My wife is cooking rice and curry.'

'We too will have rice and curry then.'

The women in our group volunteered to help Madhoo's wife while we came out of the room and looked at the farm behind it. We saw another room, besides the barn and the tractor garage, lit by a lantern.

'What's that?'

'It's the room where our old cow stays,' Madhoo answered. He was carrying water in a pitcher.

'An old cow?'

'Yes. Since it gets cold during the nights, we gave her a spare room.'

'Does she give milk?' Tarun asked. He was a computer engineer who had joined the trip with his friend Pankaj. Tarun was tall and had the rugged look of a seasoned trekker.

Madhoo laughed. 'How can an old cow give milk?'

'Then why do you keep her?' Subhir asked.

'Where else will she go in her old age?'

'In cities, they sell old animals.'

'You mean abandon them? Sell them to the butcher?'

'Not the butcher –'

'To a middleman who sells them to the butcher,' Swamiji corrected him.

'Which is the same. What do you do with your parents when they get old?'

An uncomfortable silence prevailed. None of us had expected this question.

'They are as unwanted in our lives as the cattle that grow old in the city. We neglect them,' said Subhir with a faraway gaze.

'But how can you do that? How can you forget what they have done for you?'

'Can you show us your cow?' said Swami Partibhan, in an attempt to change the sensitive topic.

Madhoo took us inside the room. I noticed that he sneezed a lot. He would then wipe his nose with his palms and rub them on his clothes. I winced in disgust.

We saw the cow in the middle of the room, lying over dry hay, with a generous quantity of green chaff, which she was nibbling. She was clean and her skin sparkled, unlike the dirty city cows.

'You bathe her and dispose the dung?'

'Everyday.' Madhoo puffed his chest.

What pride and devotion was this? Why did they care for a useless animal until it died? The argument was against all financial logic.

'You treat your cattle better than I treated my parents – '

'Babu, you're crying,' Madhoo touched Subhir's shoulder with the hand with which he wiped his sneeze.

'Let him shed the burden of his heart,' Swamiji said.

Subhir didn't say anything. He kept looking at the cow.

'Feeling awful?' I walked up to Subhir.

'I moved my parents to an old-age home two years ago.'

'Are they well kept?'

'Yes, it's the best. Still ... the way these villagers look after even their useless cattle ... I feel guilty. I shouldn't have sent them away. They didn't want to go and were heartbroken –'

'In absolute terms, it appears wrong. But think of what should take priority: a life that's blooming or a life that's ending?' I looked around to see if anyone in the group would respond to my question.

'A life of balance,' said Swamiji, before turning away.

'Food is ready,' said Madhoo – and sneezed.

Together, Madhoo and his wife served us food. I was anxious to know if Madhoo had washed his hands before serving.

Mercifully, he didn't sneeze while we ate, or I would have vomited.

Many in the group insisted Madhoo and his wife join us, but they refused.

'We don't eat before we serve guests.'

Half an hour after we finished dinner, Madhoo returned with logs of wood.

'This'll keep you warm. We have some bedsheets and quilts, but they won't be enough.'

'Why are you taking so much trouble for us?'

'Because you are our guests.'

ᘓ

We got up well rested in the morning and had a bath in water Madhoo had heated for us. He served us tea with roti and *subzi*, which he and his wife had made even before we got up. However, his sneezing had gotten worse.

To repay our night stay and his hospitality, we helped Madhoo with his domestic chores. Subhir bathed and fed the cow and removed the cow-dung, the women dusted and mopped the house, while the rest of us cleared weeds from the field and watered it.

When we left at 11 a.m., the sky was overcast. It would be a cold and bleak day for us.

80

'Where's your sweater?' At noon, when we rested near Nasik, Shruti noticed that Swamiji didn't have his sweater on. It was rumoured that she was Partibhan's fiancée. I had never seen her at the ashram and she had joined the group only in the morning when we started.

'My sweater?'

'You must have forgotten it at Madhoo's place,' Piyushi said.

'Yes, maybe … . Yes, I think I left it there.'

'How could you forget it? It was cold when we started,' said Shruti.

'I just forgot.'

'Then we must fetch it,' said Tarun, getting up.

'No –'

'But Swamiji, the nights can be very cold,' Ruchika voiced her concern. She was a manager in a multinational bank. A divorcee in her late twenties, she had come to the ashram to seek solace after a turbulent and unhappy marriage.

'I'll manage,' said Swamiji. 'Don't worry.'

'I'll go back and get it. The distance isn't much –'

'No need for that, Tarun. We'll have to wait for hours and you'll also get tired unnecessarily. Forget the sweater. Let's go.'

'Where?' Ramanujam said. 'We're in no hurry to cover distances.'

'Letting you freeze would be downright mean. Tarun isn't going alone. We'll go together,' added Mohan. He was a man in his forties, a soft-spoken government officer. He wore gray clothes and gray shoes; even his face looked gray.

'You're fussing over nothing.'

'If you're not going to cooperate, we'll leave without you.'

'As your leader, I order you –' Swamiji gave up. He simply couldn't muster enough authority.

'Let's go back,' I said.

We started walking in the opposite direction.

'Wait. I left it deliberately.'

'Now you are lying,' Shruti said with a smile.

'If I lie, then what's the use of this journey?'

'You left it purposely?'

'Yes.'

'Why?'

'You saw Madhoo sneeze?'

'Yes.'

'He was feeling cold because he didn't have a sweater. I gave mine to his wife.'

We fell silent. I remembered Madhoo's sneezes and my misgivings about his hygiene. But Swamiji saw beyond the obvious.

'Please take my half-sweater Swamiji. I have another,' said Mohan. He started taking off his cardigan.

'No, please. You wouldn't have brought it if you didn't need it. You'll not suffer for something because of me. I gave him the sweater because I don't feel that cold.'

We tried our best but he was adamant. Finally, we quit and resumed our walk.

Swamiji's gesture overwhelmed me. While insecurity about the future made me anxious about food and shelter, he gave away his only shield against the biting cold.

Madhoo's simplicity and Swamiji's sacrifice forced me to introspect. I felt the same embarrassment which I had felt when Swamiji told us that the fire was a test and I had failed. This time, I felt bad and wondered if it was even possible for humans to change their selfish natures at all.

'Not feeling good, is it?' Ramanujam caught up with me. 'Swamiji pretended to forget the sweater.'

'Swamiji says that if we can see our flaws then we can remove them,' said Dr Piyushi. 'I don't feel good either, but I'll not give up. At least we're able to see one more selfish streak in us.'

'Can spirituality change the basic nature of a person?' I asked Ramanujam. 'I keep reverting to my old self.'

'Yes. Swamiji is like a magnet that emits divine force and we are like iron pieces in touch with him. We manifest his qualities, but it will be sometime before we become permanent magnets ourselves. Right now, it's temporary and depends on our contact with him. Once we imbibe the property, we'll emit the divine force always. It will become our nature.'

Ramanujam's example of a temporary magnet transforming into a permanent magnet rekindled my hope. If I managed to achieve even a small per cent of the empathy which Swamiji possessed, I would reach an important milestone.

9 | The Sugar of Life

As we walked on the highway, we saw the dense morning fog settled over crops lifting off like the veil from the face of a bride.

'In the city, there's no time or place for beauty,' said Ruchika as she stopped to experience the magnificent sight. 'We live in concrete jails, yet imagine we're free!'

'City life reminds me of the merciless bullock cart driver who beats his buffaloes to hurry them up. We pity the buffaloes, but not our overburdened selves,' Kulkarni too, was intoxicated by the moment.

∞

In the afternoon, near Ozar, we saw a terrible accident. A car and a truck were smashed and twisted. Though we didn't see any bodies, we heard that all three occupants of the car had died. The truck driver was critically injured and the cleaner had fled.

'They were driving at more than a hundred and twenty kilometres an hour,' said a fruit vendor near the accident site.

It was yet another example of human beings in a senseless hurry. Accidents. Rapes. Robberies. Corruption. Violence. Utterly random behaviour of humans that created headlines of misery.

What made the drivers of life's vehicles so reckless? Why did people drive through life without using spiritual brakes?

At 2.30 p.m., when we crossed Ozar village, we saw farmers making jaggery. The delicious aroma emanating from the huge cauldrons increased our hunger. As we watched the villagers, they asked where we were heading.

'You're going to Ganapatipule? There, a huge natural rock resembles the head of Lord Shri Ganesha. We call it *swayambhu*, or self-created idol. May you be blessed with the spiritual wisdom of Shri Ganesha.' An elderly person smoking a hookah smiled serenely, as he peered through his thick lenses.

The villagers began the process of making the jaggery and mixed additives in the cauldrons. Soon, the sugarcane extract began to boil. After a while, it gained a chocolate-brown colour that I had never seen before. The aroma was ravishing, and my hunger now uncontrollable.

The villagers offered us chunks of jaggery on plates, for which we were extremely grateful. It melted in our mouths. When I asked for water, they told me to wait. We watched them make more of the stuff.

Swamiji, who was observing them intently, commented, 'It takes a long time to grow the sugarcane crop. Many of the seeds go waste. A portion of it withers away and pests devour some of it. Yet, the small quantity of juice most of the crop yields is the sweetest in the world. Similarly, most of our life is spent in pursuit of useless objects – merely to satisfy our egos. However, one little act of brilliance can make everything worthwhile and acquit our existence. Through it, we sweeten many lives. When we do that, despite our several flaws, our lives become worthy. We just have to do that little bit we are meant to do.'

Just when I began to wonder if the villagers had forgotten my request for water, they appeared with a huge vessel and some tumblers.

To my surprise, they brought milk instead of water.

'All we wanted was water!' I turned to my fellow travellers, surprised. We gawked at the huge tumblers of milk. Never before had we consumed such a huge quantity of milk in one go.

'If you drink water after warm jaggery, you get a bad throat,' said the woman who handed us our glasses of milk. 'Besides, you are hungry.'

'We should've offered you food, but you will like this combination no less.' Another villager gave out more of the jaggery.

This time, the jaggery, accompanied by hot milk, was even more delicious. 'I don't know what to make of them,' I turned to Sneha. 'Few city people have the natural empathy which villagers have in abundance.'

'Today's jaggery is special,' a villager grinned. 'The yield will fetch us a good price.'

'No wonder it tastes so good,' said Sanjeev, holding his piece up. 'I think it is extraordinary – a rare blend.'

'The taste will linger with me for years,' said Mohan, raising his tumbler.

∞

The highway near Nasik city was congested and vehicles had to share the highway with bullock carts, tractors, and cycles, which slowed their pace. While walking, we saw a tourist bus following a tractor at a snail's pace. The bus driver tried to overtake, but the traffic coming down the other side of the road frustrated his attempts. Furious, he shouted abuse at the poor man driving the tractor, who tried to move as far left as he could. But try as he may, the passage he created for the bus was insufficient. Finally, the bus managed to overtake the tractor, but instead of rushing on, the bus driver pulled up ahead and forced it to stop. Both the driver and conductor got down, creating a huge jam behind them.

'Why didn't you give us way, you fool? Couldn't you hear the horn? Are you deaf?'

'I gave you as much way I could. Look! Another half a foot and my tractor would have fallen off the road.'

'First you don't give way and then you argue!' The driver lifted his hand to slap the poor farmer.

'Stop!' Piyushi grabbed the driver's hand. She was trembling in anger. 'Don't take out your frustration on an innocent man.'

'Who are you, a relative of his?' The conductor smiled insolently.

'We relate to him as fellow human beings,' Swamiji said quietly. 'Like you, he too is on his way to earn his daily bread. Why should you have more precedence over him, when the situation doesn't allow?'

'Because these fools drive slow machines and block the traffic. I bet he doesn't even have a licence.'

'I have!' The tractor driver took it out quickly. He was regaining courage after seeing us rally for him.

'You call them all sorts of names, but it's their village through which you drive. Instead of thanking them for the roads they allowed to run through their fields, you curse them for slowing down your vehicles. Go away before we collect more villagers and deflate your tyres or call the police!' Piyushi raised her voice as she uttered the threat.

The driver dropped his hand abruptly. If the threat was real, it would mean a long delay.

'What the woman just said makes sense. Apologise to the farmer and let's go. Don't make it an issue,' a tourist within the bus reasoned.

'Yes. It's not his fault. Respect their rights to the road,' another joined in.

Muttering and grumbling, the driver and the conductor climbed into the bus and left in a rage.

The farmer grinned happily. 'You gave them a fitting reply. Thank you. Where are you going?'

We declined his offer to give us a free ride 'as far as we wanted' and took leave.

'Where did you get the courage to confront the men?' Swami Partibhan asked Piyushi, who had taken refuge in silence.

'I couldn't bear the injustice and my anger went out of control. Now I feel bad.'

'Being spiritual doesn't mean one has to be indifferent. Sometimes, controlled anger is necessary to check injustice.'

৪০

During the day, we were comfortable because of the warm sun, but in the evening, the cold wind had an unpleasant bite. When we rested, I checked my blood sugar. Being diabetic, I was worried because of all the jaggery I'd consumed. I had not taken a single tablet since we started, yet my blood sugar level was normal. All the walking was doing the work of a medicine.

10 | Two Banks and a River Called Life

In the afternoon, we walked the stretch between Nasik and Wadhiware and ate inside a popular temple. The devotees gave us *paisam* made with *mung* beans, with laddus. We relished the still-warm sweet pudding, enriched with golden raisins, cashews, cinnamon and cloves. To pay for our food, we swept and mopped the temple's dirty floor and left the marble gleaming. The effort was tiring but we felt happy seeing the result.

It was evening by the time we reached Wadhiware. While walking beside a canal, we saw people working on a breach. It was too big, and their attempts at repair appeared futile.

'They won't succeed if we don't help them. I'm going down.' Before we could react, Swamiji started descending the highway.

I stood bewildered, watching him rush towards the breach.

'I thought this was a spiritual journey. I wouldn't have joined if they had told me we would repair breaches in winter,' Harish, a school teacher, flayed his hands agitatedly.

'This is crazy, and I won't be a part of this circus.' Another man rested his hands on his hips, his face contorted.

'What's the connection between breaches and spirituality?' a middle-aged woman shouted. 'We're getting late. We should rather be searching for a place to put up at night.'

All three of them left the group. It seemed like we were losing seekers all the time.

I shrugged and followed Swamiji reluctantly. The journey was a good idea and I wanted to believe in him because I desperately wished to change.

The villagers were glad when they saw so many of us willing to help them.

'A few of you can dig mud while the rest can help us plug the breach with it,' one of the villagers directed us.

Glad to have a choice, I rushed to dig mud in my attempt to avoid getting wet in the cold.

The women in the group carried mud in trays and passed it to the men. Half the men from our group went to work on the breach – Swamiji was one of them.

I could immediately see that the numbers mattered after all. The plug was filling quickly. Still, the mud was unable to stick and washed away repeatedly. Just as I feared, my fellow pilgrims were soaked and their clothes muddied.

'Mix some stones and gravel with the mud,' Swamiji shouted over the rushing cold water. We were shivering and our teeth chattered.

We also uprooted some crops to add to the mix. I bruised my hands with the rough work. By now, I doubted if I had made the right choice in opting to dig instead of plugging the leak.

This time, when the women gave the gravel to the men, it stayed. Still, it was not enough to plug the breach.

Some of the men working on the breach joined us and together we mixed sand and gravel much faster.

Two hours of labour brought success, and though tired, exhausted, wet and dirty from the effort, we felt like victorious soldiers. We had gained control over a seemingly hopeless situation.

We patted one another and shook hands in celebration.

'Great work!' Wakde, the village *pradhan*, beamed. 'Your women, too, were no less than the men. They matched our efforts.'

'The water would have caused a lot of damage to our crops. Your help was timely,' another villager grinned, his teeth shining like pearls on his muddy face.

Though my hands didn't bleed, they were covered with boils.

'To which village do you belong? Where are you going?' one of them asked.

'We are pilgrims on our way to Ganapatipule near Ratnagiri,' said Swamiji, running his fingers through his wet hair to squeeze out the water.

'Then you will be our guests, at my house,' the *pradhan* offered.

The evening dipped into the night and we were cold and hungry from our efforts. Not only Wakde's family, but other families turned up to help us. They gave us warm water and fresh clothes. Since Wakde's house didn't have enough bathrooms, all of us split up and headed to different houses to bathe and freshen up.

After almost an hour, we converged near a bonfire with the village folk to eat our meals. I noticed our clothes hung on wires near the fire. The villagers had washed them. It was their way of reciprocating our help. Sharing pains and problems unites people. My doubts about spirituality becoming an inconvenient burden disappeared instantaneously.

As I stared into the fire, I realised it was important to see the self in others. If you identify the self in you alone, you become isolated. If you are able to see this self in others, you can feel their problems and help find solutions with your expanded awareness. The boils in my hands didn't ache anymore; I felt comfortable and warm beside the fire.

'You are a mahatma, Swamiji. Tell us something about spirituality.' Wakde was squatting near the fire, staring at it. 'Until now, I have seen only preaching *babas*, but today, I saw a *karamayogi baba* and I wish to listen to what you have to say.'

'Many villagers refused to help us, although it is their village. Even our youth didn't help,' another villager complained. 'They merely kept telephoning government agencies, telling us that this is not our job.'

'You were a godsend,' a woman from the group commented. 'Say something to all of us. We wish to hear you.'

Swamiji's face, reflecting the glow of the fire, looked beautiful.

'I think I'll speak about the breach today,' he said. 'Our life is like water flowing in the canal with its two banks. One is the bank of acceptance while the other is the bank of thanksgiving. These banks have to be strong for the self to reach its true potential, and achieve resonance with the force behind the universe.'

A hushed silence prevailed as everyone listened to him with complete attention.

'Thanksgiving is the spirit of gratitude towards everything we have today – our house, our jobs, our children, our farms, our cattle, our clothes, our bodies, and our intelligence. Through this spirit, we achieve satisfaction and contentment. Achieving this is not easy, because the mind constantly takes for granted what it possesses and focuses on what it doesn't have. By invoking the spirit of thanksgiving, we steer away from the cravings of our restless minds and force them to focus on what we have. We calm their turbulence and invoke peace.'

'And acceptance?' Wakde asked.

'Acceptance is surrendering the efforts we make and reconciling with the results from each effort. It's important to remind ourselves that everything ultimately helps us evolve.'

'Even when we fail miserably?' A youth raised his doubt.

'Yes, even when we face disappointments. The designs of the supreme self are beyond our understanding, but they are invariably good for us because of its undiluted love for creation. Failure in material pursuits in spite of our best efforts is because a higher cause awaits us. It's something we only realise when we look back at our journey and see how everything fits together beautifully. We must accept results cheerfully and not let disappointments divert us from our true purpose, which is to evolve. This is the spirit of acceptance.'

'It's difficult –'

'I agree it is. However, without acceptance, our lives, like a river diverted on its way to meet the ocean, will fail to achieve evolution. When we're disappointed with results, we breach the bank of acceptance. Our lives seep from this breach and lose their destined course. We become sad, bitter, selfish, aggressive, depressed or angry because we think these small goals are our destinations. Some of us turn into predators who draw satisfaction by looting and depriving others of their share of peace, happiness and joy. They look mighty and successful from the outside, but within them there is not a shred of joy or peace.

'If the bank of thanksgiving is broken, we feel jealous of others and lose our tranquility. The quest for materialistic attainment replaces our true search. We start hankering for what we don't have. The thirst for more increases, and our evolution becomes a casualty.

'Sometimes the breaches are small, and we are able to repair them, like the one we did today. However, some breaches become so big that our lives take the form of a devastating flood that creates havoc. Neighbours, society, children, friends – all who face the fury of this unrestrained deluge suffer.

'We possess nothing and will take nothing with us. Everything we own – this body, this breath and all our materialistic belongings – are perishable. So the idea of gaining and losing is a limited one when seen in this light. That's all I wish to say for today.'

Throughout the meal, I saw Wakde engaging in enthusiastic conversation with Swamiji.

'Another person has started his spiritual journey today. Swamiji has lit another lamp,' I said.

'It's not Swamiji's job alone. It's ours too,' said Ramanujam.

'Ours? How, when we are far from perfect ourselves? How can a flawed person think of enlightening others?'

'We should not forget that the journey to perfection might be spread over many births. But if we feel peace and are evolving even in small bursts, just by being in touch with our divine self, then we should spread this message to others.'

I stayed awake for a long time and meditated on what Swamiji and Ramanujam had said. What Swamiji advocated was surprisingly simple to follow. Still, what stopped me from following the practice? Why couldn't I imbibe the spirit of acceptance?

My daughter's desertion had led to my visit to the ashram. If I saw it as a catalyst that started me on this journey, then what happened was for the good. Yet ...

இ

We started at seven in the morning after having breakfast.

'I'll come to your ashram, Swamiji. I hope you'll recognise me,' Wakde said.

'You're always welcome at the ashram, like everyone else. I hope your spiritual journey is a fulfilling and enriching experience.'

On our way, we saw a dead body being carried to the cremation ground.

'Ram naam sat hai. Satya bolo sat hai,' the people accompanying the body chanted.

'I've heard that chant before, but don't know its meaning,' I said.

'The chant means "everything we perceive is unreal and illusionary. Only God's name is the absolute truth",' Ruchika said.

'Our illusionary world starts with our birth and ends with our death. We bring nothing, take nothing, and yet mistakenly believe we own everything populating our small world,' Ramanujam added.

'It's strange. But doesn't the truth behind those two sentences echo what Swami Partibhan said last night?' Shruti asked.

I vowed I would never forget the simple lesson Swamiji taught us that evening and resolved to end the duality haunting me – the pulls of the material and spiritual worlds.

11 | Being the Change

We reached Kasara late in the evening. As we crossed a gurdwara, we saw people distributing prasad -- wheat flour halwa with hot puris and aloo subzi. The meal was delicious and I checked myself from overindulging.

Meal over, we washed our hands and feet while Swami Partibhan approached the priest who'd given us the prasad.

'Do you have a room where we can stay for the night? We're pilgrims on a journey to Ratnagiri.'

'Where's your luggage?'

'We've no luggage.' He explained the aim of our journey.

'We've a hall where we hold discourses. You can sleep there, but we don't have any bedding.' The priest wiped his hands with a cloth.

At eight in the night, the priest brought tea for us in a huge vessel along with buttered toast.

'This will keep you warm for some time,' he said. 'I wish I could arrange for some bedding.'

'Please don't worry, we'll be fine.' Swamiji took the plates from him and passed them on to us. 'Thank you for this.'

The tea was excellent and I gulped it down thirstily, with a bite of toast.

'You can close the doors of the hall to avoid draughts,' the priest said and left.

Though the day was enjoyable, night turned out to be a nightmare. Time stagnated as I struggled to sleep. The hall housed an army of mosquitoes; the thin mat on the ground was rough and smelled musty. When I lay down, draughts of cold wind made me shiver and my hands and feet became icy and numb. Then I saw a cockroach so close to my face that I jumped. All the euphoria of the afternoon disappeared as I fought vainly with the unhygienic conditions and discomfort. I tossed and turned, nauseated by the smelly mat and tormented by mosquito bites. I dreamt of the comforts of home – central heating, quilts, and soft mattresses. I yearned for a mosquito repellent, worrying that I would catch malaria or dengue. What was I trying to prove by living a life of deprivation? I could spend my time in more productive ways. I felt like going back and giving up the journey, but it was too late in the night to depart.

Tomorrow morning! I promised myself.

I don't know when I drifted off to sleep. My tired body, unused to walking for the ten hours that we had put in, switched off by itself.

I woke up at 2 a.m. Someone was moaning. I strained my eyes, trying to find out who was in distress. When I got accustomed to the darkness, I discovered it was Swamiji. He was shivering and curled up in a fetal position. I hesitated. Waking him wouldn't solve any purpose – I knew he would not take my jacket. Then I had an idea: I took it off and spread it over him. Swamiji pulled it over his body and visibly relaxed. Soon, he stopped moaning and slept peacefully.

I tried to go back to sleep but my extreme discomfort didn't allow it. Giving up, I sat leaning my back on the wall. The sitting position, I discovered, was warmer. There were other lessons the long hours leading to the morning taught me – I pulled my hands into the sleeves of my shirt, stretched my trousers over my feet, and wrapped my towel around my head to cover my ears. All these made me feel warmer than before, but still not comfortable enough to fall asleep.

Watching Swamiji, I felt an intense compassion. He shivered and suffered quietly, while the others slept comfortably. How many people would willingly suffer for another person in this world, that too so selflessly? A strange peace came over me while I watched him sleep. I'd slept for five hours; perhaps with the jacket, Swamiji could sleep for three or four. I felt happy to have shared his discomfort. In comparison to Swamiji's suffering, my decision to quit the journey appeared petty. I slept intermittently while sitting against the wall.

∞

Around 6 a.m., I opened my eyes and saw Swamiji smiling at me. He wrapped the jacket over my shoulders and chest.

'What are you smiling at?'

'If you give so much love to me, I might forget my purpose.'

I tried to smile back but instead, tears started cascading without warning.

'Thank you for what you did, but as I said, in future, you will not pay the price for something I do.'

'You are selfish.'

'Why?' The look on his face was one of surprise.

'You don't want to share your good deeds with others. You want all the credit.'

'I don't understand you.'

'Perhaps heaven is a crowded place and you don't want too many competitors.'

He laughed. 'No. On the contrary, it is a place with infinite seating capacity.'

'Then why is it you teach spirituality but forbid me to practise selflessness towards you?'

'Practise it on others. Your attachment to me will stunt your progress. Ultimately, we have to become our own gurus.'

'I don't know profound philosophies about attachments and being one's own guru, but I've yet to see a child who stops growing just because he loves his mother and father.'

'I'm used to speaking, not listening,' Swamiji smiled.

'I didn't feel troubled when I shared my jacket with you.'

'God bless you,' said Swamiji. 'I can't say anything to the love you shower on me. I can only get drenched in it.'

∞

Emerging from the hall for my morning routine, I saw my fellow travellers were up already. When I took the water in my hands to brush my teeth, it felt freezing cold and I flinched. But I got used to that too, like drinking the tube-well water and the chillies in food! There was more in store as I saw disciples emerging from the three bathrooms. They were shivering and their teeth chattered.

Holy cow! Cold water bath – no hot water! I thought of skipping my bath, but my body felt sticky. No way could I skip it and be able to continue with the journey. Besides, I could never be sure if I would indeed get hot water the next morning, or the next, or ever on this journey!

'The water is cold, but after the first few splashes, it'll be all right,' Sanjeev Purie teased me. He was a tall man with a lean frame and good build. By nature, he was reticent but seeing my terror-stricken face, he flashed me a wide grin.

'I've never taken a bath in cold water during winter,' I groaned.

'But there's always a first time,' Mohan barged in. His teeth were chattering too. 'This bath reminds me of the first time I smoked. At least, it's courage and experimentation in the right direction!'

'Don't lock the door. We'll wait outside, just in case,' Tarun grinned.

I held the mug of water and stared at it in fear. With a countdown, like the ones before the launch of space rockets, I splashed its contents on my head.

'10, 9, 8, 7, 6, 5, 4, 3, 2, 1 … go, go, go!'

I choked, spluttered, and spat out the water which intruded my nostrils and mouth. The hair on my skin bristled and stung like tiny needles. My breath refused to move in or out of my lungs. I thought I had had a cardiac arrest but realised quickly, and with great relief, that I would survive after all. Even before I could think, I fired more rockets on my head.

I gasped as I stood up, flailing my arms. Then I felt a rush of warmth; my body was backing up! I grinned idiotically at an invisible mirror and felt like a teenager who has undergone a rite of passage. I had done it! I poured more water, soaped my body and emerged a winner.

Tarun, Mohan and Sanjeev were waiting outside – just as they had promised. My smile disappointed them.

'We should wash the carpets,' I suggested, when Swamiji asked what we should do to repay the temple for its hospitality.

And so, for the next two hours, we toiled over cleaning the carpets in cold water. An incredible amount of dirt poured out in muddy black streams. It took three washes for the crimson red of the carpet to shine.

Our efforts delighted the priest.

'I never knew they were so dirty,' he said.

I beamed at the results. From being just a complainer, I had done my bit to improve the circumstances I had cursed last night.

12 | Zipping Through Life on Autopilot Mode

When we moved from Kasara to Khardi, I was happy. I wasn't on a taxi back to the airport, as I'd vowed in the night. The joy of relinquishing my attachment to physical comfort dwarfed all the discomfort I'd faced the night before. I felt like a hero.

The glucometer reading revealed the sugar level in my blood to be normal. To sleep, I no longer needed a tranquilliser. It seemed as if the sun rose that morning specifically to greet me.

My innate capacity to adjust to hardships had started to resurface – something which constant work in closed offices had put to slumber. I found a new strength.

Onwards I marched with fourteen dedicated seekers. I had done a physical count after three more persons left us in the morning. They were unable to bear the cold and left gracefully, after taking Swamiji's blessings.

It was noon when we neared Khardi. As usual, we felt hungry. Human appetite surprises me: every eight hours we need something.

'I'm fed up of being hungry. Why hasn't anyone found its cure?' I complained to Tarun.

'How can you be fed up when your stomach is empty?' He was never serious, and his wit would have us laughing all the time.

'Let's approach houses to seek alms this time. What do you say?' Swami Partibhan said.

'How would we repay them?'

'We'll find a way.'

When we asked for food, some people shooed us away, some tried to give money which we refused, while others gave us their leftovers. Most people respected us for refusing money. They would then happily part with fruits, milk and eatables, clearly not leftovers! Many asked who we were, realising that we were on some special mission. Others doubted if we were genuine pilgrims and showered abuses, thinking we were rejecting petty money in hopes of a bigger donation. There was always the odd minority who suspected we were a gang of thieves and shut their doors on us. Such were the varied responses our group met.

Our lunch for the day was an odd assortment of bread slices, sandwiches, rotis, *subzi*, *puris*, milk, tea, puddings and fruits. The variety gave an impression of a feast. All of us sat in a circle inside a park, with the food we had gathered spread in the middle.

'Just as we arrange food to feed ourselves, we should strive to quench the thirst of our divine self. To achieve this, we should always keep the divine self in our subconscious attention. Just like the know-how of driving a car or bicycle is in our subconscious mind and we can think of other things while doing these,' Swamiji said.

'Are there any other examples?' Dr Piyushi leaned forward intently.

'When a child flies a kite, he doesn't do it consciously. When you write a letter, you don't think of grammar. When we speak or argue, we don't process logic. A tea-wallah doesn't consciously make tea; a housewife doesn't consciously cook food. If you want more examples, I'll have to think consciously now,' Swami Partibhan smiled.

'Still, at first we learn these things at a conscious level,' Piyushi objected.

'Yes. What we struggle to learn consciously manifests at a subconscious level after some time. We consciously struggled with learning how to drive a vehicle, understanding mathematical tables, grammar, sentence construction, etc., and now we use these skills subconsciously. Similarly, we might be struggling to assimilate spirituality today, but tomorrow it will be a part of our subconscious make-up.'

Would I identify with it like I do with my work? Could it soak into my life? It looks so easy and possible.

We disposed the foils and wrappers from lunch. To pay our dues, we cleaned the community park. It took three hours of hard work to comb the waste. The pile of plastic and junk was astonishing. The park seemed to have been neglected for a long time.

When we finished, the park looked pretty. Just then, Shruti and Ramanujam told Swami Partibhan that Kulkarni was missing. He was an accountant in the ashram, a retired government servant. He had been with Partibhan's father for several years.

'I saw him a while ago, near the park's entrance,' said Shruti.

'Maybe he's dropped out,' said Pankaj.

'He won't leave without telling us,' remarked Swami Partibhan. 'Let's look for him. Maybe he's lost his direction.'

Sure, Mr Kulkarni had lost his sense of direction and purpose, as we found out ten minutes later when we spotted him sipping coffee at a shop in the marketplace opposite the park. When caught red-handed, he grinned sheepishly, removing the cup from his lips so fast that he spilled some coffee.

'Why Kulkarni, you are enjoying your coffee alone?' Swamiji smiled without any anger.

'I ... I ... when we were asking for food, a man gave me money, a ten-rupee note. I bought this coffee with it.'

'What, Kulkarni? You let your spirit down for a cup of coffee? Broke a rule we had agreed upon?'

'I'm sorry, Swamiji.' He touched his ears. 'Many days have passed since I last tasted coffee and I succumbed to it.'

People were looking at us curiously but Swamiji wasn't aware of it.

'Then let's resume our journey.' Swami Partibhan turned to leave.

'Still, Swamiji, I would like to punish myself for what I did.'

'How do you plan to do it?'

Kulkarni's shoulders slumped in despair. 'What should I do? Return?'

'That's not a punishment. That's a return to more of your coffee cups!'

We laughed.

'Then I'll forego my dinner,' Kulkarni hastened to add.

'Do you think it's a just punishment? Can you manage without food?'

'Yes. I think it's the least I can do.'

'As you wish.'

'Swamiji!' I called as he walked at a distance from me. I wanted to ask something. The Kulkarni episode troubled me, despite an hour having passed since.

'Yes?'

'If Kulkarni couldn't resist temptation, what hope can there be for beginners like us? How do we fight this difficult battle against temptation?'

'The answer will need some explaining. Mind if we sit somewhere comfortably?'

We all moved back to a clearing beside the highway.

'Our friend Nikhil just asked me why Kulkarni couldn't resist temptation. If he could fall, then Nikhil here thinks there's no hope for the novices. Did I rephrase your doubt correctly?'

I nodded.

'Our natural state is purely divine. Temptation continuously tries to make inroads into human beings. It tries to waylay it from achieving its objective, which is evolution. When our attention's on the higher self, we don't yield to temptation. But when we aren't connected, the lure of materialism begins to blind us. It first sows the seeds of doubt and then brings us under its spell. Even if you are one day old in spirituality, if your faith is strong, you won't lose your connection with the divine self. Yet, the tiniest doubt, if left unattended, can bring years of evolution crashing down like a house of cards.'

'You mean to say that Kulkarni doubted the purpose of this journey?'

'No, it's not that simple. In Kulkarni's case, perhaps his weakness for coffee told him that Partibhan, for whom he's sacrificing it, isn't worth the effort. He justified his deviation with the logic that since I am not addicted to coffee, I don't know what it takes to be without it for so long. When confronted by others, he realised his mistake because despite their difficulties, they were still obeying a rule.'

'So how do we fight the lure of materialism and stay on course towards our evolution? Especially when temptations are continuously knocking at our doors?' Tarun asked.

'Listen to the voice of conscience, since it is the seat of the higher self. We shut the doors and windows of our houses to prevent a thief or a storm from entering. Similarly, by always preserving the divine connection and being in the company of seekers, we protect ourselves from temptation.'

'What bothers me is if God is the force that created everything, then who created temptation? From where did it come?' I asked.

'I think the clash between materialism and spirituality is a game the force behind the universe devised. He made spirituality, He made materialism, and He set us free to choose our polarity. The man who devised the game of snakes and ladders created those climbs and falls for his own enjoyment, and that of the players.'

'What is the purpose of this game of life we play, then?' Tarun asked.

'To see how we, as individuals, evolve along our journey through life. Do we attune to our higher self and try to resonate with the force behind the universe, or do we try to exist independently of Him, more comfortable with the materialistic aspect of existence? Do we choose to live at a superficial level or at a much higher level of awareness? Whatever we decide, the truth is that we have to resonate with our creator, one day or the other, in one lifetime or in several, through evolution.

'Some people achieve this goal faster by avoiding snakes and using the ladders of divine principles. Others keep falling, succumbing to the snakes. We might end up first or last in the game of life – it doesn't matter. What matters is how we played.'

'I see.'

'If your doubts are over, then let's balance all this mental activity with the simple exercise of walking meditation. While we walk, we must try to keep ourselves in thoughtless awareness. When we take our attention towards creation – flowers, trees, leaves, the mountains – our thoughts fade away. This thoughtless awareness is an uplifting experience and helps us become more aware of our higher self and its capabilities. Our attention, instead of focusing on our lower needs, soars upwards, towards evolution.'

13 | I Witness

In the evening, we passed a house in Asangaon. As we crossed the tents erected outside, a man invited us for snacks being distributed at a religious function. He served us personally with tangible love and sincerity.

'You haven't eaten anything!' Girish, the man distributing food, told Kulkarni.

'I – I have a fast today, I'm not supposed to eat,' he lied. Girish offered him a glass of fruit juice. Kulkarni looked at Swami Partibhan, who nodded. When Kulkarni finished his juice, Girish asked, 'Who are you and where are you going? On some journey?'

'You guessed it right,' Pankaj replied. 'We're pilgrims going to Ganapatipule.'

'Where are you staying?'

'Nowhere in particular. We live in God's land.'

'Where's your luggage?'

'We don't have any luggage.'

Vibha then explained the conditions of the journey to Girish.

'That means you have no place to stay. You must stay at my second home. Don't leave. Please wait for me.'

We helped him serve the others and pack up his belongings when the function was over.

Girish's second house was two kilometres away from the one in which he had held the function. The imposing height of his elegant bungalow dwarfed the other buildings in its vicinity. What struck us instantly was its beauty and the mess in it. The paint on the walls was costly but marring its silky finesse were crayon scribbles and oil paints. Childish sketches and messages defiled the beautiful walls. Scraps of paper littered the floor. The minute we entered the gates, children surrounded Girish and barraged him with their excited banter.

'Uncle, he's troubling me.' A child held his hand and pulled at him.

'You brought the decorations?'

'And the toys?'

The cacophony was endless. Girish replied patiently to each child. Assured by him, they went in to carry on with the decoration work. It was clear they were preparing for a celebration.

'They love to paint your walls,' remarked Ruchika.

'I'm happy if they are happy,' he said.

'You're different from today's youth,' observed Swamiji. We were in the interiors of the house now.

'I'm thirty years old,' Girish said. He stressed the 'thirty' to emphasise that he was older than Swamiji thought.

'Still, why do you appear so sad?'

The suddenness of the question brought an unexpected reaction – tears filled Girish's eyes.

'I lost a son, Swamiji, this day, two years ago. I hold the function in his memory.'

'And these children?'

'It's a long story ... .'

'We would like to hear it. How did your son die?'

'He died due to a tapeworm infestation in his brain.'

'It could not be treated?'

'No, though it was discovered early. No medical treatment or prayers helped. Three months later, my wife died of sorrow. She could not bear a second child and was unable to accept our son's death. I lost everything in less than five months. All my money was unable to avert the tragedy. I cursed myself, I cursed my luck, and I cursed God.'

'I can understand your grief,' said Swamiji. 'So how come you're among so many children now?'

'After the deaths of my son and wife, I had to take four tranquillisers to sleep. Even then, sleep would be fitful and tortuous. One night, when I reached a construction site to supervise a building, I heard my workers singing bhajans in their temporary hutments.

'Curious, I inched closer to the group. What made them love God so much when their lives were so hopeless? They didn't own homes, earned so little, they were barely able to feed themselves, and yet were singing praises of the Lord. Why were they thankful?

'The evening was hot and the womenfolk were making meals as the men sang bhajans. When they saw me, the labourers stopped singing and got up in respect.

'"What good has your lord done for you? Why do you sing bhajans in His praise?" I asked them.

'"They gave us you as a master. You never hold back our wages, respect our women without lusting after them like other contractors. You give us leave when we want and attend to our injuries whenever they occur. We thank God for it," one of them said.

'Their faith was surprising. Then, I saw a drunken labourer ambling back to his hut. "Why does that man drink? Why doesn't he feel like praising the Lord? I'm sure he doesn't enjoy the habit. What troubles him, not you?"

'"He has deviated from the spiritual path. He doesn't believe in God."

'"What makes you different? You live in the same poverty. Why do you believe in the Divine when he doesn't?"

'"People who fall off the spiritual path use too much of their brains. They forget the Divine is only merciful."

'"But your God wasn't merciful to me. He took away my son and my wife. I don't think it's kindness from any view!"

'"The Divine is never unkind. We pay according to our karma. Some of us have lost family members too. However, we don't stop singing His praises.

'"You don't blame God for those tragedies?"

'"Why blame the blameless, sir? I too lost my child when a drunkard lost control of his car. When he will pay for his karma, he will blame the Divine for everything." Munna said, gathering himself.

'With that one sentence, I became a witness of my wrongdoings. I think it's too complicated to explain what I felt. I knew I had paid for the serious wrongs I'd done, yet I behaved as if I were the most innocent victim on earth.

'I saw my inner self stripped of all justifications. The unnerving experience is something we have to go through at some point in our lives when our past follies finally catch up with our present.

'That night, I sat with those poor labourers and listened to their bhajans, feeling peace within. After a while, I even started singing with them, although I barely knew the bhajans. They shared with me what they cooked. And I slept without a single tranquilliser that night.

'The next day, when I reflected, I realised that most of my workers were underpaid. It was one of my crimes! I had always tried to save costs on my construction projects, sometimes even by compromising quality. That too was my crime.

'The people who were working for me were struggling to meet their basic needs while I used to spend nearly two thousand rupees on luxuries like non-vegetarian food, wine and fruit juices, every day.'

We were all quiet. What he said was true. Inequality was everywhere in society. In many ways, I too was like the rich spoiled man Girish had been.

'My relatives pressurised me to remarry, but I didn't. Today, whenever I miss my child, I drive to my labourers' hutment and take their children for an outing. They love me like a family member and come to my house in the evenings to play. We have ice cream, enjoy rides, and watch movies. I see to it that they all go to school and do whatever I can to look after their medical and educational needs. I no longer earn or save as much money as I used to. And how much money does a man need, anyway? Besides, I'm content. Today we're celebrating a kid's birthday at my home.'

So that explained the graffiti on the walls, the litter of paper and the celebrations.

The minute the children knew Girish was free, they surrounded him again and broke into shouts and laughter.

'Has the cake arrived?' Girish asked.

'Yes. It's beautiful, just like I wanted it,' a small boy beamed, shifting his weight from his left foot to the right, then back to the left in joy. It was obvious that he was the kid whose birthday was being celebrated.

How could someone hold a function in the memory of a lost son and celebrate a birthday on the same day was beyond me.

When we saw the cake, even we adults were impressed. The two-foot-high cake was shaped like a beautiful castle.

'Mohanty wants to be an architect one day. He's good at studies,' Girish grinned with pride.

Between clapping and cheering, they cut the cake and offered us a share.

'You carry on with your celebrations. I've visitors to look after today and they're tired. I'll join you after I make their sleeping arrangements.'

The house was big. Girish telephoned a bedding service and arranged mattresses and quilts for us.

'Where will you sleep?'

'I sleep in that room.' Girish pointed to a room next to the dining room.

'But it has no cot,' Swamiji remarked.

'I stopped sleeping on a cot when I saw that most of my labourers didn't have any. Sleeping on the floor is more fun.'

At eight in the night, after giving us milk, Girish asked us if it was all right if he went away for a while.

'Where are you going?' Vibha asked.

'To the hutment.'

'And what would you do there?'

'Sing bhajans. I do it every day.'

'Mind if we join you?'

'You must be tired.'

'The name of the Lord always rejuvenates the spirit and the body,' said Swamiji.

'All right then. What can be better than the company of seekers like you!'

Girish brought the labourers home, since the space in the hutment area wasn't enough to hold all of us. They came and sang the bhajans they knew, and we sang the bhajans we knew. Some of them were common. I accompanied their tabla, *chimta*, harmonium, flute and *dafli* with my guitar. The words and the music complemented each other. The whole atmosphere had an incredible energy. Many people in the gathering shed tears, tears of piety.

The bhajans went on until midnight and we forgot all our tiredness. We lost consciousness of time and place and our spirits appeared unified by devotion.

Many more joined in the singing – people from the neighbouring houses gathered around when they heard the bhajans. More than three hundred people were present when the singing ended. Amazing to think that everything had begun spontaneously, without invitations.

'What a beautiful night,' said Girish. He had brought a sweater for Swamiji.

'I can't accept this from you,' Swamiji protested.

'I'll not become poorer by giving it to you. Instead, I'll be richer in the kingdom of the Divine. Please accept this gift.'

Swamiji couldn't refuse. The circle was complete.

'You trusted us and served us out of simplicity of spirit. You recognised that we were needy and you brought us here. Your child died today, but you celebrate the birthday of a poor labourer's child. You suffered misery yourself, but for others you give out happiness. It's a rare quality you have; never give it up.'

I meditated on this observation before I slept. So much good existed in the world. Perhaps that is why the world is still an inhabitable place, despite the ugly selfishness of most people.

14 | Remembering Newton's First and Second Laws of Motion

We meditated early in the morning, just before continuing on our journey. Swamiji stressed that we meditate for at least fifteen minutes in the morning and fifteen minutes in the evening, every day. According to him, it was the key to establishing the connection with our higher selves.

On several occasions, when the fatigue of the journey would make us lethargic, Swamiji would cajole us out of our reluctance to keep up with the practice.

That morning, Vibha asked a question which had been on my mind for some time.

'Swamiji, I feel doing charity is better than meditating. Take Girish's example. What he's doing is perhaps better than my selfish attempt to evolve. If I have one hour free, isn't it better I spend it on charity instead of mediation?'

Swamiji smiled.

'Girish is an evolved soul because he has seen the futility of materialism. But the person who is yet to achieve realisation has a subtle ego which can lead him astray. It can develop despite people's attempts at being helpful to others. Have you met people who are arrogant about their humility?'

'That's a paradox,' Ruchika said.

'I've seen people who'll not wear a shirt if a kurta is unavailable. Just because a kurta to them symbolises simplicity, they refuse to wear a shirt. How do people lose their common sense? Their conditioning manifests as ego. When you say you'll be charitable, you condition yourself and risk embracing what may not be good for your evolution. Remember, being connected to the higher self implies being spontaneous in whatever you do, and this state is a gift only meditation can give. I would go as far to say, if you have to compromise between charity and meditation, compromise on charity.'

'That will sound blasphemous to many,' Ramanujam said.

'Yes, many would find it blasphemous. But if you were to be close either to the Divine or to human beings, which would you choose?'

'Swamiji, are you suggesting we ignore the deprived?' Vibha asked.

Swamiji looked amused.

'Let me put it another way. You are about to eat food and a hungry man comes along. What would you do?'

'Give it to the hungry man because I have at least eaten my last meal.'

'If in the evening, another beggar comes to your doorstep?'

'I'll give some of my food.'

'Just now you professed giving up meditation for charity. Similarly, here, you would either have to give all your food to the beggar or eat it yourself, so what will you do?'

Vibha became quiet.

'Okay, I will again part with my food,' she said slowly.

'The next day another beggar comes to your house just as you are about to put a morsel in your mouth, what will you do this time?'

'This won't happen in real life!'

'Millions of people live below poverty line. Their numbers will always be overwhelming.'

'Then I'll not give him food,' she answered at last.

'But in the eyes of society, your physical condition will still be much, much better than the beggar's. To some passers-by, you would even appear callous and selfish when you turn away a hungry man while you eat a fairly sumptuous meal.'

'I wouldn't care. I have to look after my needs too. I can't feed others while I suffer hunger.'

'Similarly, you can't do charity for others by compromising on your spiritual health.'

The logic caused murmurings within the group as the message sunk in. A minute ago, what Swamiji had said appeared insensitive to me, but now it made perfect sense.

'Just as you cannot survive without food, charity becomes unsustainable without meditation. In fact, all our activities become meaningless and lack divine presence without meditation.

'When it happens, the people doing charity work become monsters. They embezzle funds, show favouritism, and begin to enjoy power and control over the very people they seek to serve. They even start exploiting those they help.

'How common it is to see the filth which goes on in the name of charity. Why? Because those associated with charity, although beginning with good intents, degrade fast into becoming mere materialistic peddlers of comforts. Although they harbour a noble ambition, they fail because they lack spiritual centeredness. All the money, resources and power they have at their disposal corrupt their minds because they are defenseless without a spiritual cover.

'Why do poverty, disease, misery and sickness exist? Because the glorious potential and talent within every human being remains untapped. Why is one man better than another in the material world? Because he's more aware of the world! Why is still another more creative than the rest? Because he is more aware of himself and his strengths! How, then, to achieve higher awareness?'

'Through meditation,' said Pankaj.

Swamiji continued, 'If you go deeper, you will find that whatever good exists in you is because of a moral system or discipline you developed. Morality comes from spirituality. If you look at any crisis you face, you'll realise it stems from a breakdown of moral values at some point.'

'Swamiji, from the point of view of the poor, what do they need more? Charity or spirituality?'

'A poor man who is reluctant to change will remain poor in spite of the charity he gets. In fact, charity done without spirituality will *ensure* he stays poor. But spirituality will dispel his ignorance and give him wisdom that can improve his condition.'

'You are saying spirituality will help the poor more than blankets? In winters, cold can be a painful physical reality,' Sanjeev quipped.

'You're right. I don't deny the need for blankets, in the short run. But spirituality is indispensable in the long run.' Swamiji's smile was disarming.

'Swamiji, does this mean that even the best spiritual discourses at the ashram and our experiences on this journey will be ineffective if we do not meditate? I don't think I'll ever forget what I'm learning here, with or without meditation,' Mohan said.

'Do you remember all the three laws of Newton?'

'I remember only one: every action has an equal and opposite reaction.'

'But you studied three. Why did you forget the other two?'

'I didn't study them again ... .'

'Did you get the answer to your doubt?'

'Uhh ...' He scratched his head in bewilderment. 'I guess, yes ... I am not sure though.'

'When we meditate, we revise our value systems, and everything we learn. We introspect on our actions and remove our flaws. Forget to eat or sleep but don't give up your meditation. Never underestimate its value and importance. It will make you aware of your true potential by freeing you from all that's wasteful.'

In the morning, we set Girish's neglected house in order. We dusted rooms, windows, tables and doors and rearranged books and furniture. When we finished, the house looked comely.

'My wife was a perfectionist, and if she would have seen this, she would have been happy,' said Girish. His eyes were moist with unshed tears. 'But the children will ensure a short life of what you did.'

'Children will be children. But the house did need some keeping,' said Ruchika.

'I would have loved to join you, but I have an important project deadline to meet. If there are delays, I'll have to pay hefty penalties,' said Girish, as he served us raita with stuffed paranthas and lassi. The paranthas were soft and delicious.

'We would have loved your company too. But who knows, we might meet again, if God permits,' Swamiji remarked.

'I'll come to your ashram.'

'Then we'll recreate the magic of last night,' Sneha said.

When we prepared to leave, many people from the neighbourhood came to see us off. The divine bhajans we had sung the previous night had moved their hearts too. They took our ashram's address, as they wanted to know more about our philosophy.

'We created so many bonds today,' I rejoiced.

'Yes, on a regular trip, we'd have lived alone. Then we wouldn't have gotten the opportunity to meet and befriend so many new people,' said Pankaj.

'I can't hear what you're saying,' Swami Partibhan smiled as he turned back to see what we were discussing. He was walking ahead of us. 'I hope you're not criticising me for subjecting you to so much trouble.'

'We are planning a mutiny!' Shruti joked.

'Mutiny is against kings and authorities. I've nothing with me that you can possibly take. Plunder the treasures of the Lord instead. They are lying open for anyone interested in taking them away!'

By eleven, we saw a villager herding sheep, guiding those which wandered with his stick.

'Do any of you who feel that by being spiritual, you have suffered more than the people who are not?' Swamiji scratched his chin thoughtfully.

Many in the group replied in the affirmative.

'I was barely spiritual before I came to the ashram, so maybe I do not qualify yet for being singled out for suffering,' Subhir grinned.

'Singled out is what you said! Don't forget the turn of phrase,' Swamiji laughed. 'Some in the group feel they suffer more than the people who are not spiritual. If I say what they feel is true and not a misunderstanding, then can anyone explain their troubles?'

'They are living out their karma?' I asked hesitantly.

'No.' Swamiji shook his head.

'They are not properly spiritual.' Sanjeev smiled.

'No.'

'Then what is the reason?'

'I asked this question because I saw the shepherd guide the sheep. When we enter the kingdom of the Divine, we become his sheep and he becomes our shepherd. When we wander from the path which leads us to our destiny, he guides us back with his stick. So the suffering isn't suffering, it's divine guidance.'

'What of the other people who prosper despite being corrupt, cruel and uncaring? Why do they go unpunished?' Mohan asked.

'People who wander away from the path of spirituality are like wild sheep who don't accept the Divine as their shepherd. They roam freely and enjoy their unlimited freedom as no shepherd controls them.'

'The way you present it, being a wild sheep appears more lucrative,' Sanjeev objected.

'Yes. But would you grant such freedom to your children? No, because we know the effects of this complete freedom. Invariably, wild animals like wolves, hyenas or lions devour such sheep. Or it's hunted and killed. Despite the seemingly enviable free life it leads, it meets a tragic end. The same happens to people who prefer to stay away from divine discipline. Misfortune happens when their karma finally catches up with them.

'Whenever we suffer, we should remind ourselves that difficulties lead to evolution. All suffering points to erring on our parts, they serve as a reminder to us about what should be our priority. The suffering inconveniences us, but also reminds us of the false ways we have adopted.

'A piece of gold, if it has to remain just that, will undergo no trials and tribulations. If it's to become an ornament, it has to be smelted in fire, beaten into shape and polished by a file to become a useful and beautiful piece of art. Our hardships turn us into beautiful ornaments.'

Around 1 p.m., we were passing a road near Taloli when Tarun shouted excitedly, 'Look, guavas!'

We peered at the tree and saw ripe fruits. Tarun was quick to climb it.

On Tarun's insistence, I tried to relive my youth and attempted scaling a tree. I had lost my simian abilities a long time ago and settled for catching what he hurled. I was clumsy in that too, dropping several guavas. To prove they were no less, Vibha and Shruti also climbed the trees and plucked fruit. We collected a sufficient quantity. When I tasted the guava, it was extraordinarily sweet.

'Wait, let me come down. Don't finish them all!' Tarun waved the branches of the tree at me.

I gestured a guava at him, poked a thumb and continued to relish the fruit.

'Swamiji, foul!' laughed Tarun. 'You're so mild, he doesn't fear you.'

'I have no control over monkeys,' said Swamiji, smiling. 'Come down; we have enough for our lunch.'

We ate our fill of the mouth-watering guavas. Some of them were of a red hue.

'The red ones are a rare variety,' Mohan said as he chewed one. 'Delicious.'

The guavas were our first natural food since the journey and the change from regular meals was refreshing.

Meals over, I played a light tune on my guitar. My fellow seekers clapped and danced to the tune and we enjoyed the good time.

Then it was time to start again on the trail to Ganapatipule.

15 | Déjà Vu But with a Higher Point of View

'It'll take nearly one hour to reach Mumbra–Kausa,' a cyclist told us when we asked about the nearest village. We had started from Taloli at about 4.30 p.m.

'Swamiji, let's camp,' Mohan said. 'We might get late and this place looks good enough to settle in.'

'I think we should use the sunlight to cover some distance. Besides, the landscape is so beautiful and pleasant. Why not enjoy it? But not if you are tired,' Swamiji said.

So we marched on.

When we realised we'd committed a mistake, it was too late. We were caught in a long and desolate stretch with no signs of Mumbra–Kausa. It was nearing six and beginning to get dark.

A thicket of trees, shrubs and foliage populated the banks of the desolate tract. The beauty of the landscape which had prodded us to carry on with our walk now caused fear. The place didn't look safe at all, especially for women.

'Where's the village?' Kulkarni voiced his worry.

'That cyclist told us it wouldn't take more than an hour,' Vibha said.

We walked on in silence, hoping we would reach some populated place.

'Maybe he was right and we misunderstood him,' Sanjeev said after sometime.

'How?'

'Maybe he assumed we would travel by bus, like all sane people do.'

I winced at the sarcastic remark. Yet, his explanation was most likely true, which meant that we were marooned in that desolate section, on a moonless night, without a street light. The night, almost upon us, was cold and harsh. The wind was howling and the area was at least five to eight degrees cooler than the city would have been because of the green cover, open spaces and dew.

'I think we're stuck,' Swami Partibhan conceded.

'We must turn back,' said Mohan. 'I don't like the idea of moving further into this jungle.'

'No, that's pointless,' I said. 'Soon it will be too dark to continue, either backwards or forwards.'

'I think we'll have to put up here,' Swami Partibhan voiced my worst fear.

As we thought about the implications of what he said, the sight of an approaching bus cheered us. We looked at Swamiji, whose face glowed in the light from the beams. He shook his head. 'We stick by the rules. Only foot travel for us. Remember, it's the Divine's wish that we be here.'

'What of the women in the group?' Mohan asked.

'We're all in equal danger. Those who want to opt out of the trip may do so. We're a big group. The choice to stay or leave is yours.'

We looked at one another. The bus was close now. If we didn't take the decision quickly, it would leave us stranded.

'I'm opting out,' said Mohan. 'This is madness.'

'Please don't leave! Nothing will happen,' said Tarun, holding his hand.

Mohan jerked it free. 'I, too, would like to be a part of this journey but it doesn't mean I should abandon common sense. We're vulnerable, especially our women seekers ... .'

'If he wants to go, let him go. Don't force anyone to stay if they want to leave,' Swamiji intervened.

We hailed the bus for his sake. When we asked the conductor to drop Mohan to the nearest village without a ticket, he refused. However, a compassionate passenger volunteered to buy his ticket.

'I seriously think the women should leave with me,' said Mohan as he boarded the bus.

'Come on if you want; this is the last bus of the day. This is not a highway. We can't halt the bus here forever.' The conductor looked at us sternly, his face screwed into an impatient scowl. 'But no one travels without a ticket.' He blew his whistle vigorously and the bus started to move. I felt a nagging regret as I watched it disappear. The bus left the night darker than before.

'Sometimes the concern we show for others is our own fear,' I heard Shruti's voice through the darkness.

'He tried to appear concerned, but he was the one who was afraid.' This must have been Vibha. 'But I must confess, my decision to stay here is more out of faith than any logic.'

'If it is faith which made you stop here, then it will work out well.'

I couldn't help but smile at Swami Partibhan's optimism. The words calmed me, despite the situation we were in. It was so dark, we kept bumping into each other.

Without bedsheets, without any shelter and in this wilderness, where would we sleep? The place looked positively dangerous.

'We should collect twigs and light a fire. Anyone has a matchstick?' said Sanjeev.

No one spoke.

'Any ideas?' asked Swami Partibhan.

'We can try rubbing flint stones to light a fire,' said Ruchika. She had found her voice at last.

So we groped for stones in the dark. We came across shrubs, gravel and soil, but it took time to get hold of the bigger stones. When we stuck them together, they gave off a spark.

We collected twigs, dried leaves and paper, groping about like blind people. Sifting through whatever we could lay our hands on, we got hold of a sizeable collection of combustible items. We struck the stones in an attempt to ignite a fire. Half an hour went by – the sparks remained just sparks.

The wind howled and the darkness was deeper than I'd ever experienced. I shivered, and my nose ran. Sanjeev collected more paper and tore them into shards. He held them over a stone which he hit repeatedly with another stone in quick succession. As he did so, the stone would sometimes hit his finger too, making him swear. I didn't know whether to laugh or sympathise with him! But soon, he found his rhythm and created sparks in quick session. Some of them fell on the paper shards, emitting smoke, but died down quickly. He tried again and managed to create more smoke, but no fire.

'Let me roll this newspaper into a pipe to blow air over the smoke. Maybe then we will be able to start a fire,' suggested Tarun.

He rolled a newspaper into a pipe and blew over the smoke. The embers he managed to produce with his blow pipe shot out tiny flames. Sanjeev quickly took the kindled shard to the pile of combustible material we had collected and managed to light it up.

All of us clapped with delight, like children, when the fire appeared. Getting a fire started without a matchstick seemed an incredible achievement.

The overwhelming wind became an ally, helping us build the bonfire. I relaxed as I felt its warmth seeping through my clothes.

'Collect some more wood for the night, and then we can sleep by turns. Two of us can feed the fire and keep a vigil,' said Sanjeev, fanning the fire with a newspaper.

The change in Sanjeev, from a passive traveller to a man who could organise and lead a group, was impressive. Had he deliberately underplayed himself so far? Why?

Finding usable wood was much easier in the light from the fire. We also collected branches and dry twigs. I noticed that the mood of the group was again upbeat, everyone appearing hopeful and excited, and felt sorry for Mohan for having given up hope so soon. Yet my fear of the desolation remained. Our numbers were some comfort, though.

'Be careful not to let the fire die,' said Shruti, when it dipped dangerously low.

We went without food that night, but because of the anxiety, I didn't feel hungry at all. We moved away from the road to a clearing concealed by trees in case of possible miscreants. Here, we swept away the pebbles with a broom we'd made by tying several branches and leaves. We then spread the large leaves of a banyan tree to serve as a bedspread. The fire dried the dew and we became comfortable after a while, with the earth as our bed and the starry sky our cover.

The sky was beautiful and the stars looked like gems in the velvety darkness. I fell asleep, gazing at the stars.

❧

At 2 a.m., we had company. We were woken up by strange animal howls.

'Wolves!' Sanjeev's left ear turned to the direction from where they were coming. His face betrayed an unusual calm. 'They won't attack as long as the fire burns. Be on guard.'

Out of panic, we fed the fire with more wood. I saw three pairs of shining eyes. I felt insecure, anxious and edgy despite the group, because we would be defenceless if they chose to attack. But when I saw the fire deterred them from closing in on us, I relaxed. The scene transported me to those ancient times when cavemen inhabited the earth. I couldn't help marvelling at the progress we have achieved since those times. Yet, despite that, we are still as perplexed about the business of living as the primitive human beings. Will there be a time when mankind will get out of its seemingly pointless existence? Would future generations then look back on our times as primitive?

In another hour, after we got used to the menace, all but two of us went back to sleep. Thankfully, we were equipped with an adequate stock of wood.

A little while later into the night, the sound of hooves of fast-approaching horses woke us up with a jolt. We sat up, alert and tense with anxious anticipation. What kind of people would be out on a night like this, that too on horses? Suddenly, they came into view – eight men, carrying torches. From their stern faces and the silhouettes of their guns, I realised immediately that they were dacoits. My heartbeat quickened. We stood glued to our spots, paralysed by fear.

'Who are you? What're you doing here?' One of the dacoits who rode on a white horse demanded. He looked like the leader.

We told him about the journey.

'Give us all you have.'

'We don't have any possessions, we're just pilgrims,' said Ramanujam.

'Don't try to trick us. Tell us where you've hidden your cash and you won't suffer.'

'We're on a spiritual journey and one of its conditions is that we can't carry cash. We're telling you the truth,' said Subhir.

'If you don't have cash, then we'll take your women,' said another dacoit, smiling wickedly.

The leader watched with piercing eyes, waiting for our reaction.

'You'll have to kill all the men first. We're duty-bound to protect their honour,' Swamiji stepped forward.

I suddenly felt queasy. Any resistance would be futile. No one could fight those gun-wielding dacoits. If they decided to take the women, they would. Our lives wouldn't matter.

'So you'll fight us? With what? Your bare hands?' They began to laugh.

'Quiet!' said the leader sternly. 'These people clearly have nothing to give us.' He turned to us. 'We're dacoits, but we don't harm women and children.'

They were about to turn.

'You said that with much pride,' Swami Partibhan's voice sounded like a whiplash. Those men of violence were leaving us unharmed and before I could even feel relieved, Swami Partibhan called them back with his remark! What was he up to? What had happened to him? My mouth went dry and my body grew stiff.

'What?' The leader abruptly turned his horse, causing it to raise itself on its hind legs. Its whinny made me shiver involuntarily.

'What you said about not hurting women and children.'

'Yes. We dacoits too have our dharma. We live by it. But what are you trying to say?'

'If you kill a father, wouldn't you hurt a child? If you kill a husband or son, wouldn't you cause harm to a woman?'

'You talk too much. Enjoy the life we've spared, or we might change our minds,' said the leader, holding his restless horse firmly. This was surely going to get us into trouble. I wished somebody would keep Swamiji in check.

'You said it's your dharma not to hurt a woman or child, but when I ask you a question, you evaded it with a threat. Why, have I made you uncomfortable?'

The leader returned with lightning-speed and swung his rifle at Swamiji's face, who fell on the ground, spewing blood. 'You're a fly to me. I can squash the life out of you in less than a second.

Yet you talk of making me uncomfortable? Prepare to die, you fool!' The dacoit pointed his gun at Swamiji's face.

Swamiji got back on his feet quickly, never removing his gaze from the leader's face. We held our breath as we watched the blood trickle from his mouth. He did not even try to cover the wound, which was bleeding profusely.

'Why is such a powerful man angered so much by an unarmed pilgrim?' His face was expressionless.

'Don't you fear death, you fool?'

'You're the one who's afraid, not I. Why are you carrying guns? Those who make a living by robbing unarmed people at gunpoint can't be brave.'

'Shut up! I lost everything once, due to fear. Now, I know no fear.'

'Then, you were a victim; now, you make others victim of your brutality. Is that how you overcame fear?'

'I've become a beast! And if you knew who I am, you wouldn't speak so much.' The gun clicked.

'What's it you're running away from?'

I shut my eyes tight. Any minute now, I would hear the shot.

'You're running away from yourself. You don't wish to face what you've become.'

An eerie silence lingered, in which my heart beat erratically. Though he was a hair's breadth's from death, Swamiji's eyes shone with courage, mesmerising and defiant.

For the first time, the eyes of the dacoit leader shifted. He appeared uncertain, which gave me hope.

'Abandon this path of violence.'

Swamiji touched the dacoit's hand.

Out of the corner of my eye, I saw two of his henchmen getting down from their horses. They didn't like Swamiji's hand resting on their leader's. But Partibhan ignored them.

'You want money? For what? Food? We helpless people in this wood are sure the Divine will look after all our needs, even though we do not have a penny with us. Give up your violent ways. You still respect life, and have settled scores with those whom you hated. What you're doing now is worse than what those people did to you, because you have no reason for doing it any more. Give up your evil path.'

With a jerk, the leader pulled his hand away.

'Let's leave,' the leader said, just as his men raised their clenched fists. 'This man is a fool, he's itching to die. Let's not bloody our hands with his murder.' The leader turned abruptly and galloped away with the other dacoits behind him.

A few yards away, the leader stopped and turned again, to stare at Swamiji. I wondered if he was going to kill him after all. Then he kicked his horse and was gone.

We heard the noise of the hooves as they receded into darkness. The trail of dust they left behind reflected the light from our bonfire and cast a golden haze.

'Why'd you risk – why – your life for such an insensitive man?' Shruti rushed to Swamiji. She sobbed and trembled uncontrollably. 'I thought he'd fire any moment and … ! Why'd you talk … the brute … he was about to kill you!'

She applied her scarf on Swamiji's wounds. His tongue, lips and gums were bleeding profusely from the cuts.

'You were so close to death,' said Sneha, fighting to conceal the quiver in her voice.

Dr Piyushi stood still, too shocked to attend to Swamiji's wounds.

'Swamiji, what came over you?' I held his shoulders, inspecting his wounds. 'You shouldn't have been so headstrong. Anything might have happened.'

Swamiji smiled through his wounds. 'I gave the message of the Divine to the dacoit because I knew it was His will. Why do you think we got stuck in the woods? To learn to make a fire and fight wolves? No, we were here because the Divine wanted us to give a message to this man and his fellow beings. We were chosen as His instruments.'

'You could've died!' Shruti's voice was almost a scream. 'Besides, did he pay any heed to your message?'

'I thought you were brave when you told them you'd prefer to die for our sakes. But when you started giving a sermon, I thought you'd lost your mind,' said Ruchika.

'Everyone's happy while they get what they want.' Swami Partibhan looked at Shruti and then Ruchika. 'You were happy when I was prepared to die to protect your honour. Yet, I was also concerned about the welfare of the dacoit. I didn't mind risking my life for his sake too.'

'But –'

'Life has no meaning if we merely preserve it. It makes sense only if we use it.'

'I think I was selfish to have thought only of myself,' said Ruchika, immediately apologetic.

'Yet, why'd you risk your life over a dacoit? You could've reformed a more reasonable person,' asked Tarun.

'The dacoit affects many people's lives because he has power and is misled. Reforming him will save many others. So it was worth risking my life.'

'He didn't listen to you.'

'I should've been dead if he didn't pay heed to anything I had said. I saw hope in the dacoit when he talked about his dharma with pride. I took it as an opportunity to give the message.'

'Message?' I asked.

'Each of us gets messages from the messengers of the Divine – ordinary beings who tell us about His glory and the peace one gets by following His ways. We may listen to them or ignore them, but they have a habit of reappearing regularly. They are reminders to wake up from the illusionary world, which we presume to be real. In the end, we cannot complain we were ignorant.

'Our creator, who bestows upon us infinite capabilities and allows us complete freedom, makes sure our lifestyle is a choice we have executed and not some ignorant accident thrust on us. After that, it is up to us if we wish to evolve or merely survive. The decision this dacoit will take after the message I gave him today will be his choice alone, not something imposed by circumstances beyond his control which he might falsely believe and justify. You see?'

I shrugged my head. His convictions were so strong, he was ready to die for them. Whatever he said made sense, though.

By now, it was nearing daybreak and the place awakened slowly to the new dawn. The chirping of birds broke the stillness. The wilderness lost its dread and transformed into a beautiful entity. We saw a river a little ahead of where we had camped for the night.

'I think I'll go wash my wounds,' Swamiji said. 'A new day's begun. Let's see what it brings for us. I'll miss Mohan, though. He was right in worrying about staying back.'

'I'll help you,' volunteered Shruti and followed him.

It was also time to wash clothes and ready ourselves with the morning ablutions. The women went one way and the men went in the opposite direction.

I had to relieve myself in the open for the first time. The experience was humbling and embarrassing, and I made sure I was far away from the group. Then I walked to the river's edge, took off my clothes and washed them. Once again, I bathed in the river's cold water. This time, it was much easier. I wrung out as much water as I could from my clothes and then wore the other set I carried. Swamiji had asked us to bring the thinnest clothes because they dried faster.

Ablutions over, I walked towards the group, ready to face the challenges ahead. To my surprise, I saw Tarun perched on a tree, hurling *ber* fruits at Pankaj, like the previous afternoon. Pankaj and Subhir caught them expertly and passed around the fruits within the group. We ate as much as we could and wanted to carry more with us. However, the rule of not hoarding anything for the future precluded that possibility.

'How this stretch of our journey has changed in a few hours!' said Swamiji, munching the fruits. 'In the night, it seemed fearsome and dangerous. Now it looks so benign and beautiful, we feel a reluctance to leave.'

Despite the beauty around us, I still couldn't forget the terror I had felt in the night. We could have lost Swamiji and this morning would have been so different, so horrible.

Swamiji's face was swollen from his injuries and he smiled self-consciously. 'I'm afraid I don't look pretty,' he said, when he caught me looking at him.

I looked away. Remembering the way his eyes had sparkled defiantly, I wondered if he overcame fear or ignored it. Only he knew best. He looked so ordinary, so unassuming in nature. Who would suspect the mighty reserves of strength, wisdom and conviction he possessed?

I marvelled at his unique talent and felt inspired anew by his practical spiritual insights.

16 | Sit in the Cradle, or Walk and Excel

In the afternoon, when we approached some houses near Kolkhe village for our meal, something strange happened. Two brothers, Ajoy Ghosh and Bijoy Ghosh, were so impressed by the idea behind our spiritual journey that they joined us immediately. This was a reversal; so far we had only seen a trend of desertions. From thirteen, our ranks swelled to fifteen.

'Don't go with them! They might be kidnappers!' The wife of the younger brother Bijoy fidgeted near the gate of their house. 'They've hypnotised you. You're under their spell.'

'Relax Vinita. Nothing's going to happen to Bijoy. I'm with him,' Ajoy tried to assure her.

'What do you know about these people? How can you trust them?' said their mother, supporting Vinita.

'Before I married Vinita, what did you or I know about her?' Bijoy grinned at his mother. 'Calm down, it will work out well. Stop worrying about us, we are grown up!'

'I experienced a similar scene at home,' said Pankaj as he observed the concern of Ajoy and Bijoy's family members. 'My mother was almost hysterical.'

'So how did you tackle her?' I asked.

'I told her I was going anyway and if she was so concerned about my well being, she could join me. That settled the issue.' His eyes twinkled with mischief.

'She didn't trouble you?'

'She thought all of us were mad and refused to be a part of what she called a "mad carnival".'

'All relationships last only up to a point. Beyond that, we're alone.' I gazed at the road ahead as I was suddenly reminded of my loneliness.

ფე

Next day at Vashi, when we asked for food, an elderly person started contradicting us.

'Spirituality grows from being still, not unnecessary movement. To me, your journey is more like an adventure, not for seeking the truth.' The man chewed his paan vigorously. 'Your pursuit is immature and naïve.'

The man wore white clothes with a huge tilak smeared on his forehead. All his fingers bore gem-laden gold rings. Some of the fingers even had two rings! He spoke on spirituality with a tone of authority.

Our silence encouraged him.

'We can see God easily without having to do all this. I know a shortcut.'

'What is it?' I asked.

'Tantra.' He spit out the word and sprayed my shirt with red betel juice. I tried to wipe it clean with my handkerchief but my efforts created a red patch. Alarmed, I moved backwards.

'Meet me at my home, at midnight. The cremation ground's just nearby. I'll initiate you into tantric worship. Also, bring these.' He jotted down a list.

I was shocked when Sneha passed me the list. Pigeons, live chickens, human bones, ashes, a butcher's knife, an iron poke, ghee, wood, black clothes, vermillion ... the list was endless.

'We won't take the women to the cremation ground. They'll stay at my house, with my wife. Here's the address.'

'Why?' Ramanujam asked.

'Women were responsible for the decline of mankind's moral values. Manu Rishi has said that animals and women are fit to be beaten.'

'I don't believe it ... .'

'That's why you are so naïve. Come to the cremation ground tonight and you will start believing everything I say.'

'But –'

'We are getting late Nikhil,' Swamiji interrupted me abruptly. 'We'll meet you at night, sir,' he turned to the man and said.

We parted ways.

'Why did you lie to him Swamiji?' I asked. Swamiji's indifference to the tantric bothered me. 'That man was completely misguided. We should have reasoned with him. Tried to change him.'

'No Nikhil. That man is completely lost. No one can save him.'

'But he was at least better than the dacoit you risked your life for,' Vibha objected.

'The dacoit was misled but he still believed in dharma. This man is not only misled, he's so rigid in his beliefs, nothing can change him. In trying to change him, we will lose our perspective and energies, our connection with the Divine.'

'That looks callous,' said Sanjeev.

'When you are in touch with the Divine, you develop discretion. Just like a doctor who knows which disease is worth fighting for and which is hopeless. They can either expend their time on hopeless cases or devote their limited energies to patients they can cure, who need their services. It's not that the tantric will never evolve: it might take him many lifetimes to realise that his approach to the Divine was a delusion which he held on to, despite the many contradictions he experienced.'

I grinned and shook my head.

'Just because you are spiritual, it doesn't mean you should be compassionate to anyone who crosses your way. To maintain your state, you must know whom to give the divine message and whom to avoid.'

'I remember arguing with an atheist once. I knew whatever he was saying was wrong. But at the end of a three-hour debate, I lost my faith,' admitted Subhir.

'That's exactly the point I was trying to make.'

By now, all my preferences for a particular vegetable or dislike for another was gone. Food was no longer a luxury, but a means to complete the journey which was precious to me. Despite the insecurity, I was careful how much I ate. Enough to fill me for eight hours but not to interfere with the seven hours of walking we did between every meal. I learnt that if I ate too much, walking became difficult because my body would feel sluggish.

We sat upon small rocks at the centre of a park. Behind us was a beautiful fountain. The day was breezy but the chill pleasant, warmed as we were with the mild sun. We passed whatever we collected to one another, enjoying the afternoon sun.

'Bijoy is lost in his thoughts.' Swami Partibhan laid out some papers on which we spread the food.

Bijoy took an apple from the assortment and looked up. 'I was wondering why I fall short of spiritual standards. One minute I'm flying in the sky of divinity and the next minute, I'm trying to swim out of the swamp of desires. Sometimes I feel materialistic people are better off than me. At least they don't have confusions. I constantly toggle between spiritualism and materialism.'

I reflected on what he had said. I, too, experienced the same whenever I gave in to temptation. The desire for intimacy with my secretary had evoked similar reactions in me.

'Have you seen a child trying to walk, Bijoy? He tries and falls down. Again he gets up, tries and falls. Again, and again. For some time, his state appears to be worse than crawling. However, who's better off? The child who just sits or the one who learns to walk? You can compare materialistic people with children who are comfortable sitting in their cradles. But we have to keep trying despite failures because our self is tired of squatting in the darkness of ignorance when it can run towards divine light.'

'Your words are encouraging.' Ajoy was thoughtful. 'Still, I feel spirituality is a difficult and lonely struggle. Like a night without end. I'm unable to see this light you mention.'

'Whenever you lose hope, remember the parable of water kept on fire,' Swami Partibhan continued. 'Initially, while it is getting warmer, we see no evidence of anything happening to it. A person who's ignorant of the process might think nothing's happening. Then suddenly, we see bubbles and the water begins to churn – it's achieved a change of state. Being self-aware takes time. How do we know if the water's changing its state? By dipping our fingers. And how do we know if we're evolving? By comparing ourselves with what we were and what we've become. Though we may be far from perfection, we improve.'

'But –'

'All the hours of the night appear no different from each other. Though the moments towards dawn may be the darkest, they are the ones that deliver the morning rays. Only the patient and determined see the light of pure knowledge.'

'I find it surprising how different people worship different forms of God throughout the world. Christianity believes only in Jesus and dismisses every other religion as pagan. The Hindus have so many gods and goddesses. If one is devoted to Krishna, the other is a follower of Rama. We also have Kali *bhaktas*, Hanuman devotees and so on,' Piyushi said. 'Who's right and who wrong? All of them can't be right!'

'All of them are right about the incarnations they worship being great. But they are wrong in excluding the significance of other incarnations. Jesus, Krishna, Rama and Kali – all of them give different blessings to the entire humanity. Rama taught us about dharma, Jesus about forgiveness and sacrifice. Krishna preached detachment, without giving undue importance to results. Kali freed humanity from oppression. Hanuman represents unquestioning devotion to the Supreme Being.'

'So we are an assimilation of their qualities?'

'Yes. These incarnations set off a chain reaction that led to our evolution. We assimilated their qualities and today, anyone who decides to walk on the spiritual path can easily attain them. Before the arrival of these incarnations, it was impossible for humans to achieve the qualities they bestowed. Can you see a lion, even by exception, who is forgiving?

'The essence of these incarnations gets lost when, instead of absorbing their qualities, we relegate them to mere symbols for various religious cults. These incarnations blessed us with higher awareness. From being the relative of an ape with no purpose or values, the caveman became a conscious being. No other living creature can match human beings because the human race is an integration of the values gifted by these incarnations.'

'Still, different people have different opinions about the Divine. Some believe He's a sadist enjoying His creation. Some feel He is all-powerful while others think of Him as powerless, citing the poverty, disease and starvation that affects most of humanity. How can we perceive one God in so many different ways?' Sanjeev enquired.

Swami Partibhan looked at Sanjeev for sometime without any expression. Sanjeev became uncomfortable and looked away.

'You can compare it to people's relation with the sun,' Swami Partibhan remarked. 'One sun affects different people in different ways, but essentially what is it: a star emitting heat and light. You can dry clothes and say that the sun is for drying clothes. You can power a car with its energy and say it's an energy source. You can warm yourself and say it's for keeping the body warm. You can go blind looking at it and claim it is harmful.' He paused.

'I see. It depends on how we align with it,' I said.

'How many of us live according to the laws of the scriptures?' asked Swamiji. 'Most of us lead a life that denies spiritual precepts. We violate all divine laws and smother our consciences. We lie, cheat, commit adultery and indulge in lavishness when others struggle to survive. Yet, when nothing wrong happens to us, we think we've gotten away with our wanton ways.

'Were those saints who wrote about karma and the need to abide by spiritual laws fools? Try to look for spiritual people in this world and you'll have to search hard. If the majority of this world is inclined towards a corrupt value system, then in what manner will it reap the karmic fruit of the seeds it sows? You get a result where eighty per cent of the population lives in misery.

'Where do you think will all the people who voluntarily choose to live outside the shelter of the Divine go? What will happen to all those disbelievers who laugh at the idea of the Divine and plunder resources for their limited gains? Reverse the trend which exists today – connect eighty per cent of the people to the Divine, and all the miseries you mention will disappear. We create misery; we pay the price of our own actions, but blame the Divine for it.

'When we have the choice, we negate all the positive value systems which spirituality preaches, and then we wonder why there is darkness on earth. I didn't want to say it in such stern terms, but you insisted and there was no other way. I don't wish to put fear of the Divine in you because the Divine only loves us. But how would a mother treat a truant son who troubles another noble son of hers? She'll have to punish him if he doesn't improve. The Divine is also like a mother to us. He's neither sadistic nor vengeful.'

What Swamiji said made a lot more sense than any other explanation I had heard or read.

'So what hope do we have of uniting with the pure Divine, when we have so much filth in us?' Sanjeev persisted.

'As much hope as a stream of a polluted river has on its way to the ocean. Only our intent separates us from the Divine, not our filth. His power to make us pure is infinite because He cannot be polluted.'

At noon, Pankaj complained of a headache. He'd caught cold in the jungle. He tried to walk with us but couldn't. We took an hour's rest to see if he would get well, but he didn't. Dr Piyushi touched his forehead with her palm, then took his temperature. '103 degrees. The fever's rising,' she said, examining his tongue and eyes. 'Looks like viral infection to me. He needs rest and an analgesic. I wouldn't advise him to continue on this journey.'

She gave him medicines and waited for the temperature to subside. We placed wet towels on his forehead and chest to bring down his temperature.

In another hour, it came down, but his eyes were watery.

'Feel better now?'

'Yes. I would like to continue.'

'No. You're going back home.' Dr Piyushi stopped him from getting up.

When Tarun tried to escort him on his journey home, Pankaj vehemently refused.

'I'll manage. I wouldn't want you to give up this journey.' His lips were dry and his face pale.

With sadness, we bid farewell to our friend. Piyushi gave him some medicines for the way.

'Don't worry about him. What am I there for?' The jovial taxi-driver assured Dr Piyushi, who kept checking Pankaj's forehead. 'You'll get the money from the ashram,' said Swamiji.

'I don't feel like leaving,' said Pankaj, as the driver closed the door. 'I'll miss all the fun.'

'Some other time, my friend.'

'Sure you'll manage?' asked Tarun.

'Of course. I'll be fine. Don't worry about me.'

'Take care of yourself.'

'You too, and Swamiji, even you! You scared me last night with your bravery.'

The taxi left.

A boil on my toe was a cause of worry: even I might have to opt out of the journey if it worsened because of my diabetes. When we halted for rest the next time, I picked up a piece of rag and cleaned the boil thoroughly. I was about to wrap it around my toe when Swamiji came to me.

'You've done only half the job, my friend. Let me do the other half.'

He got up, approached the *neem* trees on the side of the road, and plucked some leaves. Using a stone, he ground them to a paste and applied it on my wound. He then tied the makeshift bandage, a little clumsily because instead of a forefinger, he only had a stub.

'What happened to your finger? It appears you lost it recently.'

Swami Partibhan smiled. 'The night I lost it looked terribly violent and bleak. But looking back, I see there was a design even in that mayhem. And it is so true about everything in life.'

The paste felt cool and soothing. My heart melted at his humility when he lifted my foot and placed it on his lap to apply the dressing.

'Are you seekers of the Divine getting the worth of the efforts you're putting in?' he asked when he finished the job. 'I mean, take a look at you. You're falling ill, getting boils, facing hunger and wild animals in the woods, not to talk of dacoits. Is it worth the while? Or do you wish to call it quits?'

'No. I'd like to continue!'

'No way do we wish to quit, Swamiji!'

'We're enjoying it!'

The garbled replies were spontaneous.

17 | Life's a Stage, But Do You Hear the Message?

As we walked into a village on the stretch between Vashi and Nagothane, a few people rushed to meet us. They abandoned their shops and chores to surround us.

'Are you Swami Partibhan?' One of them stared at Swamiji strangely.

'Did you confront the notorious dacoit Virendra Pratap near Mumbra–Kausa?' another asked.

'During the early hours of the morning?'

'He hit you with his rifle butt on the face?'

They rained questions on us, while we stood confused, unable to understand what was happening.

'Yes. Here.' Swamiji showed his wound to them.

'You asked him to leave his violent path?' A woman brought her hand to her mouth.

'Even when he pointed his gun and threatened to kill you?' A child held Swami Partibhan's hand and looked up at him, awestruck.

'How do you know all this?' Swamiji's eyebrows knit into a frown. 'You weren't with us! Why do you ask me all this? Is something wrong?'

'Dacoit Virendra Pratap listened to you and surrendered at 1 p.m. today. He gave an account of what happened in the wilderness to the newspersons.'

'He surrendered with his entire gang. He was impressed by the way you wanted them to change their ways even in the face of death.'

'All the channels are flashing the news with your photographs.'

'We recognised you from the photographs on TV.'

Everyone talked excitedly at once.

'So the message went home.' Swamiji turned to us and smiled. 'You see the power of the Divine? We were stuck in those woods for a purpose. God bless him. I respect him and bow to him for the courage it must have taken to surrender.'

The way he said it, it appeared the entire credit belonged to the dacoit and not him!

'Come, see the news on TV,' shouted a man in the crowd. 'You're the hero of the media.'

'I am but a messenger. The real hero is Virendra Pratap. He deserves your attention and love because he chose to act on the message and make amends.'

'You are very humble, Swamiji.'

'Please stay with us today. Take a day off from your foot march to Ganapatipule.'

'Is that on the news too?'

'Yes.'

'God help us all,' said Swami Partibhan with a frown. 'Now we'll not be left in peace.'

Sure enough, a couple of media reporters found us and pressed us for an interview. At first, they tried to tell Swamiji to comb his hair and rearrange his clothes for the camera in the typically arrogant way of the press. The make-up artist wanted to highlight his wounds. Behind us, the cameramen were taking out their equipment and setting up a live telecast. The whole town seemed to be in a grip of excitement.

Swamiji laughed gently at the suggestions of the reporter on grooming and rejected them outright. 'I'm not an actor who needs to look good before giving a shot. I've no wish to look different.'

The clever interviewer sensed immediately that a high-handed approach would only put Swamiji off, so he softened a bit.

'If you sit, we can interview you better. You'll look more presentable under the lights.'

Again Swamiji laughed like a child.

'The journey is my priority, not appearing on channels as a celebrity.'

The reporter reluctantly began to walk with Swamiji to interview him.

'Where did you get the courage to stand up against an armed and merciless dacoit?' He shot his first question.

'When you are in touch with the Divine, it doesn't need courage to give the message of God,' Swamiji said simply. 'It becomes a habit.'

'How does it feel to have made him surrender?'

'He *chose* to surrender, but I do feel good that the man listened to reason.'

'From a spiritual guru to the hero of the masses – how does the journey feel?'

'I'll say it again, you've got it all wrong,' said Swamiji. 'The dacoit is the real hero in all this.'

'Why?'

Swami Partibhan paused and turned to face the interviewer.

'How often do we tell people to change their ways? When we ask others to give up anger, lying, smoking, dishonesty and cheating, or to give up drinking alcohol, do they change? If at all anyone gives up his bad habits, who do you think is a better person: the one who gives free advice or the one who listens? Is giving advice worthier than giving up a habit?'

'I didn't see it that way.' The interviewer's eyes widened in surprise.

'Go to the dacoit. He's your hero, not me. Leave us alone; we've a job to do.'

'Thank you, Swamiji.' The interviewer snapped out of his thoughts. The crew was waiting for him to end the interview.

'The humble guru Swami Partibhan refuses to take credit for the dacoit's surrender in his typical self-effacing way. Yet, how many of us will stand up to a gun and risk our lives? How many self-styled gurus, who live in palaces but promote ascetic lifestyles, undertake a *pada-yatra* without money and any belongings? The whole nation salutes Guru Partibhan, who travels on foot and spreads the message of practical spirituality.'

The reporter signed off with the typical smile they all have for viewers.

People on all sides surrounded us. The experience was overwhelming. They wanted to talk to us, to shake hands with us, and see for themselves the people whose photographs were appearing on all television channels. Many touched Swamiji's feet and sought his blessings. After much pleading and requesting, they allowed us to resume our journey.

'I'm surprised you could change him. You risked your life for it. *Jai Swami Partibhan!*' Tarun chanted with enthusiasm. He was joined by Ramanujam.

'*Jai Swami Partibhan!*' I too shouted as loudly as I could, with the others. Until then, I had never raised slogans for anyone. Yet Swami Partibhan's courage in the wilderness deserved praise, and praise flowed spontaneously from my heart.

PART TWO

Sanjeev's story

Immaculate conception is impossible. Shri Krishna was a petty magician. Shri Rama was but a glorified king. Accept all these convincing allegations as true, and what have you? The Divine is just a myth.

Deny the Divine and live the 'free life', and soon, all peace evaporates. The snakes of anger, desire, temptation, jealousy and competition infest and torment the mind.

Faith in the Divine brings bliss and peace.

So is being spiritual a brainwashed response? But then, isn't every conviction brainwashing? If you don't believe in the Divine, then you have been brainwashed into believing there is no Divine. What kind of brainwashing is good? One that gives peace or one which disturbs?

We make all the choices and we alone are responsible for the results. No person or circumstance is responsible for what we choose to become.

18 | Shouts of Doubts

I watched the group with amusement as they sang the bhajan in ecstasy. They swayed and clapped with joy, eyes closed like zombies.

These people singing the cleverly crafted song seemed like addicts who had found an escapist fix. Those who had invented the hoax called God had pulled off a good job. They created a myth foolish people like these seekers readily accepted. The whole idea about this stage-managed journey without money and personal belongings was too good to be true; these people were blind.

Guru Partibhan is an accomplished rogue, an actor and a cheat. His ploy to gain popularity impressed me when I got the first briefing. A publicity stunt like this would guarantee huge media attention. The way the so-called miracles kept occurring one after the other, and the ease with which we got our food and lodging, merely confirmed my suspicions.

Madhoo, the fairytale contractor, and the dacoit – they were puppets on a thread Partibhan and his organisation pulled. His syrupy lectures, friendly homilies, and banal summaries after each stage-managed act filled me with nausea and repulsion. All around me, I saw bobbing heads, worshipful smiles and tearful eyes as the fools believed everything.

How easy it is to take the masses on a roller-coaster ride, especially the believers! His blatantly self-effacing manner was a publicity-seeking ploy, and it made me sick.

'How many self-styled gurus would leave their palaces and walk the streets?' the reporter had asked the audience. Only clever Partibhan! He was shrewd enough to see the huge potential of a well-scripted spiritual *pada-yatra*.

∞

'I have an assignment for you.' It had been raining the day Ranbir came to my home. I had been watching the raindrops from my portico, sipping tea while relishing the pakoras my mother had cooked for me.

'What does it involve?'

'Exposure.'

'Whose?'

'Swami Partibhan's.'

'Partibhan? Swami Parmanand's heir?'

'The same guy.'

'What's he done?'

'We believe he is taking his devotees on a trip.'

'By "trip" I guess you mean the journey?'

'Exactly.'

'And what will be my job?

'Spying on him, of course!'

I am a private detective. For ten years now, I have been involved in the investigations of some of the biggest industrial crimes and leaks, while also detecting celebrity level adultery. The cases I have investigated have involved names that would shock the masses. I once caught a high society serial killer and in another case, nabbed six embezzlers, long after they thought they had escaped with millions of rupees. Far from being a popular Sherlock Holmes, I am an unknown face and happy about it. Anonymity is of utmost importance in my business, and I like it this way, ensuring that nobody I investigate should ever know who was after them or what hit them.

My reports on this particular situation have brought all the actors in the script under the scanner for their beautifully thought-out roles and picture-perfect performances. Looking at this self-styled sage, I became even more sure that all miracle-performing gurus are cheats. Why did miracles suddenly reduce in the age of science, when detecting frauds became so much easier?

For me, all that these saints have managed to achieve is to start new cults and personal followings. I haven't seen anyone transformed by listening to the sermons of these gurus in the times I live in. Human beings are constantly going towards darkness instead of enlightenment and the world is rapidly becoming a place fit only for the wealthy and the manipulative.

Each generation of ours, though progressing rapidly on the scientific frontier, has been worse than its predecessors when it comes to the quality called humanity. We've been evolving, not into refined human beings, but manipulative, cunning and selfish beasts. Where is the human evolution and emancipation promised in the scriptures? I don't see it in the world I live in.

The primitive man needed someone to fall back on when he faced unexplained thunder in the skies. In those desperate moments of helplessness, he discovered the notion of the Divine. The primal fear of a benevolent yet vengeful almighty Divine, who watched our every move, passed from generation to generation. The fear of being punished for sins became embedded in our genes.

Some people freed themselves from the crippling influence of these ideas and philosophies. They went on to disprove the claims made by saints, scriptures and religious preachers on the Divine's behalf. These men of science marched into uncharted frontiers of astronomy, physics, cloning, genetic engineering, artificial intelligence and ageing – directly challenging the Divine's domain and the karma theory. In the future, scientists will cure AIDS, diabetes, cancer, Alzheimer's disease and other life-crippling ailments, which, according to spiritual people, are caused due to bad karma. These so-called gurus simply dismiss the notion that it could be random.

'When you live sinfully, you get afflicted by diseases. If you are spiritual, no disease can touch you,' a very popular guru who appears on TV had once said in his lecture.

Scientists of today give a resounding slap to the religious fanatics who think of disease as the Divine's punishment to humanity for their sins. The idea of suffering because of karma makes me laugh. Just think about all those people before the nineteenth century who died of malaria or tuberculosis. If they paid for some of their karmic sins, it was with their lives. Yet people in the twentieth century suffering from malaria or tuberculosis need not balance their karma by losing their lives. God has written off death from malaria and tuberculosis causing karma. Could it be the result of an amendment in heaven? A reprieve? Cheers! Carry on with your malaria and tuberculosis causing karma, it's no longer a crime in God's present, altered world!

Science will one day, by conquering death and disease, take the air out of the karma balloon, refuting life after death theories and the notions of heaven and hell. Will man become immortal, and therefore, God? And what would he be doing then? Exploiting the weak and the poor! No different from the man of today.

Bang! I would love to be there when the karma theory explodes. I'd love to see the reactions of the propagators of this theory when science will snatch their favourite toy from them.

I am convinced that people who fall into the rut of spirituality are mostly those who don't fit in anywhere else – they are the biggest losers.

Just like my father.

19 | Cult Insults

I observed these religious cults at work when I was a child. My father's strong religious leanings and beliefs were seeded by a cult.

My father found it difficult to get along with society – his brothers, parents, and neighbours. In the cult, he felt he had discovered another universe where people loved him for what he was and did not reject him for his failures at a materialistic level. He felt welcomed, despite his lack of achievements and poor social standing. He imagined that while society respected only the rich, the famous, the doers and achievers, his cult treated every member equally. But he was wrong. Cults accept people just to flaunt their numbers, not out of brotherhood or love. With these numbers solidly behind them, they attract the ones who matter.

So many people cannot be wrong!

The group needs the rich and successful for funding its programmes and earning profits. A herd mentality achieves this objective.

'He will take care of everything. We are just puppets,' my father used to say.

Like every non-performer, he, too, had to face the consequences of running away from the challenges of life. We suffered quietly on account of his misdirected beliefs.

'Why couldn't you become a doctor or an engineer, like your brothers?' people would ask.

'Why don't you seek their guidance?'

'Why don't you take help from your brothers who are so successful?' a relative had once asked.

'My brothers may be wealthy and famous, but they are not spiritual. My spiritual wealth is far superior to their achievements,' he would say, while sitting on a cot outside his shop, which saw few customers.

Though he would try to put on a brave front in the face of such questions, I knew he used to get upset. He would go into long meditation sessions to forget the pain.

'You'll have to run the shop, I need to do *seva* for my guru,' he told Mother on one very difficult day, when many people had troubled him with their comments. He was packing his bag with the clothes to be worn at his ashram and other basic necessities.

'Don't let customers trick you into giving loans. Will you be able to manage?'

'Do you have to go? You know I can't run it as well as you.'

'Don't tell me you can't even run a shop.' He stared at her, his eyes bloodshot due to lack of sleep because of the late night puja.

Mother started crying.

He picked up his bags and left without another word.

In the days that followed, my mother cooked and washed clothes and utensils in the morning, then ran the shop till late in the night. All this while, my father cooked meals for his guru, served him milk and fruits, and washed his clothes in return for spiritual instructions.

One day, my mother fainted after a bout of giddiness, and it was some time before she regained consciousness.

'What happened to you, mama?'

'Nothing, I was a bit tired ...'

'I'll help you at the shop, mama,' I said through my sobs.

'You're my only hope, Sanju! Don't kill it by entering this hell,' she said, wiping my tears.

The next day, I walked to the ashram where my father was staying. The long, four-hour walk tired me out.

'We are unable to cope in your absence. Mama is not well ... .' I didn't look up, just stared at the tips of my shoes.

'I know these are difficult times. God's testing our patience. I will pray for your mother. She'll be all right.'

'But –'

'Go back and look after her.' He raised his voice the way he usually did to signal the end of the conversation.

I returned home and wept at my father's cruelty.

The people at the ashram dropped him back a week later. He had suffered a paralytic stroke, and they were unable to cope with him. That was how they repaid his selfless work at the ashram. While someone else took on the job of serving my father's guru, we spent all our money on his treatment. When the money proved inadequate, we sold the shop, which was our only means of income. My mother became a well-paid housemaid in the house of a rich and sympathetic acquaintance, and I gave tuitions between my studies to meet our expenses.

My father never recovered from the paralysis. He died, hoping God would cure him. I wept bitterly at his death. My tears were not for him, but for the god who existed in our lives as a curse.

My father would have managed adequately without God, but he ruined everything in his mistaken ideology and faith. People who get miraculously cured, whose businesses suddenly start doing well, or those who are saved in an accident, all give credit to God for his kindly intervention. Yet, what of those thousands of believers like my father who die despite getting proper treatment? What of those hundreds on ill-fated trains, buses or airplanes that crash and pulverise – some of them bound for holy pilgrimages? When they die, who is to blame?

Spiritual people explain everything with one word – karma. They would even say that my father was not spiritual in the true sense. However, I wouldn't blame him. His anger at his frustrating circumstances pulled him to the ashram. Deep down he was good, but misled. He drove himself into spirituality – that was his fault.

I've evolved since then. I don't believe destiny or karma binds people to their fates. Everyone is free to become whatever they want. With this belief, I was able get rid of our poverty. I struggled hard to reach where I am.

Today, my mother and I have status, respect, and wealth. Mercifully, we have no God in our lives. Because of my painful past, I looked forward to this assignment. I would derive great satisfaction if I could somehow expose this rogue. Killing the 'Practical Spirituality' movement in its infancy, before it became another cult, would be immensely satisfying. I will do everything to prevent it from ruining more homes like ours.

What did the gurus give the world? Merely Sikhs, Muslims, Hindus and Christians. These cults created essentially selfish predators in different garbs. They didn't create any paradise on earth. They only led to communal riots. If I did nothing to stop this guru, soon people would be wearing T-shirts flaunting his cult.

I had to stop it before it was too late.

20 | One Can Have Many Dimensions

The day after the encounter with the dacoit, the publicity gained by Swami Partibhan ensured decent meals for all of us. News of the charlatan's conquest over the dacoit spread everywhere and people on the streets insisted on serving us tea, coffee and snacks wherever we went. The days of begging and barely managing a fire in the woods were behind us. The dacoit drama ensured that the journey would be self-sustainable!

'Welcome to the Age of Practical Spirituality' proclaimed banners and T-shirts, just as I had predicted. People hailed the new messiah. My fears had become real.

In the evening, as we entered another city, some villagers came up with a strange request.

'A youth in our village is ill, Swamiji. He's suffering from cancer. He's the only hope of his aged parents. Please visit his house to bless him.' A man spoke with folded hands, his head bent low in respect. A large group of people stood behind him, their hands also folded.

'My blessings are with all of you.'

'No, we want you to meet Brij Mohan personally and give your blessings.' The man bent his head even lower.

'But –'

'Please fulfil the last wish of the young man.'

'All right.'

'*Swami Partibhan ki jai!*' The crowd became joyous when Swamiji agreed to their request.

As we walked to Brij's house, it was possible for me to fall behind the crowd. I hastily retrieved my cell phone and called my contact Ranbir Singh at the agency.

'We're going to meet a man named Brij Mohan. The villagers claim he's a cancer patient.'

'Is he also a doctor by profession, this guru?'

'No. Brij has sought his blessings. Just run a background scan on this man and his family. Find out since when he's ill, the works. I think the guru's planning a miracle cure,' I spoke rapidly.

'But where are you?'

'Nagothane,' I paused. 'Anything on that Girish fellow?'

'We're investigating.' Ranbir's tone was non-committal.

The house was rundown. Brij's face was pale and he looked wasted.

'His cancer is in its final stage. Doctors at the local hospital have given up hope,' said a youth.

'What happened?'

'A year ago, he developed fever and it didn't come down. He was a wrestler, and now, just look at him.'

'Swamiji, give me your blessings. I don't want to die. I have to look after my parents.' Brij folded his hands and broke into sobs.

'The Divine is merciful. Don't despair.'

'Please,' he begged, 'bless me with a long life; it's all I want you to do.'

'Life's in the Divine's hands –'

'I haven't seen God but when I saw your face on television, I knew, if anyone can save me, it's you.'

'But –'

'Please pray for me; that's all I ask of you.'

The guru seemed uneasy when he placed his hand on the young man's head and closed his eyes. Then he murmured loud enough for us to hear, 'O, Divine, spare this life and use it as an instrument to spread your glory here on earth.'

'Swamiji, if I live, I'll dedicate my life to serving humanity. I promise this to you.'

The flustered parents of the young man offered us dinner, which the villagers prepared. We were served fruits and milk after we finished dinner. In return for the hospitality, we cleaned up Brij's extremely neglected home. The villagers installed us in a good *dharamshala* and gave us quilts and blankets.

'Phew, what a day!' Subhir said as he stretched himself on his mattress.

'Your bravery in the jungle has changed the shape of this journey.' I was sitting close to Partibhan. 'From a difficult to sustain *pada-yatra*, it's transformed into a hero-worshipping, guru-felicitating trail.'

'People are bowing to me, a mere human being. If they were wise, then they would bow not to me but to the one within all of us!'

'Now you are trying to be humble. It was you, and none among us, who displayed the courage to deal with the dacoit.' Ruchika applied oil to her hair from the bottle she carried with her. Typical of her routine – she would be washing her hair tomorrow.

'Where did the courage come from?' Vibha asked.

'From divine connection.' Partibhan applied some medication on his finger stub. The wound was fresh, and I knew how and where he had lost that finger. 'The one who's always subconsciously connected to the Divine, the higher self, can actuate all the qualities the Divine grants to human beings.'

'All qualities? How?' I asked. 'Can a sprinter preparing for the Olympics boost his talent with this connection? What should he do? Meditate or practise?' Though I knew I should avoid discussions and arguments, I couldn't restrain myself.

'Like the sports you mention, several other talents like creativity, genius, courage, compassion, and love too, exist for a reason,' Swamiji said.

It was impossible to provoke the icebox.

'Yet many Olympic athletes don't believe in the Divine. Aren't they somehow worthier than those who sing prayers, yet do nothing exceptional with their lives?'

'That's the purpose of this journey. To inspire ourselves to get over our insecurities and evolve. But it appears your perception about the Divine is different from mine. For me, the Divine is the greater being in us. One who is above petty greed, desires and other traits that actually block our evolution to a higher state. He's not someone else, but you, me, all of us. When we connect with Him, we create happiness for ourselves and others with our unique gifts. This happiness is different from the feeling of temporary elation that comes from materialistic achievement – though materialistic seekers mistake it to be the same. If the Olympic medal-winning sprinter is not connected to his higher being, then he'll be as miserable as all those disconnected from the Divine are – medals notwithstanding. I agree with you that mere praying is not enough, we must be attuned to our higher self, or the Divine and remain in balance while working on our strengths and gifts.'

'But most people are convinced that to achieve perfection, you have to stress on one quality.'

'That's a narrow view – the one in which the misled world believes. In the evolution I speak of, all of us can enjoy life as a play and the best will simply flow out of us. Leonardo Da Vinci was a painter as well as a scientist. Albert Einstein was a great philosopher and a scientist. A great man has more to him than the one facet which defines him.

'I find it difficult to imagine that to become a sprinter, you have to give up loving people or turn your eyes away from art or shut your brain to science. Those who do this, close their personality. When such people are past running their races, they find themselves unhappy and ill-equipped to face life.' His logic was precise and irrefutable.

'We were speaking of your courage to face the dacoit,' Piyushi reminded, 'not sprinters in Olympics.'

Partibhan laughed. 'Our friend Sanjeev has many doubts. Heave the burden you are carrying as an "over-responsible" adult Sanjeev, and run through life like a child.'

The carefree world he described mesmerised me. But I quickly snapped out of the hypnotic suggestion. I didn't want to be brainwashed!

'What you say is so simple to follow. But the immediate "I" in us breaks the connection with the higher self you keep referring to.'

I could see Nikhil's restlessness. He wanted to live like that child, the one Partibhan described.

'What a beautiful state it would be, if we achieved it.' Shruti gazed into the distance, dreaming of the ideal state the guru painted with his lies.

'Just like a drop of ocean separated by a tiny floating leaf is a drop of water and the ocean at the same time, we, too, have to realise that our higher self and "I" are two sides of the same thing separated by the veil of ego.'

These gurus have one great trait in them. They talk well, and why not? They dig their places in the hearts of the masses and rob banks with the tools of clever words and examples. Often, even I came close to believing he was genuine. His logic was hypnotic. Such gurus are dangerous and difficult to resist.

How could anyone talk so intensely, yet be acting out the part? It's something I could never do. I hadn't seen any lowering of guard in this man in all the time I'd spent with him. He talked consistently, behaved consistently, and did not contradict himself at all. No chinks in his armour. This one would be tough to deal with.

It now dawned on me why so much money was being spent in investigating him. Whoever wanted to expose him must have realised that this unconventional guru could be a threat in the future. The sting operation was a desperate measure to fish out some weakness in him. Maybe they would uncover something about the cancer patient. If the guru cured this man, then he would prove himself a miracle healer as well.

I felt tired and sleepy, and decided to stop asking questions. Enough for one day.

21 | Jesus Anonymous

I got up early next morning to avoid the villagers turning up to meet Partibhan and contacted Ranbir from a bathroom at the *dharamshala*. Ranbir didn't pick up immediately – he was probably sleeping. I envied the luxuries surrounding him while I was spending time in the wilderness. Still, good money and an exciting assignment were my compensations.

'Hello?' Ranbir yawned.

'Still sleepy?'

'No, just a late night.'

'Busy with this case?'

'You pull the strings and then ask if I move!' Ranbir complained.

I grinned; the suffering was mutual.

'Why'd you call so early? Any development?'

'Brij looks seriously ill, but you must investigate. Despite what it looks, this could well be a prefabricated drama. You checked with the doctors at the hospital?'

'Yes, it's cancer beyond doubt. Reports and prescriptions prove the claim. They go as far back as one year; we have a genuine history. Tests to prove he has cancer. Besides, every doctor at the hospital knows Brij is a cancer patient.'

'Is it? If it's true, then –'

'It's a small community. Even the old villagers we checked with confirm the story.'

'But it could still be an elaborate lie.'

'Despite the dead ends we met?'

'The ashram could've been preparing for this big day.'

'And all the villagers and all the doctors are a part of it? Your imagination's working overtime, Sanjeev. Admit it; your intuition's wrong this time.'

I looked at the bathroom wall with a row of ants crawling across in a line. Just one ant moved alone, out of sync with the group. 'I think you don't need so many people to perpetrate a scam. You need just one person – the lab technician who conducts tests. All this person has to do is to write false reports. Brij then appears at the clinic for treatment and the doctors assume he's suffering from cancer.'

'But –'

'Brij meets the unsuspecting doctors regularly, but disposes all medicines because he's not ill. For the money, he fasts and loses considerable weight. A wasting wrestler leaves no scope for any doubts. Repeated tests, with the help of the technician, only confirm his condition getting worse.'

Ranbir whistled in shock. His response made me smile.

'What you say makes sense, and maybe explains everything. In fact, I hate to think why it didn't strike me.'

'What'll be your next step?'

'Leave it to me. But what makes you so sure Brij will be cured? Do you have some evidence you don't want to give now?'

The one who didn't give any of his cards away wanted to know if I possessed any!

'I've an intuition, just wait and watch.'

'You could be wrong.'

'Wanna bet?'

'No. You have the advantage of being where the action is.'

'This man is clever. I've yet to see him lower his guard.'

'Jesus!'

'That's what he intends to become,' I said. 'My mobile battery may not last long. Arrange for three more.'

With that, I ended the call.

When I emerged from the bathroom, a huge crowd had collected outside the *dharamshala*.

'*Swami Partibhan ki jai!*' they shouted.

'What happened?' I asked a man in the group.

'Brij got up today with a good appetite. He went to the toilet on his own.'

'He'd been so weak he couldn't even get up?' I looked at the crowd; it was jubilant.

'He was bedridden for the past five months. His friends have taken him to the hospital. Doctors will conduct fresh blood tests.'

In another hour, all of us headed to the assembly hall, where the villagers served breakfast.

The villagers brought Brij to the assembly hall too, as they awaited the test reports. He'd shaved off his beard and looked well-groomed. The extreme pale look was gone. He looked thin but healthy, yet his face betrayed tension.

Take up a crash diet course and lose weight abruptly. Apply a paste of yellow pigment, sport a beard and a dishevelled look, and you would look like a patient suffering from leukemia. The whole village would believe you have the dreaded disease. Wash your face to remove the pigment stain, shave your beard, comb your hair – and behold! You have a miracle! How easy – the step-by-step construct and deconstruct for a miracle cancer cure.

Our breakfast was more like a feast, but I didn't eat much. The devious ways of the false guru nauseated me. There must be a way to check Partibhan's fame before he ascended to glory. There must be a way out. I brainstormed furiously.

The suspense of the next few minutes weighed on me. Despite my hunch, I wanted to hear that Brij hadn't been cured by this charlatan. Then a man came running towards the assembly hall. He carried a slip of paper in his hands. He was excited and breathing heavily.

'What does the report say?'

'Great improvement! Our Brij has shown great improvement. The doctors are hopeful he might survive!'

'I knew you would heal me!' Brij said with tears in his eyes. 'When I got up in the morning and felt hungry, I knew I'd been cured.'

The villagers lifted him on his shoulders and celebrated by dancing to drum beats. The drums appeared remarkably quickly.

'*Swami Partibhan ki jai!*' the villagers shouted.

'This is what I don't like,' Swami Partibhan protested over the din of the drums.

'Who cured this man?'

'You cured him with your blessings.' The noise from the drums was deafening.

'Don't mistake me as the healer,' he said in his soft voice. 'The Divine cured him, not me.'

'You have special miraculous powers, Swamiji. You tamed a ferocious dacoit and cured a cancer patient. The kindness of God flows through you.'

An old villager came up from the crowds and said, 'Why do you pretend to be an ordinary man when you're a saint?'

People began to garland the guru. I watched them, amused. They didn't care much for spirituality. They only understood and bowed to a miracle, just as in the medieval ages. Man benefitted from the miracles of Jesus and then crucified him. If this was a movie, then our guru had delivered a hit and was now enjoying a fan following. God be damned!

Despite my suspicions, Brij's health surprised me. The change was too glaring to ignore. A part of me wanted to believe in the miracle. The professionalism of these people was phenomenal. What would happen now? Would it result in more media coverage for Partibhan, more news and more fame?

'In all these jubilations, young man,' Partibhan said as he rested his hand on Brij's shoulder, 'don't forget the promise you made – to serve humanity in whatever small way you can.'

'You tell me what to do, Swamiji.'

'If your desire to serve is pure, you will find a way.'

The man bowed in respect.

Partibhan turned to face the jubilant villagers. 'I want one promise from all of you.'

'Anything you wish, Swamiji!'

'The grace of the Divine cured this man, not me. What I don't want you to do is tell the press about this. Already the dacoit episode has affected us. I don't want newspersons to follow us and make a mockery of this journey.'

If he was asking them to go immediately to the press, then this was the best way to ensure it.

'All right. However, once you complete your *pada-yatra*, we will tell the media.'

'That's up to you. Now, I wish to leave. Do I have your word that this healing will remain a secret? I want your word. Everybody's word. If you don't do as I say, then we'll have to cancel this *yatra*, which is dear to all of us.'

'We promise you, Swamiji!'

When we were at a twenty-kilometre distance from Brij's village without any media activity, I felt sure the villagers had abided by his request. The development confounded me. If Partibhan were a fraud, he would be seeking publicity, not smothering it. Any news is news only while it is hot. After many days, when the *pada-yatra* would be over, if these villagers approached the news channels, it wouldn't be as juicy – no media channel would be interested in covering it. Live news made a big impression. The buzz and excitement of witnesses – doctors, reporters and the patient – would have created a huge impact. But two weeks from now, it would appear like a documentary, an advertisement of the ashram.

க

'Like you'd predicted,' Ranbir said. 'A miracle happened.'

'What are you doing at your end?' I asked.

'We have the lab technician under observation. All his moves and his bank accounts are under scrutiny. And we're watching Brij too.'

'I'm not sure anymore.'

'Why?'

'Partibhan turned down the publicity he could've got from the episode. If he didn't want publicity, then why would he –'

'You think this is a case of genuine healing?' Ranbir voice sounded incredulous. 'You're growing old, man. You believe this shit?'

'What I believe or don't believe shouldn't matter. You follow your end of the investigation.' I ended the call.

Had the man not shrugged off publicity, I would have been sure. Anyone in his position would want results. If he was a fraud, then his aim would be to get many more followers.

Did it mean this young man was a real saint? So far, I had held unshakeable convictions about everything. But why did the guru ensure the cancer cure wouldn't draw media attention?

This man had confused me thoroughly.

22 | Music of the Meddling Medley

We were on a highway towards Mangaon in the afternoon when a truck driver told us the city was nearly fifteen kilometres away. Stranded, and with no other choice left, we approached dhabas near the highway to satiate our hunger. Which of them was on the payrolls of Partibhan this time?

When we approached them, they ridiculed our 'begging'. The truck drivers who stopped at these dhabas lampooned us for trying to live off the income of others. It was humiliating.

'Swamiji, let's give up our lunch today,' Ajoy suggested.

'Let's try again, one last time!'

This time, when Swami Partibhan approached a restaurateur, I assumed it was a prearranged, prepaid dhaba.

'Swamiji, I don't like the look of that dhaba owner. Let's try the other dhaba across the road.' I tried to deflect his move, just to see how he would react.

'To me, he looks all right,' Partibhan gazed at the dhaba owner intently. 'What's wrong with him?'

Partibhan's attempts to justify his move towards the dhaba he headed confirmed my suspicion it was already fixed. I decided to be assertive.

'He'll refuse and then we'll all have to go hungry. Let's try the other dhaba.'

'All right, as you wish.' Partibhan conceded easily, much to my astonishment.

I congratulated myself for having deflected Swamiji from going to a 'prepaid' dhaba.

The language the previous restaurateurs had used was so abusive that I didn't have the courage to face the situation, so I hovered in the background.

'Let me talk to him,' Partibhan offered gallantly. He explained the idea behind the journey to the restaurant owner who listened with patience.

'You're thirteen people. In feeding you, I'll have to lose a lot out of my profit. I can give you food, but only on one condition.'

'What is it?'

'Can you do some work for me in return? Pay me in kind.'

'Of course, I already told you we're willing to repay you through services. What do you want us to do?'

'I'd planned to paint the restroom, but three of my employees have fallen ill and are on leave. Two of you can paint the room. Three of you can serve the drivers. Then, in preparation for our evening meals, you'll peel and cut vegetables, wash the unclean vessels and leave the place clean. For all this work, you can eat free of cost.'

'None of us have ever painted before.'

'I've never given free lunch to anyone,' he grinned. 'So both of us can do with some learning. I'll teach you; it's simple.'

'Right,' Swami Partibhan said. 'Yet, we might mix up the orders as we are not used to the job.'

'Tell me something.'

'Yes?'

'Do you have the will to work or not?'

'Yes, but we are afraid we might commit errors.'

'Don't worry; leave it to me. Now, which three will take orders?'

Swami Partibhan volunteered; Tarun and Bijoy too stepped up.

'Who will do the whitewashing?'

Ajoy and Subhir raised their hands.

'The rest of you can take out the vegetables and cut them.'

I was stunned with the way things turned out – I wasn't prepared for doing such a menial job. Since no one raised any objections, I fell in line unwillingly.

We started on our jobs as waiters, painters and cooks. Everyone enjoyed their work. What learning experience was this debasement and humiliation? I think the restaurateur had been sure we would decline the offer. Even if we accepted, he only stood to gain, the clever scoundrel.

Swami Partibhan was already moving among the customers and taking their orders with Tarun and Bijoy. The dhaba owner helped them. I couldn't suppress my smile watching Partibhan, though I still disapproved of him. He looked so much like one of us. Not a high-flying guru at all, despite the vast fortune his father had left behind.

I went inside the kitchen and brought out the several kilos of vegetables we were forced to cut. Ajoy and Subhir disappeared into the restroom, where the restaurateur showed them how to paint.

I didn't know which job was worse. The painters climbed a ladder, scraped surfaces, and painted them. More than the walls, they painted themselves, yet they came out grinning, proud of their accomplishments.

The guru and his team rushed to meet orders. They tripped over one another, spilled water from glasses and mixed orders. The person who wanted chicken got dal and the driver who wanted fish got salad! Yet they zipped through the hotel with nonstop enthusiasm, ignoring the choicest abuses the victims of their messed-up servings hurled at them, as if they were congenitally deaf. They were hurried and harried by the hungry and sped like sprinters in a hurdles' race.

As for my job, the less said the better. In peeling potatoes with a knife as sharp as a razor's blade, I cut my fingers twice. My hands ached while doing the unaccustomed activity. My eyes watered while slicing the pungent onions, and I suspect half my tears were real. I detested what lengths human beings went to, to fill their stomachs. I'd been unaware of the work which went into cooking food and wondered at the hardships my mother must be facing every day. The job was so mechanical, repetitive, and boring, I went to sleep with my eyes open, only to cut my finger again.

'I used to take my wife for granted. In future, I'll help her with the household chores instead of reading my newspaper from morning till night,' Kulkarni said.

'You can help her by chopping onions.' Sneha took a moment's pause to look up at him. She was the fastest in the group.

'I'll try. However, I think giving up onions altogether might be a better idea.' His innocent statement made them laugh but didn't amuse me. I stared at the pile of sixty kilos of vegetables in front of us.

'I pray some scientist would invent a capsule that could douse a man's appetite for his entire life or maybe, a year. Then we can get rid of this menace,' I said.

'Life's a synonym for difficulty. All problems disappear only when we die – even cutting vegetables,' Nikhil laughed. 'Better to cut onions than lie over a flaming pyre.'

What made these people so joyous? Ajoy and Subhir whistled as they painted briskly. They stopped occasionally to marvel at their brush strokes.

We were starving when the work was over and hot food was served to us.

'I thought you would run away at the mention of the deal. Now I believe you.' The restaurateur served us with love and generosity. He brought vegetables, dals and chapattis and made us eat at least one extra chapatti each.

When we finished, he surprised us by serving *kheer*, which he had kept in the refrigerator. His generosity was unexpected. He could have easily avoided giving us the *kheer*, which he sold at ₹40 per plate. The dessert, rich in roasted almonds and raisins, was delicious. This unexpected gesture erased my earlier impression of him.

At three, we were ready to leave. But not before we had tea, which the man insisted on. Swami Partibhan thanked the dhaba owner for his generosity, who in turn thanked us.

'Because of you, I could do such brisk business today. You turned out to be a godsend. Thanks.'

We took leave of him. A short while later, Partibhan fell in step with me. 'You were right about this dhaba owner. Despite the work he made us do, he was a good man. Besides, the experience was enjoyable. You judged him correctly.'

What could I say? I merely deflected Partibhan because I wanted to test him. To my surprise, it turned out to be another fairy tale experience.

At six in the evening, the physical work at the dhaba, coupled with the heavy meal we had eaten, began showing effects. We felt tired.

'Swamiji, I don't think we can make it to the city today,' Ramanujam spoke for everyone. 'We should take a break.'

We found a flat area and cleared it of pebbles and shrubs. Our previous difficulty at starting a fire had compelled us to carry a matchbox, so we didn't have any problems starting a bonfire this time. We huddled close to the fire and talked about our lives in the city long into the night.

Two of us kept watch as we dozed by turns. The highway traffic shattered the silence now and then.

Mercifully, this night passed without any melodramatics, and we drifted into a peaceful slumber.

23 | The Judge in the Witness Box

The fair one was the best. Ruchika was in her late twenties but her figure could put a teenager to shame. She exuded a sexual aura I found hard to resist, and it penetrated the professional cool I maintained. No woman had affected me the way she did. I was attracted to her and indulged in risky behaviour, quite unlike me.

The journey lulled the women's defenses and they began to believe that everyone was spiritual, just like them. When they bathed, the five women were not self-conscious. And when the opportunity presented itself at Goregaon, I decided to take advantage of it. It wasn't difficult to fool the group. I moved away with the excuse that I felt embarrassed. Then I took a circuitous route to intercept the women, who'd moved in the opposite direction. In quiet solitude, I enjoyed the sight they presented. My detective training helped me in outfoxing the group without raising suspicion.

After telling Ranbir about the developments of the previous day, I squat down, keeping the women in view. They were bathing now and though I could see them all, I concentrated on Ruchika. The opportunity to bathe and do the morning routine in the wilderness had appeared twice before, but this was the first time I was taking advantage of it.

After some time, I got up. It was time to leave, or the others would start getting suspicious.

'That was not right.' The voice from behind startled me.

I turned to see Partibhan standing solemnly, his eyes fixed on me. My ears went hot with shame.

My career and this journey are over. What would I say to those who had hired my services? What reason would I give for my inglorious exit? I stood speechless, my mouth dry. Such a stupid mistake!

'You realise what you did just now was wrong?'

'Yes. I ... I'm s-sorry.'

I had botched up this job. Word would get around that I was sleazy, therefore unreliable.

'You indulged in peeping, thinking you'd get away.'

'I was ... I feel s-stupid.'

'You didn't while you were at it, sure of getting away.'

I remained silent.

'Answer me!' His stern voice made me shiver.

'But ... Krishna ... did the same ... with *gopis* ... .'

'Krishna lifted a mountain with his forefinger. He killed a huge sea snake with his bare hands. He killed Kansa. Can you do the other things he did? And you compare this lewd act of yours with Krishna?'

This was the first time I had seen him so angry.

'I'm sorry.'

'Only now. Rapists, murderers and thieves have similar logic. And you equate yourself with Krishna!'

'I'm sorry.'

'Tell me, how you'd have felt if your wife, sister, or daughter was bathing and you caught someone ogling lecherously at them?'

I dug into my shoes out of shame and repentance. 'I'd have beaten him up.'

'Think about this reaction of yours whenever you do something that can harm others. How would you feel if you were in their place?'

'I won't do this ever again.' I couldn't bear to look at his piercing eyes.

'Then go and join the group. Forget this ever happened. Forgive yourself and resolve today never to repeat anything like this.'

When he turned and left me as abruptly as he had appeared, I couldn't believe he spared me. Found guilty but left unpunished – it was incredible.

I walked back, feeling wretched. Ironically, until then, I had been judging the guru smugly, writing him off as a fraud and pretender. I had laughed at his philosophies as if I were a greater human being. Yet, this incident reversed the equation. Rather than punish me for my folly, he wanted to improve me. I felt rotten.

'Forgive yourself ...'

His compassion filled me with remorse. Nobody else would have forgiven me. In the world I understood, I would have been thrashed, not to talk of the exposure and scandal I would have had to face for the rest of my life. This incident would have ruined my career. The way Swami Partibhan forgave me showed he not only preached spirituality but practised it too.

I was quiet and thoughtful when we reassembled and resumed our journey. Partibhan pretended as though nothing had happened.

The burden of guilt weighed heavily on my conscience.

24 | Fight with a Snake Bite

We had barely travelled for two kilometres when I saw a black snake emerge from the bushes. Before I could warn him, it had bitten Tarun and disappeared again.

Tarun shouted and writhed in pain.

'Give me a long piece of cloth,' Piyushi demanded as she inspected the wound. Kulkarni passed his handkerchief to her which she tied about two inches above the bite.

'His leg needs to be lower than his heart, so it would be better if someone lifts him and lets his leg dangle. And Tarun, don't move, just relax. Any movement will spread the venom quicker.' She turned to face us. 'Let's take him to the hospital immediately.'

Seeing the urgency, I heaved him on my shoulders and rushed to the highway. The early morning traffic density was low and none of the vehicles we hailed cared to stop. Finally, a truck halted beside us.

'A snake has bitten our friend. He needs urgent treatment,' Kulkarni told the truck driver. Tarun was semi-conscious now, gasping for breath. Twenty minutes had elapsed.

'Climb in,' the driver said.

We stretched Tarun on the back of the open truck.

'We've lost a lot of time,' said Piyushi. 'Let's try to reach a hospital as quickly as possible. They might have an antidote.'

'How far is the city?' I asked the driver.

'At least an hour from here.'

'Since we can do nothing, let's pray and sing a bhajan,' Swami Partibhan said.

We remained quiet, none of us having the heart to sing. The guru began to sing alone. His voice was melodious and its words pulled the strings of the heart. Gradually, everyone joined him.

The guru kept his hands on Tarun as he prayed and we joined him, keeping our hands over each other's. Tarun's body was turning blue.

'His pulse is dropping.' Piyushi tried to look calm. 'We're too late.' She whispered.

'Could you please drive faster?' I shouted over the noise of the truck.

Swami Partibhan and the others continued to sing bhajans while Piyushi monitored Tarun's pulse. He was writhing in pain and she had difficulty calming him. She refused to give him water when he asked for it.

'No food or water until you are out of danger.'

The bhajans sung by the guru spoke of the glory of the Lord, his greatness and his powers. They spoke of his compassion, kindness and mercy; of annihilating the evil that lurks in all of us by immersing ourselves in his memory, day and night.

Seeing Tarun in such a critical state, I realised what a short distance exists between life and death. I remembered the conviction with which Partibhan had conveyed the message of the Divine to the dacoit. I, too, had received a message.

So far, I had ignored and laughed at spiritual people, but now I was not sure. My convictions had taken me to the brink of disaster, but Partibhan had pulled me to safety. From now onwards, like Partibhan said, my life's course would be a matter of choice, not the result of my father's actions.

Curiously, I felt vibrations pouring out of my hands, cheeks and neck. My hair stood up in needles and tears welled in my eyes as I connected with the Divine for the first time. I vowed to change. I would consciously do no wrong.

We reached the city and took Tarun to a nursing home.

'Take him to the government hospital. The poison has spread; he's turned blue. I'm afraid we do not have the equipment or expertise to treat him,' the doctor in charge told us.

His behaviour suggested there was little hope for Tarun.

25 | The Cure – Beyond Just the Physical

The government hospital was nearly fifty kilometres away. The driver offered to take us there, even when we told him we didn't have the money to pay him. 'Hop in quickly, don't waste time,' he said, as he started his truck.

Tarun was unconscious by now.

Until then, I was thinking of practical ways to save Tarun. But the doctor's attitude and the fifty kilometres seemed ominous. Seeing the hopelessness of the situation, I began to pray. I had never prayed since my father died. As I immersed myself in those beautiful bhajans, I drifted into a semi-conscious state which gave me peace and tranquility. I lost touch with time and my surroundings.

'He's gained consciousness.' Piyushi's cry brought me out of my state. Her expression was triumphant. Tarun looked bewildered and confused. His body had lost its blue tinge. Piyushi checked his pulse again.

'Normal; but still, it's too early to say.'

Tarun appeared dazed and drugged, but responded to our questions.

'How are you feeling?'

'All right ... a little giddy ... where am I?'

He then vomited three times, but said the vomiting made him feel better.

We reached the government hospital after an hour and a half – the move through the traffic was tortuously slow.

'He's fine,' the doctor at the government hospital said. 'His pulse rate and BP are low so we'll give him a glucose drip. We'll keep him under observation till evening.'

At seven in the evening, they discharged him. We welcomed him back joyfully. It was hard to believe Tarun was alive and amongst us!

'We have two choices,' Swami Partibhan addressed us. 'One is to end our journey for the sake of Tarun. Or, one of us can escort him to our ashram while the rest can continue with the journey.'

'I'll take him to the ashram,' Ajoy volunteered.

'You continue Ajoy, I'll take him,' Bijoy, his younger brother, offered.

'No, I'll go. You're enjoying this journey. I've never seen you this happy.' The sight of each brother trying to outdo the other in sacrifice was touching.

'Since you volunteered out of compassion for all of us, you've accomplished this spiritual journey in the true spirit.' Partibhan patted Ajoy's shoulder.

Before leaving, both Tarun and Ajoy touched Swami Partibhan's feet and shook hands with us.

'I wouldn't have survived the bite if it was not for your prayers,' Tarun said.

'I think it's Piyushi you should thank, especially,' Swami Partibhan said. 'Her first-aid probably saved your life ... .'

'No way,' Piyushi shook her head. 'His entire body turned blue. Didn't you see? What we witnessed was a miracle; don't pass it off as first-aid!'

'I know,' Tarun said, getting into the taxi. 'Those prayers stalled my death. I'll never forget this journey. And Sanjeev, it was fun creating fire with you. We'll try to recreate fire again, another time.' He lingered with the handshake as he said those words.

The words brought cheer to my heart. I'd become a dry twig, without emotions and feelings; Tarun's words stirred something within me that I hadn't felt since my father's death.

Then they were gone.

'Swamiji, it's a miracle he's still alive. I've seen the power of your prayers. They do heal,' I said. I could no longer think of him in disparaging terms like Partibhan, or the fraud guru, as my new respect and reverence for him grew.

'It was not just me. All of us prayed together, including you, while Dr Piyushi did the best she could. You played as much a part in the cure. Didn't you feel the vibrations?' his voice exuded love. There was no malice – as though he didn't even remember what had happened in the woods.

'Yet, we couldn't bring ourselves to remember the Divine in the crisis,' I said.

'I, too, thought it would be much better if we searched for hospitals instead of singing bhajans,' Subhir added. 'At the time, your singing bhajans appeared crazy to me.'

'I, too, thought praying was somehow wrong.' Kulkarni, though behind us, was listening to the conversation.

'We did what we could as human beings. When it proved inadequate, it was the most natural course for us to turn to the divine within us. What people call a miracle is like tapping power from the right source in the most natural way,' Swamiji said.

My association with Swamiji made me realise that my father had been exploited by unscrupulous people. I was convinced that not all gurus were alike. I wanted to believe Swamiji when he said we made the miracle possible. This meant there was hope for a person like me. Despite my flaws, I could still connect with the divine within me.

⒭

'He's above suspicion,' I reported early next morning, recounting the miracle to Ranbir.

'Still, it could have been a trick,' Ranbir said. 'Tarun could have been a part of the setup. Maybe the snake wasn't poisonous. Maybe it was not a snake at all, just a rubber toy.'

'I saw it myself.'

'Did you see it real close?'

'No.'

'Can you rule out the possibilities I just mentioned?'

'No, I can't ... but what about the blue hue, the vomiting, and what the doctors said at the hospital? It *was* a snake bite.'

'A powder or chemical rubbed by Partibhan could have turned Tarun's skin blue. Remember he kept his hands on Tarun's body. Did they conduct any tests at the hospital you first went to?'

'No. At the private nursing home, the doctor said they couldn't help us. They merely saw the bluish hue and told us to take him to the government hospital. By the time we reached the hospital, Tarun had recovered.'

'You see? The story rests only on physical symptoms. What a fantastic ruse!'

'And the vomiting?'

'Vomiting's easy,' Ranbir argued.

He explained every turn of the event plausibly and yet ... my hunch said something else. Over the years, I had come to trust and respect it. I couldn't bring myself to be dismissive of what I had witnessed first-hand.

'I believe he's genuine. Though I'll keep reporting to you about the developments, I don't think we'll find anything.'

'On the contrary, we've mounted a full investigation on Brij and the lab technician. We'll nail them so hard, they'll rue the day they agreed to help Partibhan.'

'You'll find nothing. Brij will do social service, like he promised to Swami Partibhan.'

'You're entitled to your opinions, Sanjeev. Doing and promising are different. I've heard these gurus have hypnotic powers. You might be under his spell. Break free before it starts affecting you.'

Then I remembered.

'What about the low pulse and the low blood pressure?'

'Could be an error. Doesn't look right to me, Sanjeev. Stop behaving like a brainwashed fool!'

I ended the call. For the fraction of a second, I wondered if I was being naïve by believing Swamiji. Ranbir's logic explained every trick that could have led to the so-called miracle. Yet, while the brain could explain everything, the heart was a different matter. I couldn't bring myself to believe that Swamiji had perpetrated a fraud. I knew I had to do something.

Finding him alone, I told him all about the assignment to spy on him. 'What should I do now?' I asked.

'I suggest you should do this job like you have done every job before this. Carry on with it, without the slightest hesitation.' He was not the least disturbed by my confession.

'But Swamiji –'

'Getting to the bottom of the truth is your job. Continue with your investigation and let the truth prevail. I'll pray for you to achieve the Absolute Truth each of us seeks.'

'I've a feeling the people who are investigating you are out to tarnish your image or harm you.'

'They're misled and will change with time. You report whatever you see to your agency, honestly. I have nothing to hide or be afraid of.'

'But –'

'Why do you worry so much? Just heave your burden!' He smiled as he kept his hand on my shoulder.

The tiniest doubt that might have lingered in my mind disappeared like a flame blown out by a strong wind. Swami Partibhan's simple ways had won me over. Then I did something which would have surprised my mother, friends and relatives. I bent down, touched the feet of this great man, and folded my hands.

'Hey, don't touch my feet because today, I see the divine self shining within you. You have realised the goal of the journey; may the Divine bless you,' he said as he pulled his feet away abruptly, embarrassed by my action.

My conviction about God, spirituality and this man took an about-turn for ever.

26 | Which Came First – Faith Or Divine?

'Why does our faith in the Divine falter?' Vibha washed her face and dried it with her towel as we rested near Rajewadi. 'So many incidents in the journey should be enough to convince us about the existence of a benign power within us that can help us achieve much more than we do presently. Yet, when I return to my job, I know that doubts will surround me.'

'Faith falters only when the connection with your divine self breaks, when we stop our morning and evening meditation. Meditation and being in collectivity are our protection against the onslaught of doubts.'

'You have talked about meditation in the past, but collectivity ...?' Vibha raised her eyebrows.

'Yes. Meditation is internal while collectivity is external. When we meet other, like-minded spiritual people, it strengthens our beliefs.'

'You mean meditating alone is not self-sustaining?'

'Being in collectivity is as important as meditating because it realigns our priorities.'

'All this will need time,' I complained.

Swamiji shook his head and laughed. 'For a man who falls on evil ways, what about the time he wastes? An apple a day protects us from disease: spirituality protects us from illnesses, consequences of wrong and hasty decisions and bad reactions.'

We were in the last phase. Pale golden sunlight highlighted the green stretch and gentle wind swayed the branches as though they were dancing. Swamiji held a fixed gaze towards the sky, where the clouds became a golden fluff.

'Yet how to have unshakeable faith, despite the contrary evidence that sometimes appears?' Piyushi adjusted her specs with her forefinger. She did this unconsciously whenever she was thoughtful.

'Faith is peculiar, in the sense that you have to have it before you start walking on the spiritual path. Shri Rama took the support of humble monkeys and their army to get his wife back. He wept like a child when Inderjeet grievously injured Lakshman. It was Hanuman who brought the medicine to treat Lakshman and saved him from certain death. At that moment, for the doubters, Hanuman, not Shri Rama, would have appeared more powerful.

'By maintaining our faith in our higher self, we continue to evolve – to the next, higher stage until we reach the highest awareness about ourselves and the universe. This is the state of nirvana, or moksha, where we experience the joy of joys. From a crawling life form to a complete, holistically evolved being. Immortal. All powerful. Capable. Benign.

'When this happens, we achieve a state that resonates with the universe. There is no conflict, no strife, no cross purpose, no clash of interest. What a beautiful reward we get for so many lifetimes of struggles and striving. What a beautiful finale of this great drama of life. Our faith in this higher being within us decides whether we attain this godhood or not.'

A long and thoughtful silence lingered as we meditated on Swamiji's words. The picture playing in my mind was beautiful. If I could somehow preserve this faith, then what I would achieve would be far better than anything I now possessed.

'You talk of the carefree ways of the sparrow. You talk of excelling with our unique talents. You talk of nirvana. You speak of meditation and collectivity. Aren't these conflicting messages?' Ruchika fidgeted with her ring, her forehead knotted with furrows.

'Are they? I don't think so! Clearly, it's evolution which happens between the time we're born and the time we die. So everything will logically lead to it, provided we are aware of it and in harmony with our environment. By freeing ourselves of conflict, we do what is fulfilling and become more and more aware of ourselves, our capabilities and strengths. With emancipation comes the awareness about the higher, divine self and we reach the pinnacle of evolution. None of the things you mentioned are in conflict with one another. They clash only when the path we choose deviates from the goal of higher awareness to mere existence.'

'If it is really a fight between doubt and faith, then what's the need for a spiritual guru? Isn't having faith enough?' Bijoy interrupted Swamiji. 'I didn't mean to insult you, Swamiji! But –'

His remark made me laugh: it was so spontaneous.

'That's a question I asked myself before becoming a guru.' Swamiji gazed at his dismembered finger stump for what seemed a long time. The smile on his face was enigmatic. Then he looked up and cleared his throat, 'Why is there a need for a middleman between the seeker and the sought? Middlemen are only interested in commission.' Everyone laughed.

'I once asked myself, when I was a student,' he resumed, 'why do parents who want to make their children engineers and doctors send their children to a school with teachers with just a B.Sc or an M.Sc? It's because the wide disparity of education between the teacher and the taught is enough to justify their teaching capabilities. Similarly, it's the gap in spiritual knowledge between a guru and his disciples which makes a guru a necessity. A guru brings you to a point in your spiritual journey when you become aware and conscious of the self. From here onwards, if you have to go any further, you have to move on the evolutionary path more like an explorer or adventurer than as an apprentice. You may even go further than your guru, just like the pupils of a teacher invariably outshine him.

'When this awareness or realisation comes spontaneously from within, it's blossom time for the disciple. From a tiny plant which needed care and protection, the disciple undergoes a beautiful transformation! As your guru, it's my wish that each of you spread the unique fragrance of divinity in you. If you merely existed as Swami Partibhan's followers, then as your gardener, I would have failed.'

After travelling further, we saw some pear trees. The night was approaching, so we decided to eat fruits as a meal. As we collected the fruits, someone shouted at us.

'You don't have any shame? How dare you pluck those fruits and eat when you don't have permission!'

'Who are you?'

'I'm the watchman of this private orchard.' The man's expression was belligerent.

'Sorry, we didn't know. There are no walls or fences. We're travellers and mistook your orchard as a part of the wilderness.'

'And you took liberties as if it's your ancestral property.'

'Why insult our ancestors for the offence we have done?' Sneha laughed. 'What can we do to compensate for this damage?'

'Pay money, of course!' thundered the watchman.

'What will the owner of such a huge orchard do with whatever little money you expect of us?' We knew he merely wanted money for himself.

'That's none of your business. You've damaged my orchard and you must pay.'

'We don't have money with us. We're travelling without a penny. It's the reason we plucked your fruits,' Ramanujam tried to explain.

'Why do you lie? You're twelve adults and you say you have no money? You're forcing me to call the police.'

'Then do what you want. Call the police.'

The watchman was shocked by our unexpected reply.

'How shameful! You are prepared to go to jail, but not ready to pay for the damages.'

'Look,' Swamiji went up to the man, trying to calm him. 'We are weary travellers going to Ganapatipule on a spiritual journey. We were hungry and plucked what looks like two kilos of your fruit –'

'What did you say? You are on a spiritual journey to Ganapatipule?' The man's manner changed at once. 'Are you Swami Partibhan who was in the news for the dacoit's surrender?'

Swamiji didn't say anything. He did not like the constant references to the incident. By now, he was tired of denying he was the hero in the incident. Taking his silence for acceptance, the man knelt down at once and folded his hands.

'Forgive me, Swamiji!' He prostrated himself on Swamiji's feet. 'I have committed a grave mistake by mistreating you.'

The change in the man was astounding.

'I'm no one to forgive or punish you. Yet, how does my being a guru who appears on TV make me superior to a poor man in need?'

'I wanted to make some money out of the incident. Please forgive me!' The man pulled at his ears. 'Come to the farmhouse and rest there for the night.'

That night, we settled comfortably in the sprawling farmhouse, surrounded by huge trees. It had a swimming pool and was centrally heated. The watchman arranged for our dinner, which was delicious. He joined us in meditation and sang bhajans with us.

When we switched off the lights, I gazed at the night sky from the huge windows of the room. The sky, littered with thousands of shimmering stars on that moonless night, made me smile. The universe looked beautiful.

I drifted to sleep with thoughts of nirvana and becoming one with all the beauty that held me spellbound. Until then, the thought of never being born again had scared me. The thought of not having an identity of my own and a life to live – no matter how painful and full of misery it was – seemed scary. The agony of being human, despite an inconsequential existence, had seemed much more attractive a proposition. Now, I understood that being one with our creator and all the beauty in the world was the aim of this journey.

PART THREE

Partibhan's story

The butterfly, when it flaps its wings in the springtime, enchants the world with its magnificent beauty. Yet it has a humbler origin – it was an ugly caterpillar once, which could only crawl.

The past is dead. The present is the living truth. Change brings with it transformation. Once something is transformed, there is no connection whatsoever with its past.

When people become butterflies, they no longer remain caterpillars, whatever anyone may say of their past.

They become different human beings altogether.

27 | Back to the Future

I sat at the beautiful beach, lost in my thoughts. We had finally reached Ganapatipule. The natural beach running along the sea road was beautiful. The snowy white froth of the waves, and their roar as they rushed to the shore, filled my heart with joy. The complex creation of the Maker awed me. Air, water, earth, fire – all the elements were so different, and yet they evolved from the same source, interacting to create myriad patterns. Their integration created all living beings.

What a finale to the wonderful journey this was! Though we had accomplished a difficult task, I felt sad that it was ending. The spiritual expedition was packed with surprises and proved to be a perfect vehicle to learn spirituality at a practical level, beyond my wildest expectations.

Just before the sojourn, I had witnessed the negative tendencies of several of my disciples at the ashram, which filled me with despair. For many of them, spending time at the ashram was like coming on a holiday. They ate like gluttons and slept like Kumbhakarans, forgetting why they were there. Their indifference to something for which they had devoted so much time and energy bothered me. I wanted things to work for those who genuinely wished to change. The journey to Ganapatipule on foot was a big leap.

As we progressed, the entire group evolved, and the transformations were very evident. My insights surprised me. From a diffident man, who'd questioned his right to preach to people, I became comfortable with the idea of being a spiritual guide. Until then, I had been uncomfortable in every other role thrust upon me.

As a child, I was a misfit in every game we played. I watched with awe as Bittoo, my childhood friend and a cricket prodigy, played his shots as if he had been specially trained from the 'skies' – my word for heaven when I was a child. When Karan ran like a bullet to win medals at the school races, I wondered from where he got the special burst of energy while I struggled to finish the race. Ranjit, another childhood friend, could manipulate the bicycle in a way that left everyone spellbound. He would drive blindfolded, balance on the still bike, drive backwards, and pedal with his hands instead of his feet! Arti's poems were exceptional in maturity. And Nitin, he surprised everyone with the lightning speed with which he solved the toughest mathematical sums. He was my friend in class ten.

I had struggled, whereas these gifted prodigies had excelled. I wasn't jealous, but the wide gap between me and those exceptional children was insurmountable. I was turning out to be an average student, and my mother, who had been optimistic for me, was beginning to show her disappointment. Yet, try as I did, I could do nothing to improve my performance in studies, sports or co-curricular activities. Trying to get just five per cent more in mathematics, when I resolved to beat Nitin out of sheer frustration, was a draining experience. I put three hours extra everyday to score those five marks! Nitin got 100 out of 100 almost effortlessly.

In college and in my job, it was no different. The gifted people zipped past every hurdle, while people like me struggled. Aptitude, talents, propensities, inclinations, destiny, etc. were merely labels. They named the differentiations, but did not explain them. Now, after discovering this spiritual strength in me, I think I know the answer.

Each of us is best suited to a specific vocation. Most of us land in careers not conducive to our key strengths, for various reasons. Status, honour, money, fame or a herd mentality tempt us to stray. Only a few lucky ones land into careers where their true self finds an outlet. The inherent quality within them to tackle this vocation comes effortlessly, while people doing a job not suited to them, in contrast, struggle.

There is a big difference between a fish swimming in water and a man copying it. Man can never duplicate the effortless ease of the fish and its graceful movement in water, because water is the natural environment for fish. Most people are like human beings in water – struggling with their careers and vocations. Those whose inborn traits and qualities match their chosen profession become like fish in water. For them, work is not a burdensome exercise, or an endless struggle to survive, but something they accomplish with ease.

Despite my reservations about my father's profession as a spiritual guide, I found myself excelling in it. I hadn't realised until now that I was meant to be a spiritual guide rather than an engineer. Somehow, all the situations and circumstances that previously appeared negative led to this beautiful present. They taught me the lesson of acceptance and surrender. Adverse circumstances displace our attention and almost always result in our improvement; that is, if we don't get bogged down by them.

However, the incident with the dacoit surprised me. I hadn't been sure that Brij's cancer could be cured, or that Tarun would recover. Maybe the divine force sometimes intervenes to lessen suffering – I could see His divine love flowing everywhere.

Yet, miracles scared me, so I didn't encourage the people who came to me seeking them. Helping people understand and overcome their limits was the biggest miracle of all – making them rid themselves of their masks, stop being someone they were never meant to be. Anything else is cheap magic by comparison. The seekers of miracles begin to depend on them and eventually lose sight of the higher self they originally sought.

'What are you thinking?'

I hadn't realised Shruti had joined me. She was my childhood friend, and my fiancée.

'I'm thinking it would have been much better if I could be more spiritual than I am. Then I would have relished the grace the Divine showers on us. Right now, I feel unworthy and ashamed that such an impure body receives so much divine love.'

'That's your humility speaking. You've transformed. You look so ... so different. Where did you get those insights, that courage, and this almost mad concern for others?'

I laughed. 'You're thinking exactly like I used to think. Where did other people get their talents?'

'Talent, that's the right word. But sometimes, the change in you makes me nervous. I feel you might leave me to live your mission.'

'Once we've surrendered to the divine self within us, only the best can happen.'

She smiled. 'We've achieved what I thought to be impossible.'

'Where are the others?'

'They're busy plucking tender coconuts with the help of local people. We've kept some for you. Won't you join us?'

'You carry on. I'll come after sometime.'

I dipped my feet in the sea and found the water comforting my tired feet. The weather turned pleasant as we approached the coast, though the nights were still cold.

How time changes everything! Some turning points shake the foundations of our lives. I remembered the storm that had transformed the course of my life forever....

28 | An Offer I Could Not Refuse

*J*ust six months ago ...

The harsh ring of my cell phone woke me up. My immediate reaction was confusion. I stared sleepily at the watch. 6 a.m., it blinked. Who needed to talk to me at this unearthly hour?

The ring tone died as suddenly as it had sounded. I turned and pulled the sheet over my head. Just then, the cell phone intruded on my privacy again.

The same number.

I bolted upright. Had the loan sharks traced my number? I grabbed the mobile before it played hide and seek with me again. 'Hello?'

'Is that Partibhan?' The faintly familiar female voice at the other end stopped me from packing my stuff to flee.

'Yes?'

'Guru Parmanand wants to see you.'

If I had been expecting a bolt from the skies, then this would be it. I recoiled at the mention of the name as though I was holding a snake in my hand.

'Hello?' I was familiar with the voice at the other end, but couldn't recall who it belonged to. 'Why? And after all this time?'

'He's going to depart from the world in a short while.'

'That's a roundabout way to say he's dying. Pity the great, all- knowing, all-powerful Swami Parmanand can't tame something as simple as death!'

'He isn't dying. Your father's taking samadhi, a voluntary renunciation of the body. But I don't think you'll understand. Are you coming to see him?'

'Is that a threat or a request?'

'A request; why should I threaten you?' The woman sounded calm. My verbal assault failed to irritate her.

'No, I don't wish to see him. His physical death has arrived twenty years too late for me.'

'Harsh words for your father. I called not only about performing the last rites, which is your moral duty, but for a more practical and pressing material side.'

'My father can't have a material side to him. He's so spiritual, so holy.' The sarcastic edge in my tone surprised me.

'If you take no interest in him at all, then we'll have no choice but to donate his fortune and close the ashram.'

'You can all go to hell, or paradise – whichever way you please. I have nothing to do with his ashrams and followers.'

'Partibhan, don't pass judgement so casually on us. You're unaware of the eternal spirit within you.'

'It's because we can't see it on an X-ray, can we, Sneha?' I finally recognised the voice of the woman speaking to me. She was my father's first disciple. Fair, tall and almost thirty-five – her picture came into sharp focus in my memory. She had been with my father from the time he was a non-entity to his present status as a world-renowned, miracle-performing saint.

'Are you coming?'

'Don't you understand simple replies anymore?'

'I'm talking about the trust your father owns. About three billion dollars, and all legal. You wish to say goodbye to all that? This, when you're on the run from loan sharks? You've lost a finger already; you want to lose your life?'

I gulped. Now I was awake. I mean really, really awake. They were thorough with their homework. Three billion dollars. Dollars! Mine! I looked at the suitcase I had hurriedly picked up in my anxiety to leave the hotel. It reminded me of my constant state of panic. I was a desperate man on the run.

'Are you still there?'

'Yes –'

'Just to inform you, both wills are ready. One of them donates all the fortune owned by your father to hospitals and NGOs, and the other is in your name. If you see him and accept the plan he has for your future, the fortune could be yours. If not –'

'I don't care … .' My lips were dry. I was afraid she might believe me.

'We'll wait for you till this weekend. You decide. Goodbye!' The phone went dead.

I stared at my cell. From being a poisonous snake, it had transformed into a magic wand which could change my financial health! Three billion dollars! And she said it could belong to me. The only question haunting me was how I would contain my hatred towards my father without jeopardising the inheritance.

I decided that I couldn't postpone the trip. I was tired of living in dingy rat-holes. The opportunity was irresistible.

In less than five minutes, I was heading towards the railway station to catch a train to Manmad.

29 | Someone's Loss, Someone's Gain

It was evening when my auto-rickshaw stopped at the gates of my father's ashram. The mellow sun cast a rust-brown sheen over the building, giving it a resplendent look. No one could have imagined that this ashram run by my father was worth three billion dollars – it seemed incapable of such prosperity.

As I stood mesmerised by its beauty, the guards managing the gate approached me.

'I'm Partibhan,' I told them. 'I'm here to meet Sneha.'

From the way they reacted, I think they knew who I was and were expecting me. They saluted and opened the gates quickly.

Moving deeper into the compound, I saw fountains lining the road to the main building. The water cascades, replete with pebbles and ferns, seemed real. Flower beds of many varieties lined the sides of the manmade stream. Further down, a tall, majestic, pyramid-shaped meditation hall made of glass created a spectacular silhouette against the sky. A group of people sitting on the lawns outside were singing a bhajan. Was all this going to belong to me? Did I deserve it?

For the first time ever, I was in awe of my father – before this there had been just one dimension to our relationship, that of hatred. More than the stamp of wealth, the place bore the signature of heart on everything visible. I felt serene and content for no reason, after a long time.

How my father came to own this ashram was a story the media repeated *ad nauseam*. An industrialist's only son was afflicted with a tumour in the brain and the doctors gave him a maximum of six months to live. Left without hope, the man took his child to my father for help, who at that time, had a very small but dedicated following. Guru Parmanand asked the industrialist to bring his child to the ashram every day. In six months, the child seemed to have made considerable improvement. The doctors pursuing the case were in for a surprise when a CT scan showed no sign of tumour. From the hospital, the industrialist went straight to Guru Parmanand. He fell at his feet and wept with joy.

'You saved my son! You saved him!'

In a spontaneous gesture, the industrialist donated twenty crore rupees worth of idle land to my father with a request. 'I would like you to build an ashram for the good work you're doing. I'm sure whatever happens here will be for the good of humanity.'

Since the industrialist was famous, the news of this gift hogged headlines for days and stirred a controversy. The cynics and believers kept arguing about the reasons behind the cure but my father refused to comment or engage. He quietly went on with the construction, with the complete cooperation and support of the industrialist.

The incident proved to be the turning point in my father's life. His fame spread, both through the lanes of India and the skies of foreign countries. In another decade or so, he became a world-renowned spiritual leader, whom both Indians and foreigners were eager to meet. His refusal to migrate abroad met with praise and his popularity with the masses as a man of ascetic values soared to heady heights.

'You can come to India because you can afford it, but most of my fellow citizens are poor and can't fly to your countries. I would rather stay with them,' he would say, whenever rich and influential people asked him to migrate to their countries. No talk about spirituality was possible without his name cropping up.

All this was that facet of his personality the world knew. His private side, however, was one which only two individuals suffered and endured – his wife and me. He abandoned us on the night he fled on his selfish spiritual search. We remained bitter, while the world heaped praises on him.

He tried to reach us when he could afford it, but it was too late. To us, he wasn't a saint but a charlatan, who merely got lucky.

When the media tried to raise a juicy scandal by unearthing our whereabouts and interviewing us, my mother flatly refused to participate. She rejected the large sums of money they tried to pay her for her story because she didn't believe in mud-slinging.

There was a large crowd outside the entrance to the main building. Every face I saw reflected anxiety. No single quality could describe the gathering. It represented different classes and backgrounds, yet the people appeared united in concern for my father.

'He isn't dying of ill health or suffering from any disease ... .' I heard Sneha say as I got down from my auto-rickshaw and walked towards the assembly. 'It's a wilful abandonment of the body. So be joyous for him, like he wishes.'

Like me, nobody bought her views. The gloom in the crowd didn't abate.

She saw me and nodded perceptibly. Before she could meet me, she fielded questions about my father's health. People swarmed her with requests to meet him one last time or to donate money. It took quite some time for her to disengage from her duties.

I waited patiently, feeling lost and confused in a place where I didn't belong. With nothing else to do, I watched her. She radiated good health, efficiency, patience and kindness – despite the endless and sometimes unintelligent questioning by the disciples. Anyone at an 'enquiry' counter would have lost their nerve a long time ago. At last, she was free.

'Sorry to have kept you waiting for so long,' she said. 'So you've seen reason at last.'

30 | Freedom, on One Condition

We marched through the corridors. The building had a high roof and a series of recurring ventilators made the corridors breezy and well-lit. The place was so quiet, I could hear the clatter of my shoes, and it made me uneasy.

'Why didn't he choose you or someone from the ashram as his successor?' I voiced what was uppermost on my mind.

'Because we're not as worthy as you.'

'How does being his son make me worthy?'

'Swami Parmanand can never be wrong in his judgment.'

It was obvious her faith was blind. 'I think my father's just promoting a family tradition. I smell a hierarchical stink rather than a spiritual flavour in this dish he's trying to cook.'

'Your father's a great man. If he's chosen you, he must have some good reasons.'

'Which are apparently lost to you and me?'

She ducked my comment with a stoic silence. Eventually, we came to a large room.

'Please remove your shoes.'

The room connected to another room through a door, which Sneha opened, leading me inside.

He was sitting in meditation, eyes closed. His body was so thin, he appeared malnourished. He sported a flowing beard. His forehead glistened with a supernatural radiance and my immediate reaction was to look at the roof, to find the bulb which must have been casting the luminance on him. There was no bulb!

My father looked different from his appearances in the media and his presence felt electric. My hair stood on end like bristles; I felt a cold rush of air over my head. We approached him on tiptoe and waited. The complete silence lingering in the room amplified all sounds beyond proportions and made me aware of all the noises we create – the sound of our breathing, heartbeats, and the rustle of our feet over the floor.

'So you have come.' He spoke without opening his eyes, his voice a soft melody of a flowing river. 'Welcome, my son.'

'I have no time for niceties. Will you come straight to the point, please?' How did he see me with his eyes closed? I searched the room for CCTVs through which he may have seen me coming, but found none.

'Why are you so stuck with the business of hating me? You must forgive me now that I am leaving this world.'

'You're only leaving this world now; you left ours twenty years ago.'

He didn't reply.

'Will you open your eyes and talk? Surely, you are not meditating. This way, I have a creepy feeling, as if you are blind. I mean, in the real sense of the word.'

My father opened his eyes. They were big, languid and hypnotic, having depths that made me uncomfortable.

Why did I ask him to open them at all!

His penetrating gaze tore away the mask of indifference I wore. He might have been lean, but he was healthy beyond doubt and far removed from death. Was this a cheap trick to bring me here, then? I remembered the anxious followers outside and Sneha's replies to their concerns. It puzzled me. Could the claim of samadhi as promoted by Sneha be true, then?

'Your stay in the ashram will change the way you see the world.'

'As much as criminals change in a jail.'

'Then let me come straight to the point. Day after tomorrow, when I take samadhi, you will become the next guru of this ashram – you'll take up from where I leave. All my life's work will then become your responsibility.'

'Is that all one needs to become a guru of your type? No training, no education? Nothing except being the son you discarded long ago? I simply have to sit on your funny-looking throne to become a world-famous guru like you?'

'I'll give you *shakti-paat*.'

'What's that?'

'A transfer of my divine knowledge to you through a special ceremony. You'll receive all the knowledge I gained in my lifetime and all my experience.'

'You mean you'll give to me all that you don't have and I'll own the nothing that is in you.'

He smiled again. I was simmering in anger but could not provoke him.

'This game of finding and pointing out my flaws is something you can't amuse yourself with for too long now. I request you to focus on the future. Do you want me to leave everything to the government institutions, NGOs and hospitals?'

'Why are you so keen that it shouldn't go to them, even when they are more deserving than me?'

'It's heartening to know you're still concerned about right and wrong despite your financial difficulties. Remember those times when we used to give alms to the poor children near our home? You were ten years old then.'

'Yes I do. Why do you ask?'

'How did you feel the first time?'

'Good. I felt as if we were looking after them.'

'They were malnourished and we gave them clothes. They slept outside our house and smiled on seeing us, all of which made us happy. But soon they became a nuisance.'

This was true. From priding myself as their saviour, I soon become furious at them. They would shout, fight, and create a ruckus. Their pranks interfered with my studies. They picked up quarrels with other children and littered the street. Twice, they broke windows when they hurled stones at each other in street fights, which became routine. One day, I offered them chocolate out of sympathy. But rather than feel grateful, they pounced upon me the next day and rummaged through my bag – throwing my books, tearing pages in the hope of getting their next chocolate, which they thought I was hiding from them.

'Where are you hiding it?' one of them demanded.

'I don't have it *baba*,' I reasoned.

'Trying to act smart? Take this –'

They didn't believe me and beat me black and blue, tore my clothes and sent me wailing and crying. Finally, someone complained and the authorities took them away. It was a big relief for everyone.

'I spent sleepless nights after the day you returned home with your torn clothes and a lost school bag. I realised that those kids, and in fact every human being, needed something other than alms, without which they would keep straying from their potential. I also realised that a much bigger task awaited me, instead of just feeding my family.'

'You mean to say that we harm people by helping them? The jobs being done by NGOs and the Red Cross are futile?'

'Who deserves alms, and when you need to stop giving and instead focus on making them self-reliant is something which you can know only when you become self-aware. Then you know who is living at an animal level and who is ready to connect with the higher being in them. Sadly, help and charity are exploited, both by the users and the givers.'

'Yet that's what most NGOs are doing.'

'For me, a much more rewarding job would be to invoke the deeply buried higher self in every human being. If this higher self is activated, then automatically, not only will all their other needs be fulfilled, but they can also excel as human beings. For that to happen, they have to align to the superior force of the Divine present in them and not to the pulls and pushes of an NGO.'

'Are you suggesting that running this ashram is worthier than running a hospital?'

'Yes.'

'Anyone can see how the work done by charitable hospitals and NGOs helps humanity. But your work is abstract and vague, maybe, even questionable, because who has seen the Divine?'

'We're running charitable hospitals and NGOs too.'

'Still, you think that spiritual healing is worthier?'

'Yes, because it works at a higher level, aims at a higher goal. It's not about surviving or existing, but sublimating. It makes them independent of NGOs and helps them have a higher awareness and vision.'

'Then why choose an unworthy candidate? I am a rogue, hounded by loan sharks. My interest in this ashram is limited to money, and you know that well enough.'

'Yes, I know. I also know why you took that loan and lost your finger.'

So he was aware. I'd borrowed money for my mother's treatment, but I failed to save her from death. She'd succumbed to her insulin-shock-triggered coma, despite the best efforts of the doctors, and I had lost my finger in the brutality that followed because I was unable to repay the loan.

'You think you are unworthy and you even accept it,' my father continued. 'You never justify yourself but feel guilty about being thrust into a place and position you feel you don't deserve. Is that the sign of a rogue? No, it's a sign of a humility only the aware can have.'

'Flattering, but I still don't feel I'm suited for the job.'

'As I mentioned earlier, shakti-paat is a powerful ceremony that will change you. You have another twenty-four hours to decide. After that, I won't be here to change the will. So think carefully.'

At that moment, I knew he was not lying.

31 | On the Path with *Shakti-Paat*

I knew Shruti would never forgive me if she got to know about the life I was leading. I took a loan of ten lakhs for my mother's treatment and because of the time I spent with her in the hospital, I lost my job. With no money to pay the monthly installments, I tried to buy time. But when those loan sharks chopped my finger off with the warning that they would return for more, I was left with no choice but to flee to another city. I took up odd jobs, like working at factories as a supervisor, to meet my expenses, always with the fear that they would find me one day.

Now, I was on the verge of becoming a guru!

All this while, Shruti believed that I was still working at the automobile plant – a job I had managed to secure after quitting my government job. But for the abnormal circumstances, she would have been my wife by now. She was almost twenty-seven. Her father was anxious to see us married.

Before revealing the details of my new career to her, I had to tackle my confused state of mind. My becoming a guru would shock her. However, I had reached a point where the 'coward' label didn't bother me. I needed time to regain my bearings in this new world.

In the past, I had criticised the ways of spiritual gurus like my father to everyone I knew. I had always believed that gurus preached spirituality to the gullible to earn money, fame and comfort for themselves. But soon, I was going to become one of them.

Shruti would be angry with me for not having sought her father's help in clearing my financial dues. But he was the last person I would ever seek help from. I never felt comfortable with him – he was always scrutinising me, as if measuring my character.

I can't forget the day he had invited me over for lunch. During those days, I was struggling with my career after my disastrous stint at Bangalore. I'd resigned because of the deep-rooted corruption prevalent in my government job and was finding it difficult to secure another one. Most of my friends and relatives didn't see my quitting a corrupt job as something heroic. From their perspective, I'd run away from a battle, like a coward. My confidence wasn't very high either. Though I was in no mood to socialise, he insisted on a lunch.

When Shruti went into the kitchen, he offered to set up a factory for me. 'You're unemployed and I was just wondering … you know.'

He was testing me for what I was worth. Those searing eyes watched me like a fisherman watches the waters after spreading his net.

'You are offering me what my father did some time ago, and I refuse for the same reason. I don't want any favours.' I toyed with the chopsticks, having lost my appetite.

'You have a father? Shruti never told me.'

'Everyone has one. What she doesn't know is that he's alive. I am the son of Guru Parmanand.'

His head jerked back and his face mirrored his shock. It turned out that he was my father's follower. I revealed my tumultuous past and his cynicism turned to respect. From a despicable, to-be-avoided son-in-law, I became a cherished and desirable one.

Next week, we were engaged!

I kept thinking about these incidents on my way to signing those damned papers, still hoping that a last-minute reprieve would extricate me from the inescapable gravity of financial matters. Then I need not tell Shruti anything.

'The ashram won't be the same after Swamiji.' Sneha startled me out of my reverie.

'I suspect it will be more like a circus, with me playing the joker!'

'Not a joker, but a guru.'

'In my dictionary, they are synonyms.'

'Wait and see. You'll need to revise the old edition soon and remove the errors.'

'Fat chance!'

A lawyer delivered the papers in full view of my father, Ramanujam, Sneha and some other old disciples of his. Shifting my attention from the lawyer to the papers, I tried to spot a loophole in whatever I was being made to sign. But there were none. Several clauses filled the pages.

I would lose my inheritance:

If I spent more than two months a year outside the ashram.

If I stopped giving lectures to my disciples.

If I called my father a fraud.

If I made fun of religion.

If I spent lavishly towards pursuits not helping spiritualism in any way.

Sneha could veto all my expenses, unconditionally, but I could spend money – thirty thousand every month – without her permission. However, if I spent this money improperly, I would cease to be a trustee and also lose the right to the monthly stipend. The pocket money would double when I married. The list went on and on, typical of a father who knows his son too well and tries to pre-empt all his weaknesses with one masterstroke. Acutely aware that I didn't have any choice in deciding matters, I signed awkwardly, using my thumb and middle finger.

Goodbye, freedom!

My father instructed Ramanujam to clear all the pending interest I owed the loan sharks.

'But you can easily pay the entire sum I owe. Why pay only the interest?' I protested.

'Your dues will be cleared after two years.'

'Why not now?'

'Because then you will be tempted to reconsider your freedom and discard the ashram after it has served your desperate purpose.'

'I can do this after two years too.'

'Two years is going to be more than enough for you to realise your higher self. One day, you will know that all these steps were for your welfare. You are in a terrible crisis right now and most people in such situations behave in self-destructive ways. I don't want you to destroy this ashram or yourself.'

Glad that the ceremony of my utter humiliation was finished, I went to my room to celebrate my slavery to a profession I hated.

My father was right when he said that the game of hating him, which I'd played so far, was about to end. I had already made a beginning in which I was going to hate myself more than I hated my father. I compromised only because I was tired of hiding from my creditors.

'So Partibhan, you're no longer an engineer in the materialistic world, but a guru in the spiritual world. You are a guru from today …' I laughed spitefully at my reflection in the mirror.

Shakti-paat, or transfer of power from the guru to his disciple, was to take place in an hour's time. The preparations were elaborate. Word had spread that I would succeed my father, who was going to take samadhi. Before he left his earthly home, he would transfer all his divine powers and spiritual knowledge to me. I suspected it to be a lousy trick to establish my succession without stirring controversy.

My father's disciples threw flowers at me as they led me to the stage. I gasped when I saw the spectacle: massive cheering crowds of at least ten thousand people. What had I done to deserve the honour? Signed the death warrant of a free life?

A short while later, my father appeared. He greeted the crowd with folded hands. The entire gathering saluted him. Some of them folded their hands while others prostrated on the ground.

'Guru Parmanand ki jai!'

He waited for the noise to subside. Then, in his clear baritone, he addressed them. 'My children, I'm going to depart at 6 a.m. tomorrow. But I'm going to leave a part of me in the young Partibhan. My voice and my advice will exist through him, because I'll give him realisation today. After the *shakti-paat* ceremony, there will be no difference between him and me, spiritually, that is. Respect him the way you respect me now. Listen to him as you listen to me.'

'Guru Parmanand ki jai!'

'Guru Partibhan ki jai!'

I looked around, bewildered at the sudden change in the chants. He had achieved the transfer with mere words! The message to his followers was clear – they were to respect my authority.

My father sat on the floor, facing me. He closed his eyes and raised his right palm towards me, in a gesture of blessings. He then began to chant what sounded like mantras.

Was this man really going to die tomorrow at six? Or was he going to commit suicide because he was fed up of the ashram life? Maybe this was his revenge for my refusal to accept him as a respectable father figure. He was locking me up in this jail for two years – among these mad people!

The entire gathering watched us in silence. Then my father raised his hand further and placed it on my head.

'Guru Parmanand ki jai!' People shouted repeatedly.

My father was reciting some Sanskrit *shlokas*. All this while, I sat inertly, surely looking like the fool I felt I was. Abruptly, my father opened his eyes and said, 'I have given *shakti-paat* to your new guru Swami Partibhan. A new chapter begins and my time has come. I have served you to the best of my capacity. Forgive me if I unintentionally hurt anyone's sentiments.'

'We love you, guruji!' Many in that hysterical congregation were sobbing.

'Long live Guru Parmanand! Long live Guru Partibhan!'

My head buzzed with a strange sensation. I felt drowsy.

Later, alone in my room, I closed my eyes and remembered the madness of the crowd.

Was *shakti-paat* real or just a clever gimmick? Was it an auto-suggestion that would make me believe I had received spiritual enlightenment? Or was it a catalyst that would trigger my dormant capabilities? I felt confused and at a complete loss.

And what were all those people seeking? What did they see in my father which I failed to see? I would never understand these people.

I realised I would have to talk to Shruti about my predicament. I needed advice to survive this madness.

The buzz in my head increased and I felt cool draughts all over my body. I was overcome with drowsiness, despite having slept enough for the day.

I stretched on the bed and immediately fell asleep.

32 | Fuzzy Logic

I was flying among stars spread so densely, they formed a river. The universe looked beautiful with its suns, planets and galaxies. It seemed as if I wasn't alone but accompanied by a benign force. As I drifted along the river of stars, I experienced a sense of joy and freedom, as if I was liberated from all binds. I felt surprisingly light.

'You have to return now to your world and do the job meant for you,' said the invisible force.

'I don't want to leave. I've never been so happy.'

'Your job awaits you. When you return, there won't be any turning back.'

'Promise?'

'Promise.'

When I woke up, I felt sad for no reason, as if I'd lost something precious. The beauty of the state persisted. Still groggy from sleep, I reached for the glass pitcher.

Was it a dream or something real that I had seen? I didn't know. I looked at my chopped finger, a constant reminder of my financial failure. For five years, I had struggled to make a career out of my engineering degree. I couldn't compromise with corrupt superiors and unethical practices. Now, to escape the consequences of my financial problems, I agreed to be a guru to so many people who would repose their faith and trust in me. I was clueless as to what I was supposed to do, with no learning or experience whatsoever. Should I go and tell everyone the truth? Should I tell them to seek salvation at a more deserving place?

If I did this, the loan sharks would never leave me in peace when the next installments came up. And what to make of the dream? It perplexed me. It was loaded with overpowering significance. What of the joy I'd experienced in the flight, which still lingered? Only my father could answer these questions. Just three hours remained between now and 6 a.m. If I slept now, I might never see him again – if his intent to take samadhi was real.

I felt compelled to talk to my father.

The lights in the corridor were dim, but I found his room easily. I pushed the door from the outside and it gave in. It took me some time to get accustomed to the darkness.

He was sleeping on the floor without a mattress or bedsheet beneath him. It was very cold because the heater was off. The sparsely furnished room smelled of the sweet fragrance of incense sticks. It was more like a temple than a bedroom.

I stood watching my father as he slept peacefully, without even a pillow beneath his head. His face looked serene. I saw his caved-in stomach, his undernourished body, and realised that though my father was surrounded by luxuries, he lived a severely austere life. Automatically, my gaze went to his forehead, which seemed to glisten with a halo. As I stood, uncertain of what I should do, my father opened his eyes.

'What are the questions troubling you, my son?'

I was shocked. How could he have read my mind? I stared into those hypnotic eyes with unfathomable depths. 'I feel like a fraud and am leaving this ashram.'

'Why? What fraud did you commit?'

'I can't fool people into believing I got *shakti-paat* and have moved to a higher spiritual plane, and give sermons. Because I haven't changed in any way. I have neither the knowledge of a saint nor the grace of a holy person. I feel every inch a fraud.'

'The *shakti-paat* was real. In time, you'll understand it fully.'

'What's the need to lie when we stand here alone?'

'I believe in it and one day you will too. For now, sit and close your eyes to take an inward journey and tell me if you see something.'

'But what has this got to do – '

'Go ahead, just do it. You and I are not going to lose anything by this simple exercise.'

I closed my eyes and sat motionless for what appeared like five minutes. Gradually, a joyous state enveloped me. Abruptly, I saw the same river of stars, the Milky Way and the universe in slow motion I had dreamt of in my sleep. I also saw a huge ball of light in the middle of this universe. The repeat experience startled me. What was happening?

'What did you see?' My father broke the spell. I opened my eyes and stared at him. What had he done?

'I saw the universe and a huge ball of light – exactly the same I dreamed of when I fell asleep, after the *shakti-paat*.'

'You just saw the inner light of your divine self, which is present in all of us. It's divine light. However, the darkness of ignorance eclipses it. During *shakti-paat*, I merely raised the curtain of ignorance and let the divine light fill your being. The light you saw was your own divine self.'

What he said appeared incredible. The ecstasy I had experienced was unique. 'Still, it's difficult to believe that spirituality is like cooking instant noodles.'

My father laughed. 'Spirituality is an inherent, ever-present quality in all of us. When awakened, it becomes accessible instantly. Just like the force of electricity comes alive with the flick of a switch.'

'I don't know if it's available in me and I don't know what to do with it.'

'Different people put electricity to different uses. Someone uses it in a torch to light a path at night and someone else lights huge mercury lamps to flood an entire auditorium. Our spiritual force is present in all its strength and ready for us to use. It's present in the meanest of human beings, as in the most saintly. With an ancient process, I've merely given you ready and easy access to your own spirituality, switched it on, like electricity.'

'You mean you have put me on a fast track? I find that hard to believe. What about my disciples? How would I be able to help them access their spirituality? I see that as my key role, of which I have no clue.'

'Good concern. The spirituality I've invoked in you is more like a seed I've planted. But it's you who'll decide whether to nurture the seed and make it a tree or let it wither. If you make it a tree, then the fruits of your effort will be available to all those who come in touch with you. However, if you deviate from the spiritual path, this light will dim. Just stay steadfast on the path, and the light will glow like a thousand suns. It will bless many by its radiance. You'll be able to dispel the darkness that lingers in ignorant minds with the light of your knowledge. Unleash an exponential chain reaction by giving everyone their self-realisation.'

'Self-realisation?'

'The *shakti-paat* I gave is just one-to-one, from me to you, limited to two people. But if you remain steadfast, you will ignite self-realisation in millions of people with this light that is in you.'

I smiled disbelievingly. 'What are you doing on the floor, in this cold? You don't even have a bed and you haven't switched on your heater.'

'Those are materialistic comforts, not necessary. The joy I feel with the Divine is what I relate with. I don't need them because I rarely identify with my body.'

'I wish I could believe what you said. What about the samadhi? Is it possible? Or is it suicide you'll commit tomorrow?'

'Suicide is a cowardly act. Death comes to all of us; I'm choosing the time to leave my body. Only blessed mortals can do so, that too after several years of attuning to the Supreme.'

'Your austerity could be a ruse to impress the gullible, and the samadhi could be suicide, despite what you claim.'

'And what you saw just now is the result of opium we mixed in your food? Our mind can do nothing except destroy everything sublime. I can't extract you from the swamp of intellectualism. To come out, listen to your heart. It's easy to destroy what the heart builds. I have given you a glimpse of the absolute truth. But faith is something you'll have to build on your own. Even God can't instil it in human beings.'

His word signalled that the discussion was over; the spell had broken.

The temporary bridge of friendship built in those beautiful moments lingered in my mind long after I closed the door gently behind me.

33 | Death by Invitation

At six in the morning, I heard a knock at the door.

When I opened the door with eyes half-closed, I saw Ramanujam peering at me, his eyes red and swollen.

'Your father has left this world. He's taken samadhi.'

My hand went automatically to my chin. I found myself at a loss for words.

'He's left this earthly abode for his heavenly journey. We're all waiting for you to begin the last rites....' Ramanujam found it difficult to continue.

His body lay on the floor, with a half-smile on his face. He appeared serene and calm, even in death. I was now the guru of the ashram and its followers. The realisation brought with it resentment; he hadn't even trained me for the job. Just abandoned me with the responsibility and the assumption that I would take up where he left off, on such short notice. Once again, I felt the same disorientation I had experienced years ago, the same insecurity of an abandoned child. What would happen this time?

I'll survive, like before. A desperate belief, rather than any real conviction.

The samadhi was not a myth. What I was seeing was a near-perfect exit. Could someone take samadhi like that? Just step out of the roller-coaster of life whenever they wished? Until now, I had viewed death as something which happened because the body parts stopped functioning due to disease and aging.

My father's death brought me face-to-face with the issue of life after death. If someone could take samadhi, as described in the scriptures, then was everything else they said about a life after death true? I believed the scriptures were for reining in the moral conduct of a society. This was alien territory. My brain reeled with the implications of it.

Fifteen years ago, when he left a void in our lives, we faced insecurity and acrimony. These were good enough reasons for a weak man to run from the battlefield. Why did he leave now, when the world was falling at his feet and he had earned fame and recognition? Who would feel like quitting an empire worth three billion dollars? It must have been for something superior to what he already possessed.

'He left a note for you.' Ramanujam interrupted my thoughts.

I found myself staring at a long white envelope.

My dear Partibhan,

I haven't chosen you as the successor of this ashram because you are my son, as many would dismiss, including you. I chose you because I can see the Holy Spirit living in you. At the moment, your pain traps your spirit, but when it crumbles, it will set your spirit free. Then you and the world will know the wisdom and correctness of my decision.

The divine presence is waiting to blossom in you. Contrary to what you imagine, it doesn't need coaching. The force is a spontaneous one, which flows to its natural destination freely

200 so The Quest of the Sparrows

and with the greatest of ease. Follow your heart and surrender
everything to the divine self in you. It will guide you and look
after you.

May the Divine be with you.

Parmanand

At 12 p.m., after elaborate ceremonies, I consigned the body to
flames. I not only lit my father's funeral pyre that morning but
also extinguished my hatred for him – nothing left for me to hate
now. I could never come to love him, though. They say death
is a healer of wounds. My father's death ended the bitterness in
me. Before his death, he ironed out my financial creases, though
not in a way I liked or appreciated. But is anything in life ever
close to being perfect?

I didn't cry for my father, but felt a void. I had sensed something
other than his mere physical presence and now it was gone. Yet,
I felt different from the day my mother died. I had wept bitterly
then and felt more of an orphan than I felt today. My mother
had sacrificed her life for me. I saw her bearing all kinds of
hardships for my sake. She starved herself, didn't take milk and
fruits; wore cheap, torn clothes, so that I could buy expensive
books for my education and wear the best of clothes to college.
Yet, my mother died an unknown martyr. Nobody saluted her
motherhood. Nobody praised her. This wasn't so with my father.
The world sought him. His disciples cried and became hysterical.
They gained from him what I lost. They shed for him the tears
I didn't have and wept for him as I wept for my mother. I was
objective about my father's death – objective because he didn't
arouse any emotions in me.

Standing there and watching the flames go up, I felt as far from spirituality as a drunkard is from logic. I didn't feel forgiveness; I didn't feel guiltless over my mother's death. Not light or free. Nothing at all. Would the spiritual seed my father had claimed to have planted in me become a tree? I was a poor example, a wretched candidate for spirituality. What was I going to preach?

As I stood there, I drew parallels between my mother's and my father's lives. They were just that – parallels in the real sense. I couldn't help noticing that while my mother surrendered to death by giving up her struggle to live, my father outwitted it by exiting on his own terms, at a time and place of his choice. The smile on his face was one of triumph, of a man who had conquered the fear of death.

Despite my prejudice, I couldn't help but notice the ease with which my father had lived, and the difficulties my mother had faced. It was not because of the difference in their riches, but a result of the bitterness she had felt. She always appeared bottled-up and in emotional turmoil. Always sad and depressed about the way life had treated us.

In contrast, my father had transcended all emotions. Despite his immense wealth, I knew he possessed peace which only few human beings do. It is a quality independent of money, power or glory – it is innate and intrinsic. So what was the source of his peace and why did it elude my mother? To me, the bliss he experienced while dying was an enigma, since most of us are afraid of dying.

'It's time to leave,' Ramanujam reminded me.

34 | Eureka in a Dhoti!

A day after I returned from Haridwar, after immersing my father's ashes in the Ganges, a guard came running towards me. 'Someone wants to see you.'

'Who?'

'A woman named Shruti. Says you know her.'

I stood like a frozen chicken, shocked and stupefied. I looked down at my dhoti and vest – my traditional dress within the ashram.

'Your instructions, sir?'

Realising that wishing her away was not going to solve my problems, I took a deep breath and barely managed to murmur, 'Allow her in.'

I knew what would have happened if I had refused her permission. She would have gatecrashed and created a scene! With quick hops, the best I could manage with the darned dhoti, I converted the walk to my room into a trot. While at the semi-sprint, I was careful not to lose the dignity of a guru. If she was to laugh at me, it better be in private, not with so many people standing and watching us. Her reactions would be embarrassing; especially in front of the people I would be preaching to in future.

Inside the room, I considered changing into my jeans. Realising that it would only postpone the issue, and her laughter, to some other potentially more embarrassing time, I decided to field whatever she would throw at me. I had to adapt to the uncomfortable parts of my decision to become a guru some day – and I had decided that this day was going to be the beginning.

Shruti stood speechless when she saw me. Her jaw dropped and her mouth formed a shocked O! Then she started laughing uncontrollably. Her whole body heaved, in direct proportion to her mirth. It was worse than I had feared and I blessed my presence of mind to see her in a closed room.

'Won't you sit, Shruti?' I pretended to be unaffected by her outburst.

'What's this you've gotten into, all this guru stuff? Don't tell me the speculation in the media is true.'

'It is.'

'What?' Her body stiffened.

'Shruti, it's a complicated decision. Why don't you sit?'

'Did your father blackmail you into accepting the job? You hated gurus! Now you are one of them?'

'I didn't take up this profession because my father blackmailed me. I was left with no choice.' I brought my left hand forward, the one with the missing finger.

'No choice – what happened to your finger?' Her eyes widened with horror.

'It's a long story –'

'You lost a finger and didn't tell me? You became a guru and I come to know of this from the news and not you? You've changed. You're avoiding me. You aren't the Parti I knew –'

'Yes, I changed because I didn't have any choice. I'm now into this profession whether I like it or not.'

'What happened? What?' she demanded, her voice so shrill, it must have travelled through the ashram.

'Calm down. Shouting won't help.'

Before I continued, I insisted she should sit. It was an effort, but she obliged.

I took pains to explain the circumstances which led me to the decision.

'You went through so much while you made me believe you still held a comfortable job? You didn't trust me enough –'

'I ... I was afraid, with all those people chasing me and threatening to take my life. I didn't want your involvement in the mess I'd created.'

'But it was for your mother, damn it! You could have asked me for the money. My father would have lent it to you!'

'That would have amounted to begging. I think of this as a job I've taken up to repay my financial obligation to my father.'

'The news about you was shocking. It was difficult to believe it was you. All kinds of stories are circulating in the papers.'

'I know. I don't deserve to be here. Naturally, there's bound to be controversy.'

'What about our future? Does this sect need you to be celibate?'

'Oh, no. I can marry you today if I wanted.'

'But?'

'I'm in mourning, and for one year I shouldn't do anything celebratory in nature.'

'Oh. I see. Still, how do you plan to go about being a guru? You always mixed up the characters of the *Mahabharata* with the *Ramayana*!' A tiny smile played on her face. Her cheeks were stained with tears and her nose was running. The emotions she portrayed were a curious mix which made me smile.

'I'm doing extensive reading to fill the gaps.'

'And would you give discourses?'

'Yes. It's expected.'

'And how do you intend to achieve it?'

'I've figured out a reprieve. I've been going through my father's lectures. They're simple, and I think I can expand them and present them in different ways, with my interpretations and commentaries.'

'Isn't it strange?'

'What?'

'You always wanted spirituality to be practical. For it to work for everyone and here you are –'

'Practical!' I almost jumped out of my seat. The word triggered an idea.

'What're you thinking?'

'You're right as to why I hated gurus and religion. All these gurus and religious books preach theory but in practical life, human beings achieve very little.'

'So?'

'So what if I can conduct an experiment with spirituality? Test the truth of what's said in the scriptures!'

'What if the results are contradictory?'

'It would be the most exciting part of the experiments: verifying without prejudice what's right and what's wrong!'

'What do you have in mind?'

'From now on, I'd concentrate on practical spirituality!' My previous gloom had vanished. Facing reality has its benefits; Shruti's visit changed my depression into optimism. This is one thing

I like about Shruti. Talking to her always brings me in touch with myself, helping me think through abstract thoughts and take them to their logical conclusion. Maybe, there is divinity in what we share. For the first time, because of the ashram and the ambience of spirituality, I thought that there is Divine presence in between the two of us. Our love was a manifestation of the Supreme.

Her eyes sparkled. 'I'm confident you'll make a good guru.'

'I hope you're right.'

After our dinner, we strolled on the ashram grounds on a full moon night. The ashram was large and expansive and submerged in the silvery blue hue of the moon. The whole landscape looked incredibly bewitching.

'You have a beautiful haven,' Shruti echoed my thoughts. 'I get this soothing feeling of contentment and peace here. I think it's going to be a more fulfilling experience for you than the desk job you were doing at your bleak office.'

'Of course, there's a big "if" about me being able to cope with the job. It could end in disaster.'

'You're merely nervous, but once you start, you'll be comfortable.'

With some reluctance, we turned away from the magic of the night to return to our rooms.

'See you,' she said as she climbed into the car the next morning. Her white salwar-kameez lit up her face with a vibrant radiance.

'I'll miss you. I wanted you to stay for my first discourse –'

'I would've loved to listen too, but I have an important assignment to finish. Good luck! I'll pray for your success.' She smiled, squeezed my hand and slipped a note in it.

'Read it after I leave.' She started the car, and was gone.

Immediately, I was gripped with worry about the difficult job of delivering my first lecture to an audience who didn't know me at all. I was almost in my room when I remembered the note in my hand and opened it.

Dear Parti,

I had known for a long time that there is a Divine. There were always signs of His existence. However, I wasn't sure where He was. I thought, maybe He resides in me and you, and in all His creations. I hadn't ever seen or sensed Him.

Since I have met you, things have changed. In the sparks that flew when I came close to you, I saw a light. Not in me or you, but between us.

Now I know where the Divine is. Maybe, He is not in me and you. But I have sensed Him in the space we share. There is Divine between us, Parti.

Always yours,
Shruti

Her love gave me the strength I was missing.

Maybe it won't be as bad as I had feared. Maybe I can do it after all.

35 | Mirror, Mirror on the Wall, Make Me See Where I Fall

I couldn't watch television at the ashram. There was only one TV, in the lecture hall. Before taking samadhi, my father would deliver a lecture in person but if he wasn't present because of some reason, they played a DVD of his older lectures on this TV. Since the death of my father, the ashram had been playing only those DVDs. Although no one said anything, I knew everyone was awaiting my first discourse.

I couldn't rent a movie because no video library existed within a ten-kilometre radius from our ashram. Even if I could lay my hands on a movie, the lecture hall was not the right place to watch it. I was supposed to be in mourning, and watching TV or movies would appear inconsiderate in those circumstances.

'Your father used to do yogic asanas and gardening,' Sneha suggested one day, sensing my restlessness. This wasn't of much help. My muscles were rigid and I felt my limbs would break rather than bend doing those asanas. Also, I had never liked the idea of disturbing mother earth and was sure she didn't like it either. With these contorted excuses, I dismissed Sneha's advice.

Apart from the absence of any entertainment, I missed good food. The stuff they served at the ashram was minimal. They were promoting the 'food for survival' theory – eating only healthy food in amounts adequate for surviving and avoiding any indulgences. But I think they carried it a bit too far.

'Life's as much for enjoyment as it is for spiritual practices,' I justified my craving for food with the brazen declaration. 'If it were not so, why would there be colours, flowers, fruits and joy? We have to watch our greed, not suppress it. Even the scriptures don't ask us to give up eating good food in pursuit of spirituality. Let food be simple, not tasteless!'

With this message, I ordered a drastic change in the menu. Many people, I am sure, felt relieved. Good food also reminded me of my favourite, mouth-watering, non-vegetarian dishes. Yet, non-vegetarian stuff was strictly off-limits within the ashram, which preached ahimsa. I tried to figure out some way to satisfy my need without inviting a scandal.

A week later, Sneha brought an important-looking hand-delivered package to my room.

'It's confidential.' She pointed at the large bold letters on the package. 'I wonder what it contains.'

'I ordered some spiritual books.' I was sitting on my bed reading the newspaper. Though it was roughly nine in the night, I jumped out of my bed and went to the bathroom to shave, just to avoid her questions.

'Won't you open the parcel?' She strained over the noise of the running tap, curious to see what the package contained.

'I'm too embarrassed to show you the catching up I have to do, now that I have become a full-fledged guru. I don't even know whether Eklavya is in the *Mahabharata* or the *Ramayana*.'

'But we have an extensive library,' she objected.

'They are boring research books, with unnecessary commentaries and details. An abridged version is what I need to fill my gaps as quickly as I can.'

She left the room, not too convinced.

Alone, I tore open the parcel. Neatly packed between spiritual books was a plastic box. Inside it was my treasure, wrapped in a KFC bag: a roast chicken. Shruti was a genius, God bless her. I drooled over the packet, and then closed the plastic container quickly. The room reeked of it. Any seasoned non-vegetarian like me would detect the smell of delicious spicy chicken.

In sheer panic, I conjured a terrible urge to meditate with incense sticks. Lighting six of them at once, I cursed myself for impatience and vowed a hundred times that next time I would open the package after preparing for 'meditation'.

I took a bath too, and somehow suffered the hours to dinner. My mind was on nothing but the chicken.

'You haven't eaten properly,' Sneha commented. She was in charge of serving me food and was disappointed that I had barely eaten a few mouthfuls.

'I don't feel like eating today.'

'Have you started meditating?'

'Yes, how did you know?'

'Your room is full of *chandan* essence. Just like your father.'

I suppressed my snigger with difficulty. Had my father been up to the same mischief as me?

Alone, I lit six more incense sticks, then settled for the biggest dinner I had had in almost a month!

'How was it?' Shruti laughed.

'Delicious!'

'Your next spiritual set of books, sir?'

'Hot wings, chicken strips with salsa dips, written by my favourite author KFC.'

'Express or ordinary delivery?'

'Ordinary. How do you manage it?'

'That's a secret gurus don't need to learn. But this isn't right.'

'Are you joking?'

'Yes,' she giggled. 'Still, I feel guilty. You're a guru, an example to others. People trust you.'

'I resent vegetarianism thrust forcibly on me. I've every right to eat what I want.'

Over the next few weeks, as promised, Shruti delivered the packages. Instead of feeling satiated by the food binges, I found myself constantly thinking of them and dreaming about them. Slowly, my life started to spin around an axis of non-vegetarian food, just because there was little else for me to do.

I put on weight and my belly started protruding like a watermelon. The light I saw while I meditated became dimmer. My logic justified my actions, yet something made me uneasy. I couldn't put my finger on it.

One night, while I was busy gobbling up the stuff in a hurry, I choked on a piece of meat. I tried to cough it out but I couldn't. I gasped for breath and reached for the water jug. It was empty.

The muscles of my throat were constricting and I caught a glimpse of myself in the mirror, with the lavish dinner spread in front of me, my face red and eyes bulging. I was perspiring, my lips were smeared with what I had eaten. Even my clothes were soiled. I had eaten in a terrible hurry; afraid someone would knock and wean me from the joy of relishing the delicacies.

I tried to call Sneha; no voice came out of my throat. I inched my way to the door, not sure I would live. Even if I opened the door, what would people see? A glutton who was choking on his greed, not a guru.

I kept coughing to no effect, my face turning purple. Then I put my finger in my throat and vomited.

The meat piece flew out with the river of greed. Fresh air rushed to my lungs and I breathed in relief. I'd been terrifyingly close to death.

My eyes were puffed and part of the vomit had exited from my nostrils. The room was in a mess and I stood at its centre, holding my watermelon tummy, staring at my image in the mirror.

What I saw repulsed me. I felt graceless, and as greedy as a pig. The naked greed for non-vegetarian food filled me with loathing. I had even made Shruti a party to my greed. When would the craving be satiated? Meat was bringing out the worst in me, and I hated it for making me a glutton.

In that instant, I took a decision. I would respect my environment or reject it – no more rationalising. My weakness for food had brought out the animal in me and I was appalled by its glimpse in the mirror.

'I don't want you to send the deliveries anymore,' I told Shruti in the morning.

'Why?'

'I'm through with meat.'

'Is the place changing you, or was something wrong with the meat I sent you last night?'

'I realised why this is wrong.'

'If you feel like eating again, don't hesitate to swallow your pride,' she said. 'Your giving up meat worries me.'

'Why?'

'One day you might just embrace celibacy. Religion preaches against meat and also against lust.'

'If our love is just lust then I'll be happy to let go of it, too. Right now I feel ...' I hesitated.

'What?'

'I feel our relationship is based on love. Wouldn't you want it to be that way?'

'Which woman wouldn't want love over lust? I can't even begin to explain how glad I am you think that way.'

After that decision, I began to meditate regularly every day.

The spirituality I have invoked in you is more like a seed I have planted on a land I know is spiritually fertile. Grow that seed into a giant tree or let it wither.

I remembered my father's words. You justify flaws only as long as you cling to them. I now understood why keeping the batteries of spiritual awareness fully charged was essential and meditation was the only way.

Gradually, I regained the peace I had been missing. The glimpse in the mirror of the animal lurking in me made me aware of a new technique to check other negative tendencies: I began witnessing myself with detachment. Overcoming gluttony was just the beginning.

The groundbreaking change encouraged me to experiment further. Because of the incident, I began to see others in a new light. People with flaws, whom I had ridiculed before, were in no way different from me: only, they were yet to see their reflections in the mirror. I also saw Sneha and Ramanujam's dedication: they devoted every minute of their lives to the ashram with a smile and never complained.

I saw the trust with which many of my father's followers were trying to imbibe his advice. Whatever they were doing came from their heart and their faith in him. These people who sought spirituality were different: the word 'holy' came automatically to my mind. They transcended their pettiness in a search for higher values. They were less complaining, joyous, and spread peace around them.

In two weeks, my perspective about the ashram and its people changed. When I delved deeper into the ashram life, what I saw surprised me. The ashram was not merely a place where people assembled for ritualistic worshipping or listening to religious discourses, but a place where change was possible.

It was a vibrant, fertile and sacred place.

Most of the *shishyas* who came to the ashram stayed for a month, a fortnight or a week, according to what their busy lives permitted. Many of these were doctors, engineers or businessmen who were successful in their fields, but missing in their day-to-day lives what they were obviously getting here.

Also, the seriousness towards spirituality varied from person-to-person. Some people gained much more than others. Those who didn't gain were the ones with the maximum problems. They were stuck with petty problems of life which included food, cleanliness, hot water and other arrangements. They avoided facing their problems by projecting them outside and by fixating on people and incidents. They went about their spiritual search as if they were doing everyone a favour.

Soon, distinguishing between the serious and the non-serious seekers became easy. The antics of these non-serious seekers, like clamouring for front seats, rushing for my blessings, and competing with one another in trying to please or impress me and others were nothing but amusing.

The ashram witnessed fights for first rights to the toilets, to eat food, or to have tea. People complained that the water was not sweet enough to drink or not hot enough to have a bath in; the salt in the food was high or low or the sugar in tea was not enough and the milk was watery! How could anyone get rid of conditionings when their mind was still struggling with smaller issues?

The rich wanted air-conditioners in their rooms and more comfortable mattresses. They routinely demand attached baths with western toilets. Although they wanted to enjoy the spiritual experience at the ashram, they were still attached to the comforts of the material world.

As for me, my room was fitted with an air-conditioner, soft mattresses, a refrigerator and an attached bath. Fruits, the best of them, were imported for me from different countries. An unending supply of milk, sherbets, dry fruits and sweets were at my disposal.

However, these material comforts reminded me of my attachment to non-vegetarian food. I could spend all my life enjoying them and still not be satisfied. Though on the surface they looked harmless, I feared they would lead me away from my true purpose. I checked my temptations and indulgences and was reminded of my father's indifference to his materialistic and luxurious surroundings. I understood now why he willingly renounced everything most people cling to. Even life.

Gradually, the materialistic comforts stopped giving me happiness. I felt it was better to draw a line between excess and need and lead by example.

So one day, instead of living in the comforts of my room, I shifted to my father's room, the one without an air-conditioner, refrigerator, or even a bed. I found myself thinking clearly. I could meditate better and sleep better. By living in the sparsely equipped room, my father wasn't trying to impress anyone as I'd thought; he was living a simple life for his spiritual well-being, nothing else!

A few days later, I felt an urge to give my first discourse. The nervousness and insecurity that had haunted me previously had disappeared.

I found self-belief!

36 | Another Way with Q&A

A song is composed of words, the silence in between, and music. The words slow down or hurry up. The notes climb high, and then descend low. The pace and pitch alter with grace and fluidity. A song touches our hearts in a way nothing else can. I wanted to make my spiritual lessons appear like a song of life. I wanted them to affect the listeners and leave behind everlasting impressions, like a beautiful song which lingers with us for years, long after the conversations of people die. A song is eternal. Could my efforts in preaching spirituality be like a song that will keep playing long after my death?

My meditation was the silence which was interspersed between my discourses.

Now I was trying to do something else – change the rhythm of my song. I believe that spirituality has to be interactive to be effective. There was a lot to be gained from the entire collective. Although it was far from ideal, I decided to hold problem-perspective sessions with my disciples. They would be free to ask questions on the difficulties they faced. I, or anyone in the group, could suggest a perspective. The operating word would be 'perspective', not solution, because solutions are relative, never absolute. A prescriptive approach to problems never helps. I wanted people to be aware of the possible paths. Which path to take was a decision they would have to make. What is ambrosia for one could be poison for another.

These sessions, over a period, could herald the bigger changes I wanted – finally creating the eternal song. It was important to take the first step. Once unleashed, it would have the power to transform into something else, something more important and satisfying – just like the first few words of a thought ignite the mind to write a beautiful poem, story or philosophy.

'Sometimes, we have to view our problems from a fresh perspective, which is why we will have these Q&A sessions. Even though every journey differs from another in its experiences, different people can give helpful insights.' I finished my discourse with these words and the disciples started leaving the lecture hall, one by one.

'A good idea,' Sneha said, as she peered at me through her reading glasses. She was shuffling through the administrative paperwork she carried. The hall was nearly empty as the assembly had dispersed. 'Your father used to conduct these Q&A sessions a long time ago.'

'Why did he give up?'

'I don't know. However, I've been feeling a need for these sessions. People confide their difficulties in me but I haven't been of much use to them.'

'But if you feel helpless, then how can I – ?'

'How are you able to give such excellent discourses? Why did Guru Nanak know more than the pundits? How did Jesus Christ know more than the Pharisees? How did Shankracharya achieve sainthood at the age of fourteen? You are blessed with spiritual grace and it flows from you.'

I wasn't prepared for this outburst. I stared at her, not knowing how to react.

'Shrug off your diffidence, Swami Partibhan. Know who you are. Only then can you guide your disciples to your fullest capabilities.'

The following Thursday, when I reached the hall, it was overflowing with disciples. A large gathering of devotees had assembled, bigger than any of my previous discourses. Later, I came to know from Ramanujam that many people had come from faraway places.

Before delving into the Q&A session, I thought of speaking briefly about problems.

'Problems are a part of life. Though we resent them, they'll keep popping up because they help us evolve. Man invented tools because he had problems in hunting and surviving. We discovered fire because keeping ourselves warm had been a problem, and the wheel because we had problems transporting our goods and ourselves. Now, as I've announced, we will start discussing your problems. However, please raise your hands and speak one by one. Otherwise, managing questions will become the biggest of all problems.'

Several hands immediately went up. I pointed to one of them.

'I have been a regular for four years, yet I feel far from transformation. What's the reason?'

'What's transformation according to you?'

'Not getting angry with others, remaining calm and detached no matter how provocative the circumstance. Being content with everything we own ... .'

'You're right. Most changes occur gradually. From a seed to a big tree, the journey is a long one. Think of your spiritual state four years ago and compare it to now. If there's been a change, you have your answer.'

I pointed at the next hand.

'Despite our prayers and the wish to get rid of them, old patterns keep resurfacing.'

'The habits you speak of have longer lives than your spiritual life. If you have an overflowing tank connected to a water supply and you cut off the supply, the water doesn't stop the same instant. There's bound to be a delay. Be patient and you'll get results eventually.'

A woman raised her hand. She appeared depressed.

'I have a daughter and I want her to become a doctor. But she wastes her time in sports. What should I do?'

'Are you a doctor?'

'No. I'm a teacher.'

'Who is better – a doctor or a teacher?'

'A doctor.'

'Why?'

'Because doctors serve human beings by removing their suffering.'

'And teachers don't serve humanity by educating?'

'Yes, but –'

'The society respects doctors more than teachers.'

'Yes,' she blushed.

'Most people in our society don't bother about spirituality. Then why are you here?'

'I find peace here.'

'But why don't you let your daughter remain in peace?'

'But –'

'Every individual has potential to become somebody. Give them the freedom to be what they want. In doing what they love, people can be happy and spread happiness in the world. Unhappy people torture both themselves and others.'

She nodded her head and her face relaxed.

'Your daughter will do well in life. She'll be much happier being a sprinter, a golfer or a tennis player than a doctor.'

I fielded many problem situations that day. After a point, instead of giving answers myself, I encouraged other people to answer the questions posed by their fellow disciples. I spotted the glassy-eyed, sleepy types and asked them to join in too. Most importantly, they didn't fall asleep again.

I felt like I had managed some progress that day.

37 | Perspective that's not Prescriptive

'**S**wamiji, I don't think I am doing too well financially, and this comes in the way of my spiritual growth.'

I looked at the man. He was of a short height, with a stocky build, and the lines on his forehead betrayed his confusion. This was the sixth problem-solving session we were conducting at the ashram, and the gathering was much bigger than the first time.

'I see others who are not spiritual doing better than me, and wonder what could be wrong with me.'

'Where do you live?'

'New Delhi.'

'Is it a rented accommodation?'

'No.'

'An apartment?'

'I live in a small house. I own it.'

'How small is it?'

'Two hundred and twenty-five square yards.'

'That's not small. Do you own a vehicle?'

'Yes. Three cars.'

'I don't think you lack much in life. Currently, less than twenty-five per cent of India's population would be financially better than you. Suppose you do better in your business. After years of struggle, you may have just ten per cent people above you. Even then, you will not see your progress, only the ten per cent people doing better than you. I don't think money is your stumbling block.'

'That's not my point. I was born to this position. Growth gives satisfaction whereas stagnation –'

'What will you get with this growth? Another car, another house, more clothes? Where will it stop? And what will you do with so much wealth? Just feel good because your ego is pampered? What about the things that you really wish to do? Is there a core desire in you that is unfulfilled? To which you are not devoting time?'

The man looked confused, his eyes darting to different directions. 'I think of starting an institution for spastic children, sometimes. But I need money for it ...'

'There's a possibility you may spend your entire time arranging money for it and still not be able to fulfil that dream, like so many people. You can start on that journey today. A will is all you need; your divine higher self will show you the way. You're adequately provided right now. That's the whole point.'

'I know all this. Still –'

'Focus on evolution – that's the only pure, unselfish need of your higher self. Focus on this desire of yours, don't let the material side tell you that you are small, when you can be a giant who changes the lives of thousands of suffering children.'

I paused to see if he was still with me. He was.

'To be one with your higher self, you have to evolve, give shape to your dream for helping those spastic children selflessly. Has spirituality helped you evolve in some way?'

'Yes.'

'Then it's working for you. Believe me, you neither need better food nor better clothes than what you already have. You don't even need more space. You'll evolve spiritually and personally and get the growth you seek by following your heart.'

Another person raised his hand.

'Yes?'

'Swamiji, having tasted spirituality, I wish to tell people what they're missing. No one listens. Either people treat me like a fool or they think I'm a religious fanatic.'

'Your wish to spread the message of the divine evolution is pure. Do spread the message of spirituality to all, but with a calm detachment. Those who are seekers need only a push. Those who are not, won't budge, even with the mightiest of shoves. Use your discretion.'

'I try, but fail. Indifferent people surround me.'

'Then you must find a different media to spread the message. What do you do?'

'I don't get you.'

'What's your profession?'

'I'm a chemist.'

'What else do you do?'

'Nothing.'

'What is your passion, or hobby?'

He laughed self-consciously. 'I once wanted to be a writer. My work has been published in magazines. But somewhere, I lost interest.'

'Your hobby wants to resurface now.'

'Strange!' He looked up sharply. 'Because lately, I feel a strong compulsion to sit and write my thoughts.'

'Spirituality is trying to find an expression through your writing and reach a wider audience. That might be the reason indifferent people surround you. Never forget, every obstacle in your way is there for a reason. A bigger and much more satisfying task awaits you. Maybe you have to reach out to the millions of readers in this world with your ideas, through your writing.'

'You seriously think I can reach millions of people?'

'Have you seen trees growing on hills?'

'Yes.'

'Those trees were tiny saplings, and before that, they were seeds. Just as the tiny seed found a way to survive between the rocks to become a mighty tree, you too have endless potential. Focus your attention on the pure wish, which, in your case, is to spread the divine message. It'll find a way out.'

Then the man did something unexpected. He waded through the audience and fell at my feet! I blushed and didn't know how to react. The entire gathering folded its hands and stood up.

'Guru Partibhan ki jai,' they chanted. Were they showing me respect? I think not. They were giving respect to something refined that they recognised in me, which exists in all of us. Our egos make us believe people praise us, but actually they praise the higher self within us, which manages to shine despite our terrible natures. Instead of feeling elated, I felt small. Automatically, I folded my hands and bowed my head towards them. They had conquered within themselves what I was yet to conquer within me – the wry, cynical side that dismissed everything my father had achieved in his life as unworthy or useless. More hands went up. I pointed at a person.

'Yes, please?'

'I have two questions – what's the awareness of the self, which every saint has talked about? Secondly, how can we instil a sense of detachment within ouselves?'

'Your questions are related. Detachment enables self-realisation. Let's take two people. One of them is walking over the road, another is flying at a height of fifty feet. Who do you think is further removed from his immediate surroundings, but has a better perspective of everything?'

'The one flying at fifty feet.'

'The closer you live to your life, the narrower your view becomes. The more detached you become, the more your vision expands and you can then see what you failed to see when you were too involved. Step out of your body, your physical shell, and see yourself as an observer. This will allow you to be detached from yourself and the material world and take you to a greater state of realisation. This is what we achieve while meditating.'

'I, too, have just started in spirituality,' a woman spoke the instant my gaze rested on her face. 'But instead of feeling joy, I see terrible ugliness in the people who surround me, and I feel depressed. Their selfishness, their tendency to dominate and lie and their innate cruelty towards others distress me. Before, I used to get on with them somehow. Now, I'm unable to stand them. Wherever I go, I see the same traits in people.'

'When the light of knowledge falls on us, we begin to see our flaws. Some of them, we remove immediately and some take time. Yet, beyond doubt, we become beautiful in this light of knowledge. While you've changed and become beautiful, others remain the same.

'The contrast is what makes them look ugly in your eyes. They are not ugly – but you have become more beautiful. Don't get bogged down by comparison, have compassion for them. With love and by example, you should make them see their flaws.'

Even before I could catch my breath, I faced another query. I reminded myself to discipline the crowd the next time.

'Swamiji, everyone says there is God, but why do we need to believe in God? Why can't we rely on ourselves in distress? Besides, who has seen Him? Where was He when Hitler was massacring Jews? When the atom bomb devastated Japan?' The man's voice from the last rows of the hall boomed with impatience.

I looked around and spotted a tall, lean man with piercing eyes. He hadn't even bothered to raise his hand.

'God exists as a force all over the universe. That includes you,' I said. 'God is inside us. He did not make the wars you talk of, nor the Hitlers of this world. They were created by people who needed power or special favours.'

'Still, why do we have to first assume there is a God and then go about finding Him?' asked another person. 'For all we know, the universe can be a coincidence. He may never have existed. Besides, more people seem afraid of the wrath of God than think of Him as a loving entity.'

Not one but two hostile people in the hall! I needed to be careful while handling them.

'Man has the tendency to go wayward without any authority. All of us have seen the chaos that prevails at a crossing where the traffic lights do not work, or at a billing counter without a queue.

It makes even the best human being act like an animal. God is the invisible authority that we love, respect, and fear, so that we can avoid the ill-effects of indiscipline. He governs the universe with the simplest of laws – cause and effect, which means, one has to reap the effects of one's karmas. If we fear Him, then we're into activities which need to be feared. If we love Him, then we're living in harmony with others. The equation of fear or love that we strike with Him is one of our own making, not something He imposes.

'Your question about the need to search for God is like different people coming to a waterfall and drinking water to quench their thirst. Suppose the water of this natural source happens to have a unique, sweet taste. It will cause different reactions in the people who drink it. Some will marvel at its taste, some will bottle it for future use; some people will think of sharing the water with their friends, while others will be indifferent. Another set of people would want to find the source of the sweet water. They would climb the mountain and not rest until they know. Have you got your answer?'

The man nodded his head.

'Then why has the Divine never bothered to appear? If He wanted us to follow Him, He should have been like you, revealing Himself and preaching. I think He created this mess, but didn't have the heart to destroy it. So He retired from the scene, leaving us in our state,' another disturbed soul raised its voice. I couldn't see the man who made this observation.

His insulting remark about the Divine was pithy and threw me off balance. I took some time to recover.

'I'll give you answers one by one. Why doesn't He reveal Himself? I will say again that the Divine exists without form, like air, water vapour, electricity, heat, gravity, and magnetism. How do we know they are there? Because we feel their effects! The Divine is more like a force you feel, rather than see. You feel His presence only if you attune yourself to Him, just as you feel the force of gravity when you step out of a swimming pool, rarely otherwise. The believers know the Divine is an intelligent force far superior to the elements we don't see but readily admit.

'Now, your second question – He's preaching continuously. We listen to His voice through saints, gurus, and even common people who connect to Him. His incarnations have appeared whenever He felt humanity needed a new message. The scriptures are echoes of His voice.

'Coming to the hypothesis that the Divine has given up on us because He's fed up of the absurdity of His creation – when a force permeates and sustains everything, then by logic, if the force retires, everything will cease to exist. The mere fact that we exist, the universe exists, and you are here in this ashram, suggests that the Divine is watching over His creation.'

'I'm not fully convinced, but some of what you say does make sense,' the man replied, to my relief.

'What about conscience? Is it real or a conditioning? Is it a voice created by our past values and experiences, which would make it relative, or a voice of truth?' the man at the far end of the hall asked.

'Our higher self's innate wisdom is the voice of conscience all of us hear. It remains unchanged, even when we change drastically. Those who listen to it lead much happier lives than those who don't.'

The objections I had anticipated after my replies didn't appear. I knew this wouldn't be enough. Soon, these sessions would become dull and monotonous.

I needed more ideas to force a change in perspectives and viewpoints – to make people see spirituality in a new light.

Human beings are tied to their conditioning without knowing it. It was important for me to help my disciples see their shackles. By now, I felt we needed a new creative idea in practical spirituality for all of us to move to the next level. The problem-perspective sessions were beginning to sound like theory classes – they no longer seemed to have the dynamism I yearned for. I wanted a new method through which I could prove the practical powers of spirituality to my disciples.

It was my restlessness and dissatisfaction which led to this fantastic idea, with the fire at its centre stage. The exercise, meant to instil selflessness in my disciples, took a sudden and unexpected turn when it resulted in the spontaneous decision to undertake a journey without money and belongings. Shruti readily joined me in my endeavour.

In a way, this journey would never end, because spirituality was now a part of me as well as the group. I felt as if humanity was very close to reaching a threshold of spiritual awakening and we were the pioneers.

My heart exploded with joy as this new awareness blossomed in me, with perspective and meaning unfolding in layers like the petals of a rose, fragrant with inspiration.

PART FOUR

A book had been lying on the table for weeks, yet you didn't see it because you didn't need it. One fine day, you needed it and it appeared in your conscious awareness. Until then, you were blind to its presence. Only now, when it becomes alive in your attention, do you see it.

Likewise, there are a million objects on earth lying in wait for someone curious enough to search for them. It's just that we do not have them in our attention, which is why we never sense them, or see them, even when they cross our paths.

Similarly, the people we love exist in our awareness but not other people of the world. Why? What if like those millions of objects, the Divine exists in each molecule which envelops us, outside and inside? What if we only have to look for him to find him? Yet, we remain as unaware of his existence as we are unaware of the trees ahead of and behind us. We walk through his creation immersed in our complicated thoughts and worries, unmindful of his presence in everything we see, yet not see.

The Divine exists in all forms of creation but to see Him, to feel Him, we have to seek Him out. Only then can we become aware of His presence.

He is never so far from us that we can't ever find Him.

A little quest is all that is needed.

38 | Assassin Assigned

Pathan knew Partibhan, of course, but now the nature of his acquaintance was about to change. The casual interest in the guru mutated into a professional one as he stared at the picture of the man coming through his fax machine.

'Do you know him?' The voice on the phone was muffled. The man had exercised due caution in hiding his identity, and had used the right references and channels to contact Pathan.

'Of course. But why a guru?'

'Let's just say that when the turtle cannot beat the rabbit, the rabbit has to be put to sleep.'

'So even spirituality isn't without violence,' Pathan said. He felt disgusted.

'You can talk about hypocrisy and paradoxes all you want. Or you can name your price,' the stranger chuckled at his reaction.

'If you know me, you know my price. Wire the money now.'

'I knew you'll not disappoint. But will you be able to pull it off? He's no businessman or politician. Many think of him as a saint.'

'I have learnt not to think about the morality of human beings. Good man or bad man, my job is to ensure he's a dead man.'

'Fair enough. Your money is on its way.'

Pathan hung up the phone. In a short while, the money would be wired to his overseas account, after which his job would begin.

39 | Hiccups on the Way

'I told you it would be a waste of time and money!' Subhir shouted as he pulled his car out from the parking lot. They had barely entered their professional world when they heard the news.

'You also told me why this journey was important.'

'Yes, but imagine losing the contract by a thousand rupees. Damn!'

'I was the one who was sceptical. You felt we needed the journey to get out of our rut. Those were your words. What about that?' Vibha shouted back.

'Shit! We lost the contract when we were in those fucking jungles!'

'Mind your language.'

'All right!' He honked his horn repeatedly. 'Cool down. I'm not blaming you, okay? The journey was a stupid decision in hindsight. Look what it did to us!'

'It did me a lot of good. Maybe it's a divine plan working to our advantage.'

'That's the way every fool tries to convince himself.' Subhir turned the steering sharply. 'I call it aftershock justification.'

'Is there anything wrong in trying to be sane and optimistic? Look at you! I don't think it's either creative or productive.'

'I'm being reactive and reflective. I'm reflecting on my enormous stupidity.'

'Tell me when you get over your sulk. I refuse to believe this is the end of the world for us.'

'We could have enhanced our reputation with this project. Broken into the elite circle of architects –'

'What do you mean by elite circle? The Delhi circle of elite architects, or the North Indian circle, or the entire Indian circle, or the international circle? It's an endless chase.'

'Very funny! The only circle we're in right now is called zero.'

'Zero or hero – it's your attitude. I benefited immensely from the journey. Winning or losing a contract doesn't matter. It's inconsequential in the long run.'

'I feel like a fool who was enjoying the woods when I should have been devising strategies to secure the contract.'

'What could you have possibly done by staying in Delhi? Offered bribes? Wagged your non-existing tail? Begged for work? You're an architect, not a liaison officer. We gave our quotation, the least we could, and didn't get the contract. So why do you have to blame yourself or this journey?'

'I think someone leaked our quotation. If we'd been around, we could've kept a watch and prevented the project from slipping out of our hands. But Jack and Jill took a month off to the hills when it mattered most, and at what cost. Both lost a contract but star-struck Jill is a fool, still! Ha, ha, ha.' He was amused by the venomous poem.

'It's a lousy poem –'

Subhir's mobile began to buzz. He cancelled the call in anger. The phone rang again.

'Yes, what's it?' he snapped. A long silence followed in which Subhir pulled the car to the side and brought it to a halt. He kept mumbling, 'Yes … yes … yes …,' and then, 'all right. We'll come over to discuss. Is tomorrow fine?'

Finally, he looked up and smiled.

'We got it!' He kissed her abruptly. 'We've been awarded the Bell Building project!' The Bell project was bigger and more prestigious than the other project they lost. 'Had we manipulated to get that, we would've been out of this one because of the exclusivity clause. You were right. The Divine was working to our advantage. This calls for a celebration! Yippee!'

'How you flip and flop,' Vibha frowned. 'One minute you're using the F word for the Divine, the next minute you're singing His praises. I'm ashamed of you.'

'I was rattled; I'm sorry.'

'You feel sorry now because your Divine responded within moments of your losing the contract. So, why did you undertake that journey? You thought you'd please God Almighty and he would shower contracts on you from heaven, even if they were not right for your spirit? God is not your agent.'

'I said I'm sorry.'

She didn't reply.

'Hey! Come out of your sulk now. Give me a break, damn you.' He nudged her shoulder.

'Promise me you'll respect the divine in future.'

Subhir grinned. 'I promise. Hey, snap out! What's gotten into you? Let's go to Baskin Robbins. We deserve a treat.'

'What's there to celebrate? We've merely bagged a good contract. I'll celebrate when I achieve a big spiritual breakthrough.'

'Don't be a spoilsport.'

'I seriously don't want the ice cream.'

'You used to be crazy about celebrations.'

'No more. Let's go home.'

'I said I'm sorry. Can't you forgive the one error I have managed to make in a year?'

She smiled. He was right. He gave her little cause to be upset. 'I forgive you, but I still don't want the ice cream.'

'I see. The journey has affected you more than me.'

'Even I can see that, and it surprises me. I thought we were temperamentally quite similar.'

'Does this mean you don't like my being this way?'

'I never said that. I just realised we're different.'

'In a negative sense?' He looked away, his shoulders hunched. His euphoria vanished.

'No.' She kept peering out of the window into the distance, as if in a trance.

He drove his car thoughtfully. He felt responsible for breaking the spell of the journey. Faith and surrender were the qualities Swami Partibhan had asked them to have. Looking back, he realised his agitation came from an imbalance. He looked at Vibha, who had drifted off in her thoughts.

'Stay for a few minutes and listen to the gems from this young but evolved mind. You will not regret it,' said her mother's old relative. They had driven to the ashram to drop her for the discourse.

'We are getting late ...'

'Please, just a few minutes, for my sake ...'

They'd had no choice but to agree half-heartedly to her repeated pleadings.

The few minutes' stay had stretched to an hour as they listened to the young man, mesmerised by what he had to say.

'Are you progressing? If I ask people, most will say yes. But really, all they manage is to move from a small cage to a bigger cage of gold, then one studded with diamonds, in terms of their jobs, houses they live in and cars they drive. These cages limit us. Confine us. Is that real progress? Is this the quest of our lives? What if I told you that there is no need for this constrained living that society has imposed on your mind? That unlimited freedom is available even to the person currently living in the smallest cage? The exponential evolution I speak of is just about breaking free from all cages. The sky is what the divine self has to offer. The biggest golden cage anyone can think of pales in comparison to the freedom enjoyed by a liberated self.'

She had been quite content with her life until she heard Swami Partibhan's lecture.

For years, they had struggled to reach where they were. She had been extremely pleased with their progress and there was nothing more she had wanted. But the words suddenly made her feel claustrophobic. The cage was not a metaphor. She sensed its reality that evening when she first heard Swami Partibhan.

To hear more from the man who surprised them with every thought of his, they had gone to the ashram on the fateful day he announced the journey. They were inexorably drawn to it.

'You were opposed to the journey. Now it appears I'm not as comfortable with spirituality as you are. I had the desire, you got the blessings,' Subhir interrupted her thoughts.

'It's like resistance in electricity.' Her tone softened as she emerged from her hurt. 'If it's high, lesser current flows. If you have ego, the "I am behind all that I do" attitude, then establishing the connection with the higher self is difficult. It's that simple.'

'I'm sorry. I feel stupid because Swamiji kept asking us to leave our anxieties behind, and look how absolutely unchanged I am.'

'No. You have changed. You brought your parents back from the old-age home. You were always unstable, stubborn, and headstrong earlier. Today, you introspect and watch your flaws. Could you have done all this before? Swamiji had said, to walk you have to take the first step and not be afraid of falls.'

He felt warmth enter his heart. Although he had succeeded in a near-impossible task by completing the journey, it was not as if he had reached the Mount Everest of spirituality. There was much more to overcome. He worried, not about the complications involved in the time-bound contract they had bagged, but about remaining connected forever with the higher self. In that moment, he was glad he had Vibha. She was his check whenever he faltered and he could be hers if ever she did.

40 | A Reconnaissance

Pathan spent the next two weeks disguised as a follower, studying Swami Partibhan's routine. His reconnaissance told him that the easiest way to slay the guru would be in the afternoon, when he went out of the ashram in his car, to visit the hospitals and schools run by his missionaries or the slums. Partibhan's car stopped at the gates for half a minute at 3.30 p.m. everyday for the guard to open the gate. This was Pathan's window of opportunity.

Opposite to the gates of the ashram was another building, a primary school. He found it easy to climb the roof unnoticed, using the fire escape from the back alley. Only one old sentry guarded the main gate. On Sundays, this guard busied himself with washing clothes. He decided to strike on that day.

Pathan spent another week to get comfortable with the plan. He would sneak into the school's deserted rooftop in the evenings, while the security guard was busy cooking his meals. Standing behind the concrete water tank, he would aim his rifle at the exact place the car usually stood. He went over the whole plan daily, smoothening out any possibility of error or oversight on D-day.

Swami Partibhan would be an easy target.

The weeks he spent in the ashram were tough. It was difficult for him not to get too involved in the hypnotic discourses of the young guru. It interfered with the professional distance he liked to maintain with his target. He found it difficult to be deaf to Partibhan's ideas, because his sermons had the power to change. He had to fight himself to check the impulse to quit his profession. What was unsettling for Pathan was that he started reflecting on how he became an assassin. He had also tried to live an honest life, but he had seen dishonest people amass enormous wealth and clout, and hated that. Honest people, meanwhile, barely managed a hand-to-mouth existence, and most of the times, not even that.

In his college days, he had tried to live honourably, but then he saw how the blood donated at camps by students was misused by politicians: it rarely went to the needy. He saw student leaders blowing college funds on wine and women. His teachers and professors passed undeserving students because of their 'connections' and tormented the deserving because they questioned the injustice.

Outside college, the world was no different. Intelligent and meritorious students failed to get jobs which people with contacts took away. For three years, he had found it impossible to get a decent job and had to work at petty shops. His ideal upbringing was of little help during those dark times. The shopkeepers, who thought they owned him just because they paid him two thousand rupees a month, abused him endlessly. He hoped and prayed for change but none came his way.

Those were the bleakest days of his life. Never had he felt as helpless as he used to feel then. Once, when he had asked for an advance of five hundred rupees from his employer for an emergency, the shopkeeper had abused him while guzzling the expensive bottle of wine which Pathan used to buy for him every other day. Pathan begged and pleaded but the shopkeeper refused.

That night, he cracked. He snatched the wine bottle from the shopkeeper, struck him on the head with it, and killed him. He stole from the shopkeeper's safe as much money as he could and gave it to his parents, who needed it desperately. Then he disappeared into the criminal world.

Pathan graduated from one crime to another, knowing well that after the first murder, he had nothing to lose. He was already a social pariah because there is no place in the society for the powerless and the penniless. With time, he became a sharpshooter of repute. People, more powerful than the powerful, richer than the rich, and more influential than the influential, used him in their chess games to fell their opponents with bullets. He earned a fortune for his work. This was his evolution: from an anonymous and helpless servant to an anonymous but very-much-in-demand, capable assassin.

Pathan had decided that he wasn't going to be brainwashed by Partibhan into serving society. He was now in a position much above it.

Partibhan, too, had been favoured over many other, more deserving disciples of Parmanand when he became the guru of his ashram. He acceded to the throne left by his father only because he happened to be his son. Before that, he wasn't even spiritual. Sitting on his throne, Partibhan could afford to talk about being frugal while he zipped across the world in planes and cars. Pathan remembered this every time Swami Partibhan managed to make him see the adverse side of his violent profession. That brought back the poison he nursed in his heart for becoming what he had hated once.

Pathan would now correct the questionable means by which Swami Partibhan become a guru of the masses. He had been chosen to be the instrument for balance.

He began to wait for Swami Partibhan to return from his world tour.

41 | The First Bubbles and Change of State

Acutely aware that the spiritual movement started by the journey needed a push throughout the world, Swami Partibhan started accepting invitations from abroad. His first visit was to Los Angeles, where he spoke to a large gathering. The invitation came after several groups of people started 'Operation Free Bird' on their own and shared their experiences through Internet communities. Six groups had gotten together and invited Swami Partibhan. This started a chain reaction, and more and more people were discovering joy forever.

'In the past, a few human beings learned to communicate in a new language. Until then, we spoke with grunts and screams. Their attempts to teach this language met with resistance because grunting was far simpler and the prevailing practice. Why take pains to master something new and more complicated? What would it achieve?

'But gradually, language reached a threshold where it could no longer be ignored. Those who didn't keep pace became disadvantaged. The benefits of knowing language were far greater than its difficulties. Today, we take language for granted. What was once so difficult is now so easy: children pick it up by the time they are one year old. With this leap, we achieved an explosive evolution because we could pass off to the next generation what we had mastered.

'The same is true for agriculture, the notion of having a family, the need of laws and governance instead of leading a disorderly existence. There was a time when many doubted the practicality of those things. Similarly, doubt, fear, and suspicion about the need for spirituality linger in our minds today.

'Like the early pioneers, we find spirituality beneficial. We are not only mastering it, we are trying to convince everyone of its benefits. One day, we'll take everyone with us and cross the threshold of higher awareness. Then, humanity will embrace spirituality *en masse*.

'The new generation will peel off the outer shells of religiosity, ritualism and symbolism. We will achieve the supreme enlightened state described by the scriptures. When this happens, most of the ills present in the world we live in will vanish. Hunger, disease, exploitation, suppression, violence, rape, and unequal distribution of wealth will end. They are happening because we lack peace within. We are doing things that we are uncomfortable with. We perpetuate these miseries, not knowing that they are horrific and cheap replacements to the boundless joy we can access within us. With our attempts, we'll create the paradise promised to us here on earth.'

Someone raised a hand as he prepared to leave the dais.

'Yes?'

The woman said something he couldn't hear, so he called her on stage.

'My question is ...' her nervous voice cracked under the spotlight. She cleared her throat and repeated, 'My question is why religion continues to be decadent, instead of becoming what you say. The best of saints like Jesus, Muhammad, Guru Nanak, Tao, and Buddha gave similar messages. But we made dead religions of them. What you preach can become another dead religion – just a sect or a cult of practical spirituality. How do you avoid this pitfall? I want to believe we'll cross a spiritual threshold because it's logical. We deserve to be spiritually enlightened instead of religiously blind.'

Applause greeted her words. 'What's your name, young lady?'

'My name is Anita Smith.'

'Anita, what you fear is what I also fear. Whenever a saint or an avatar appeared, he or she taught new values. While some people made religious institutions of their teachings, others absorbed their messages and understood the essence. You, me and all these people gathered here are striving to achieve what these saints preached. Why? Because we know that the gains are priceless. We follow their teachings, not the institutions. To make my point, let's see if we can find practical examples of what I'm trying to say here.'

Ripples of murmurs ran across the hall as people waited eagerly for Swami Partibhan to do what was characteristic of him: to show the truth in a practical way.

'I'm sure there are many here who've heard of Shri Krishna. What's his most important message? Anyone?'

Several hands went up. Swami Partibhan called one of them on stage.

'To work without keeping the results in sight.'

'Are you a Shri Krishna worshipper?'

'Yes.'

'What's your name?'

'David Lean.'

'Have you read the *Gita*, David?'

'Yes, a translation.'

'What do you think of Krishna's advice on detachment?'

David was quiet.

'Do you practise it?'

'I try.'

'But?'

'I fail.'

'Why?'

'Because I don't think it's possible to not care for results.'

'You said you are a Shri Krishna worshipper. Yet you don't think his teaching to be practical?'

David smiled self-consciously. 'I feel it's too noble to be practical.'

'Is there anyone in the audience who put in his or her best efforts into something without bothering about the results?'

The question met with silence.

'Anyone? Come forward. Share your experiences, please. Don't be shy.'

A woman from the crowd raised her hand at last.

'Please come on the stage.'

She was an Indian, in her mid-fifties. She faced the mike diffidently.

'I'm the mother of two children ... .' Her voice broke off. She wrapped and unwrapped her saree *pallu* on her forefinger.

'Don't be nervous. Go ahead; tell us of your experiences.'

'My husband died when our children were barely twelve. We were poor, and I struggled to educate my sons. When they got jobs overseas, I was overjoyed. Yet, my friends thought otherwise. They warned me not to send them abroad because they would forget me. I let them go overseas against the advice of my well-wishers because I had more faith in Shri Krishna than in their warnings.'

'Did they finally call you to stay? Is it why you are here with us today, in America?'

Tears began to cascade down the woman's cheeks.

'In just two years, they forgot about me. They married foreigners and stopped communicating with me. I don't even know where they live. Yet, if I get another birth and if I become a mother again, I would still do what I did.'

The crowd clapped heartily.

'Here, here, a big hand to the brave – oh, I forgot to ask your name.'

'I'm Sushma Chaddha.'

'Your children failed you, not Krishna. Then how come you are here?'

Curiously, the woman smiled through her tears. As if she remembered something happier.

'My sons would have been the same whether in India or the US. But by restricting their growth, I would have spoiled my karma. A couple lived in my neighbourhood in Delhi. In 2005, I fell ill. They looked after my needs as if I was their real mother. When I recovered, they asked me to move into their house. I refused, but they did not take no for an answer. Now we live like a family and help each other as much as we can. Today, we are on a vacation in America together, thanks to Shri Krishna. Though I didn't get the results conventionally, they are sweeter than any I would have gotten otherwise. They are my new family!' She pointed to a couple sitting with their children in the first row, who waved back at her enthusiastically. The woman started crying again.

'So Anita and David, do you have anything to say on Amma's experience?'

Anita wiped away her tears.

'Shri Krishna's teaching isn't impractical or dead; do you agree?'

Anita nodded her head, too overwhelmed to say anything.

'It's extraordinary,' David conceded. 'Our limited interpretation reduces the sublime message of Shri Krishna to a human level.'

The entire assembly hall was buzzing. Sushma's example had created a stir.

'So, Anita's fears of our attempts going futile or turning into a dead cult are unfounded. We have to carry on with our mission. Shri Krishna's advice, Jesus Christ's spiritual legacy is alive even today; as are other saints' too. The day isn't far when the so-called institutions will crumble and lose their power – many already have. From the limiting cocoon of religion will emerge the beautiful butterfly of spirituality. From imposed religion, mankind will move to self-actuated spirituality. It would be as important and as necessary as breathing and eating. May the divine self be with you all.'

The applause was deafening and reverberated through the hall as he got down from the podium. People stood up as a mark of respect. He could feel their love and was glad that he came.

The funds were pouring in like never before, with which he set up hospitals and schools for the poor. He planned to open old-age homes, cooperatives for women – help those people whom society had exploited and then discarded. More importantly, he opened centres all across the world to spread the message of practical spirituality because like his father, he too believed that selfless service could never be dispensed without spirituality.

'Go and reach the masses. Let the divine light illumine the lives of the distressed and hopelessly despairing. Help the oppressed and downtrodden, but above all, spread the message of the Divine to those who seek Him.

'What should one gift a starving man instead of merely handing out food? Give him land to plough so he can meet his own needs and those of others, instead of being dependant on someone else. What should one give someone who is drowning? Not a rope or a life buoy – give him a boat on which not only he remains safe, but is able to save several others about to drown. To the poor, instead of alms, give the priceless gift of spirituality, one which will help them achieve their hidden potential.'

His voice became hoarse, but he didn't care. Often, he wondered if he was the same man he was two years ago. He was enjoying his heightened consciousness immensely. He toiled endlessly, resting little and working hard.

Time was short, there was so much to do!

42 | The Flight of the Sparrow

At 3.30 sharp on a Sunday afternoon, Pathan positioned himself on the rooftop, behind the concrete tank. He adjusted the focus of his gun's telescope and waited for Partibhan to come out of the ashram. Then he saw the dust raised by the approaching car. As Pathan had expected, it halted at the designated place. The guards sauntered towards the gates to open them.

He had to adjust his gun only slightly to bring the crosshair in line with Partibhan's head. It was just a matter of pulling the trigger now. Only a matter of seconds.

Then strangely, Partibhan turned. Pathan got the feeling that Partibhan's eyes were disconcertingly staring straight at him. There was a knowing smile on his face. His eyes were hypnotic in their power. Pathan dared not look at them for long.

How did he know? Pathan wondered, worried that his cover might have been blown. But he had no choice now. He had to go for it.

Uncharacteristically, his fingers trembled when he squeezed the trigger.

The bullet made a cobweb on the side-window of the car before seeking its victim. Swami Partibhan slouched into the rear seat, the blood beginning to ooze from his neck.

'Damn it!' Pathan grumbled because he had missed the headshot. He had never missed it before.

He took a long and hard look at Partibhan through the telescope, in the few seconds he had before making his escape. He had to know if Partibhan would survive. He was happy with what he saw. There was no hospital close enough for Partibhan to be saved.

'Where is your God now?' Pathan grunted as he hurriedly dismantled his gun and hurled it into the overhead tank. He used the fire escape which led to the rear end of the building. Then he casually walked to his car, a silver Honda City, which stood in the nearby fields at a little distance from the highway.

In another sixty seconds, he made his getaway without raising any suspicion. Ten kilometres down, he abandoned his primary escape vehicle in the wilderness and got into an Esteem hidden in the foliage. If someone found his movements suspicious, the police would be on the lookout for the Honda City. With the Esteem, they wouldn't have the slightest chance to trace him. By the time they discovered the abandoned car, he would be miles away.

The Honda and the Esteem he had used were remarkably easy to steal.

The trail would lead to nowhere.

43 | Countdown to Evolution

Murali, a gardener, 3.31 p.m.

He heard the glass of the car window explode and saw Swami Partibhan slump on the rear seat. The guards at the gates rushed to the car, yelling. He threw the hose with which he was watering the plants and ran towards Swamiji's car.

To his horror, he saw Swami Partibhan in a pool of blood, gasping.

'Call the ambulance, immediately ... .'

One of the guards rushed to the phone. Murali took out his mobile and began to dial.

From nowhere, a sparrow swooped down and perched on the car roof.

Sneha 3.33 p.m.

Sneha sobbed, her mouth dry and her vision hazy. She was not even wearing chappals.

'Take the car to the hospital. Why are you wasting time?' She screamed at the immobilised driver.

Swami Partibhan waved his hands.

'Time ... short ... come here ... .'

She went to him. Other disciples also closed in, wishing to hear him.

Swami Partibhan placed his hands over Sneha's head.

'You are going to lead ... from where I leave ... I am giving you *shakti-paat*. You will have all my spiritual knowledge and will be my successor ... .' He murmured a prayer, despite the pain.

'God bless you,' he smiled. 'Time for me to leave and meet my maker.'

'But you're going to live, Swamiji. You're not going to leave us ...'

'I bow to His will and abide by it. My work here is done.' He folded his hands and closed his eyes.

His body went limp.

A flutter of wings made Sneha look up.

The sparrow perched on the roof of the car took off and disappeared into the sky.

Sanjeev Purie 4.30 p.m.

'An agency hired me to spy on Swami Partibhan. Their client might be involved.' Sanjeev looked at the smashed windscreen of the car and drew an imaginary trajectory of the bullet. His hand stopped at the school building's rooftop. He wiped the tears in his eyes to see clearly.

'You were spying on him?' The inspector looked up from his sheet on which he was writing Sanjeev's account.

'Yes, I'm a private detective. His philosophy transformed me. When I revealed I was a spy, he asked me to do my job. I didn't have the faintest idea it might lead to his killing.'

'He asked you to continue with your job?' The inspector raised his eyebrows.

'Yes. He was very different. Because of that I became his follower.'

'Did you see this client?'

'No.'

The police officer took down the phone numbers of the agency for which Sanjeev had worked, and other details.

From where he stood, Sanjeev saw police officers combing the terrace of the school. They were searching the overhead water tanks. Then a constable shouted.

He was holding the gun.

Sneha 5.30 p.m.

She watched them take Swami Partibhan's body away for autopsy. His followers were wailing and crying inconsolably. She had exhausted her tears while mourning his death.

Just a few days ago, she had wondered if she could ever become a guru like Swami Partibhan. Had the *shakti-paat* made the difference? Now, in a sudden twist of events, she found herself in Swami Partibhan's shoes.

Why did the world kill its good people? History was replete with such examples.

The only likely explanation she could think of was that evil could tolerate indifference, but never goodness. Good was a threat to its empire. Gandhi, Jesus Christ, and many other saints slain by evil were proof of its hostility and intolerance.

She remembered Swamiji saying that evil had penetrated deeply into the human psyche and the only way to fight it was by creating a new race of self-aware individuals. The work started by Swamiji would continue. She needed courage to lead the movement.

Swami Partibhan's interactive spirituality was now truly a global movement. People were discussing their problems and impediments to create a wave of self-awareness on various online platforms.

Spirituality was no longer a bookish idea; it was becoming a revolutionary, practical approach to life.

'Don't think of yourself in isolation. This moment, now – think of yourself as one with your divine self and the universe. Shrug off your burden and your higher self will bear it for you. Remember, you're only limited when you assume you're the doer. Limitless possibilities open when you think your higher self is the doer, not you.'

Sneha began to cry as she remembered his advice and his charismatic face. Those liquid eyes and their gaze were enough to put the distressed at ease.

Thousands of letters of gratitude were pouring into the ashram from all parts of the world. They described how Swami Partibhan's spiritual approach changed lives in a way never imagined before. People had become prosperous, achieved what they never imagined they were capable of, learned a new capacity to love, and discovered love where previously they were alienated. Followers of Swamiji's ideas wrote in about how they found friends in sworn enemies by practising forgiveness, and opportunities where none existed previously.

Several groups of men and women shared their experiences as they replicated Swamiji's Operation Free Bird, a name he had coined jocularly but that had stuck. The idea of living like a sparrow, yet evolving to the next level of human evolution, was spreading.

Faith in the higher self was the key.

A promising life had ended prematurely. Yet, he was the author of a new movement and had brought in what could be called spiritual evolution.

Now, she was in the eye of the movement, right at the centre.

She vowed she would lead it to the best of her capabilities.

Shruti 10.30 p.m.

He was gone!

One moment he was there and then, he was no more.

It's ironic how human beings plan so much when they do not even know if their next breath might be their last. If we sew the reality of death into our lives, we immediately realise how short this life is; a short time indeed to connect to our divine self. If we succeed in realising that death releases us from material attainments, then detachment and surrender will become a habit.

That was what Parti had taught, and this was what she tried to remember when she saw his dead body.

Had she not undertaken the journey, she would probably have committed suicide – imagining a life without him would have been impossible for her. Not now. Despite the loss, she felt connected. Parti had told her that the body was just a vehicle of the soul. The soul was eternal and one with the divine force. Strangely, she could still feel his vibrations.

Sneha asked her if she would support Sneha in the movement and she immediately said yes. She would derive great satisfaction to build from where Parti left; to carry on in his memory the torch he had handed to them before his death.

She decided to resign from her job. The interactive spiritual movement started by Parti would now be her full-time career. Her only regret was that she was not with him during his death. Maybe it was the Divine's way of sparing her the extreme agony of seeing her beloved die. Despite the violent method used to end his life, Parti had died calmly, and even given the *shakti-paat* to Sneha.

In his short life, Parti had achieved the status of a saint. Thousands and thousands of people benefited from his advice and sermons. People believed that his words could transform and bring about an inner change they never experienced before. They called him 'Parasmani', the legendary alchemist stone which turned everything to gold by a mere touch.

Parti lived selflessly and fearlessly. He didn't fear death when he faced dacoits in the jungle. He believed in using rather than preserving life. From him, she learned the lesson of letting go.

Parti was a river that had merged with the ocean. She would not hold him back with her grief. She would be happy for him, happy for the liberation he must have achieved.

She would live as selflessly as he did; in this would be her greatest selfishness because, by becoming a river bound for the ocean, she would one day join her Parti.

Epilogue

Nikhil returned to the UK to reunite with his first wife Priya. He has started working on the first prototype of his dream hybrid car. His daughter married Shridhar the same day Nikhil remarried Priya.

Sanjeev married Ruchika, and the couple spends their weekends at Partibhan's hospital as volunteers.

Brij survived the cancer and now works at an old-age home. He works way beyond his stipulated eight hours and is extremely popular with the elders for the selfless way he serves them. His parents, too, contribute whenever they can.

Tarun has given up his cozy job as researcher with a software firm to follow his dream of being a lyricist. He released his first music album one year after the journey.

Subhir and Vibha attend Sneha's discourse every Saturday at the ashram. They have given up volume work for niche, exceptional work and are the most sought-after architects in the region. Their Sparrow Building in Ahmedabad has become a landmark in architecture.

Shruti works with Sneha and together, they spread Partibhan's message to the multitudes visiting the ashram.

Ajoy and Bijoy have quit their government jobs and started their own restaurant. It is a hugely popular eatery. At exactly 10 p.m., they shut the restaurant and feed the poor for an hour before closing.

The journey of the sparrows towards higher skies continues ... .

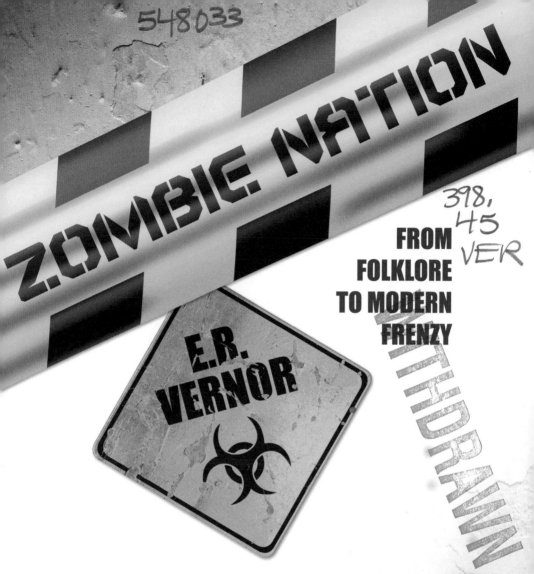

ZOMBIE NATION

FROM FOLKLORE TO MODERN FRENZY

E.R. VERNOR

Schiffer Publishing Ltd. ®

4880 Lower Valley Road • Atglen, PA 19310

OTHER SCHIFFER BOOKS BY THE AUTHOR:

Haunted Asylums
ISBN 978-0-7643-4147-2 $19.99

Cemetery Gates: Death and Mourning Through the Ages
(Written as Corvis Nocturnum)
ISBN 9780764337871 $24.99

I. Lucifer: Exploring the Archetype and Origins of the Devil
(Written as Corvis Nocturnum)
ISBN 978-0-7643-3919-6 $19.99

Designed by Justin Watkinson
Type set in Airbrake/Bad Deni/Batik Regular/Helvetica Neue LT Pro/NewBskvll BT

ISBN: 978-0-7643-4450-3

Printed in China

Schiffer Books are available at special discounts for bulk purchases for sales promotions or premiums. Special editions, including personalized covers, corporate imprints, and excerpts can be created in large quantities for special needs. For more information contact the publisher:

Published by Schiffer Publishing Ltd.
4880 Lower Valley Road
Atglen, PA 19310
Phone: (610) 593-1777; Fax: (610) 593-2002
E-mail: Info@schifferbooks.com

For the largest selection of fine reference books on this and related subjects, please visit our website at **www.schifferbooks.com** We are always looking for people to write books on new and related subjects. If you have an idea for a book, please contact us at proposals@schifferbooks.com

This book may be purchased from the publisher.
Please try your bookstore first.
You may write for a free catalog.

In Europe, Schiffer books are distributed by
Bushwood Books
6 Marksbury Ave.
Kew Gardens
Surrey TW9 4JF England
Phone: 44 (0) 20 8392 8585; Fax: 44 (0) 20 8392 9876
E-mail: info@bushwoodbooks.co.uk
Website: www.bushwoodbooks.co.uk

DEDICATION

Dedicated to all the creators and fans of zombies!

SPECIAL THANKS

The author would like to thank the following people for their inspiration and assistance with this book:

Mr. Pete Schiffer, Dinah Roseberry, Stacey, Heidi, Kevin Eads, Robert Kirkman, Chandler Riggs, John Bernthal, George Romero, Jack Wallen, Buzz, Joseph Vargo, Christine Filipak, John T. Morehead, Angel Story, Jack and Alex Sovel, Wade Davis, Boris Karloff, Everett Deger at Hornady, and all the people who have ever been a part of the zombie legacy.

CONTENTS

FOREWORD

by Kevin Eads

Eric Vernor has done it again.... He has taken a popular topic and broken it down in a way that both scholars and the masses can understand and enjoy. I have always enjoyed reading this author's works, whether written in his name or his pen name of Corvis Nocturnum. As a college professor, I find his academic approach to the subjects that fascinate me to be refreshing. He breaks each of his topics into their most basic elements so that we, as the readers, can have a greater understanding of the subject.

NIGHT OF THE LIVING DEAD. Publicity still shot available in public domain. Distributed by The Walter Reade Organization. Release date, October 1, 1968.

With *Zombie Nation*, he has now tackled the very favored topic of the zombie, but he takes a look at this misunderstood creature in a way that most other authors have not up to this point. As most people would agree, zombies today are very popular. You can't turn on a television without running into a zombie movie or television show. If you go to the comic shop or book store, you will see all types of materials dealing with zombies, from books like Max Brooks' *World War Z* to comics such as *Marvel Zombies* and *The Walking Dead*. To put it bluntly, zombies are big business.

Eric takes us from the first recorded mentioning of zombies in the *Epic of Gilgamesh* to the horror movies of George Romero in a narrative that is not only easy to follow, but enjoyable in every sense of the word. He uses his background in studying world religions to show how the zombie has been explored in religious writings over the years. He also goes into detail about the science of these "creatures." Yes, there is a science behind zombies, whether it is the concept of the slave zombie from movies, such as *WHITE ZOMBIE* and *THE SERPENT AND THE RAINBOW*, or the flesh-eating zombies in the works of Romero and his followers.

Eric also explores the zombie in modern cinema, which is the way most of us think of them. He goes into detail with the early movies, such as *I WALKED WITH A ZOMBIE* and *REVOLT OF THE ZOMBIES*, up to the works of George Romero and all of the people who have followed this director's brilliant formula, showing us the differences between films in this genre over the decades. No one would confuse the zombies of early horror cinema to those of *DAWN OF THE DEAD* after reading this book.

Eric also looks at the very fun and popular topic of survival during, what many think, will be the upcoming *zombie apocalypse*. He is able to delve into this particular subject in a way that people will find both interesting and entertaining.

I encourage anyone with an interest in the zombie to add a copy of this book to their personal library. They will not be disappointed.

Congratulations Eric,
on another job well done.

~Kevin Eads J.D.
Author of *The Amulet of Elisabeth Bathory* and
co-author of *Eerie America: Travel Guide of the Macabre*

Days of Adore art by Drake Mefestta
from *Courting the Poetic Craft: The Art and Prose of Drake Mefestta.*

⚠ AUTHOR NOTE ⚠

SPOILER ALERT! As I discuss varied films throughout this book, especially in Chapter Three, I give entire plotlines for the stories, *including* the endings. So if you have not seen a particular film mentioned and you don't want to know who gets killed by your favorite zombie, be wary of reading those sections in their entirety!

In today's world, the very word "zombie" makes one instantly think of the undead creatures featured in horror fiction, largely drawn from George A. Romero's movie *NIGHT OF THE LIVING DEAD*, DANNY BOYLE'S *28 WEEKS LATER*, and *THE WALKING DEAD* television show, among countless other films. We are at an all-time zombie high, with nearly half of all undead movies having been made after 9/11, making the topic ingrained in popular culture. *Zombie Nation: From Folklore to Modern Frenzy* looks at the facts, folklore, and fiction around our shambling friends in everything from ancient man's whispered fears, shared in tales beginning at the dawn of civilization, continuing with old European folklore right through to today's modern popular culture.

The iconic zombie is so vastly immersed in our culture that "Zombie Walks" or "Crawls," are not only found all over the United States, but also abroad, and have now become annual events, many of which are chronicled on the CRAWL OF THE DEAD website (www.crawlofthedead.com). I had no idea prior to this book that fans as far from the United States as Moscow, Australia, and the United Kingdom have been involved with these spectacular events.

I participated in one, along with my manager's son, Alex, and some other friends. Alex was scared of some of the very real special effects, but was thrilled to be a part

of it! People dressed up in zombie makeup and in costumes featuring "Umbrella Corporation" patches on military fatigues (based on the *RESIDENT EVIL* video games and the series of subsequent zombie films) and shambled for blocks, living out the fantasy of the zombie apocalypse that is the plot of the majority of these types of media.

There are also contests affiliated with zombie crawls and walk events with awards for the city that can have the most contestants; and on November 2011, Mexico broke a new world record for largest zombie gathering. *Guinness* officially counted 9,806 participants. Some organizations have used zombie walks as

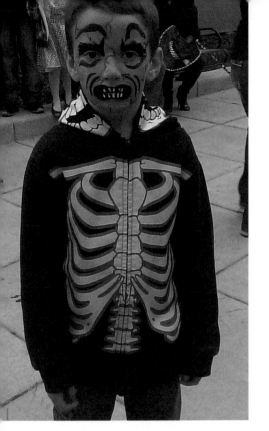

Alex from a zombie walk in Fort Wayne Indiana (2009). *Photo courtesy Angel Story.*

demonstrations to raise funds and awareness for global issues, such as world hunger. Even The Center for Disease Control and Prevention, who wanted to publicize their ideas about being prepared for outbreaks of contagious disease and other natural disasters, has jumped on the zombie-craze bandwagon, by putting together a web page in May 2011 called "Preparedness 101: Zombie Apocalypse." (http://emergency.cdc.gov/socialmedia/zombies.asp)

but why?

Why all this interest and what is the attraction? I happen to be curious about the *why* of such things, which is why I write books like this and others—I wrote in *Allure of the Vampire: Our Sexual Attraction to the Undead* that people, for centuries, have been drawn to vampires due to their power and haunting beauty, and, as much as the original NOSFERATU vampires resembled the zombies lurking outside of their graves, they are certainly not sexually appealing to most. However, very similar to ancient vampires, zombies are creatures from religions past and of modern film, equally having just as much popularity as said vampires.

As a collective, we love both vampires and zombies, but for different reasons. Both need "us" as a food source and as a replenishment for their species, yet we are drawn to them for totally different reasons. We love vampires because of their beauty and power, their mastery over death, yet fear them because they hunt us. A zombie pursues us with just as powerful a hunger, but with nowhere near the same reasons for attraction—unless you dig deeply into the original vampire tales of the Nosferatu and older civilizations. Typically, the two are very unalike. In fact, when we examine zombies as psychological aspects of humanity, they take a different and just as subtle facet within our need for the walking deads' reason for being in our minds.

When we stop to consider that zombies themselves are in fact nothing more than moving corpses, they evoke a very deep-rooted fear in us. As human beings, we fear our own mortality. As I explained in great detail in *Cemetery Gates: Death and Mourning Through the Ages*, people of all walks of life, from almost all periods of history, have gone lengths to honor the remains of our dead, and also to separate us from the next stages of life's journey, out of primitive fear. When people in our lives die, our mental picture of that person becomes static and unchanging in our memory, as we keep in mind how we last recalled them—we push out our thoughts that they soon (and quickly, according to my Forensics class in college) become nothing more than rotting remains. Rebecca Borah, an English professor at the University of Cincinnati in Ohio, agrees. She says that zombies:

> …represent our basic
> fears of death, decay and
> desecration….Who wants
> to grow old, become ill,
> and be isolated from our
> loved ones or a chance
> at redemption?

When we see a television show, such as *THE WALKING DEAD*, where the cast confronts a zombie, providing an especially terrifying scene showing what it would be like to be attacked by someone they once loved and then have to "kill" or make them dead *again*, could it be we are killing our own inner fears? Death now is not what we fear most; it is that those already dead among us will not remain that way. The zombie embodies our terror of an unstoppable monster, unlike any other man has invented. The idea of millions of mindless people attempting to destroy all other people is unthinkable.

Popular films often reflect society's fears and, in the case of George Romero's 1968 film, *NIGHT OF THE LIVING DEAD*, have overtones of the racial conflict in America in the 1960s. This holds true today, also, that zombie films still exhibit classic themes and subtle glimpses of our social phobias. I speculate that a good deal of films are reflections on the masses of mindless people as they mill about in a stupor going about their daily repetition. A prime example of this is in the opening scenes of the film *SHAUN OF THE DEAD*. Romero turned the idea of a few occurrences in previous Haitian tales into an apocalyptic scale terror unthought of since *The Epic of Gilgamesh*.

On a less subconscious level, films such as *NIGHT OF THE LIVING DEAD* illustrate society's pervasive fear of widespread apocalyptic death and hopelessness, and our trepidation of an annihilation in the form of a pandemic, the likes of which we have not seen since the Middle Ages. The implications here are basically the same as they are with *nuclear* apocalypse, but on a more personal and intimate level. If we look at it from a socio-fictional parallel context, zombies infect others by biting and the transference of saliva, and a wave of zombie films surfaced during the 80s during the AIDS scare. Stephen Joel Garver, a philosophy professor at La Salle University in Pennsylvania, believes zombies also resonate with so many Americans today because of worry about an economic collapse, as correlated with television shows like *DOOMSDAY PREPPERS* on National Geographic network and *DOOMSDAY BUNKERS* on Discovery Channel TV. People online use the euphemism of: "When the zombies come, we all need to be ready."

Stephen says:

We live in a time where we talk about "zombie banks" and "zombie corporations," the economic equivalent of the walking dead…. This points to a bigger anxiety about an "apocalypse" in which the familiar secure structures of our lives fall apart—in the face of economic collapse….

Where did all this notion of shambling corpses first originate, and how did it evolve into the mass hysteria that we're experiencing today? Let's find out!

Zombies in Folklore and Religion

Folklore

Epic of Gilgamesh

How long, exactly, have zombies been a part of man's fears? The first written reference to zombies can be found in mankind's oldest work of literature. Having read it in World Literature class during my college days, I recall the old tale, "The Epic of Gilgamesh" where the goddess Ishtar threatens the god Anu, by saying that unless he gives to her the "Bull of Heaven," that all Hell will literally break loose on Earth:

> If you do not give me the Bull of Heaven,
> I shall smash (the gates of the Netherworld) to its dwelling,
> I shall bring up the dead to consume the living,
> I shall make the dead outnumber the living.
> (Andrew George's translation, VI 96–100)

This is not the only time that Ishtar threatens to release her zombie army, as she repeats her threat to the gatekeeper of the Netherworld in "The Decent of Ishtar":

> Gatekeeper, open your gate!
> Open your gate that I may enter!
> If you do not open the gate to let me enter,
> I shall break the door, I shall wrench the lock,
> I shall smash the door-posts, I shall force the doors.
> I shall bring up the dead to consume the living,
> I shall make the dead outnumber the living.
> (Andrew George's translation, VI 96–100)

Zombie walk
Vancouver (2008).
*Photo courtesy
David Defreno.*

Zombies and
Other Religions

People of the past from all religions had burial rituals to ensure the departed spirits of loved ones would have not only safe passage to an afterlife, but also to make sure they did not return to the land of the living. The fear was so real in their minds that they would place iron cages over graves, known as "mortsafes." *Mort* is the French word for *death*, and during the Victorian period a means to deter body snatchers from stealing bodies. At that time, in the early 19th century, medical research was a rapidly growing field—especially the area of anatomy—and medical researchers needed a constant supply of human bodies on which to dissect, as they of course would decay quickly. Many countries' laws of the time made these corpses difficult to come by, so those less-respectable physicians turned to the so-called "resurrectionists," or grave robbers, who would sell them to physicians for dissection. Is that truly the only reason? Doubtful, as this was also a time when Bram Stoker's *Dracula* was written; and in the Victorian age, it was a time when fear of the deceased attacking the living was prevalent. The cage could very well have been intended to trap the undead within, were a corpse to become suddenly reanimated.

David Murphy, the author of *Zombies for Zombies: Advice and Etiquette for the Living Dead*, says Americans' zombie fascination has a religious origin. He believes zombies are people who have "lost track of their souls." Murphy says:

> Our higher spirit prevents
> us from doing stupid and
> violent things like, say,
> eating a neighbor.... When
> we are devoid of such
> spiritual "guidance," we
> become little more than
> walking bags of flesh,
> acting out like soccer
> moms on a bender.

John T. Morehead, in his work, *Toward a Zombie Theology* and *The Undead and Theology* says:

For some time now horror has been the focus of academic study, especially within religious studies. Turns out the final episode of THE WALKING DEAD was a case study for the intersection of zombies and theology, and a pointer toward the evolution of both scientific and popular thinking on the soul.... I find it fascinating that an aspect of popular culture, and a horror television program no less, includes aspects for reflection on human identity that is the focus for academic reflection among scientists, philosophers, and theologians alike. Perhaps if more theologians become comfortable with engaging the texts of popular culture, including the fantastic genres of horror, science fiction, and fantasy, then we might discover examples of what Peter Berger called "signals of transcendence," windows into the divine or the sacred in the mundane things of life.

Mr. Morehead's ideas are not that far of a stretch, when you recall the words of character Hershel, the religious doctor of THE WALKING DEAD television program, when he mentions:

Christ promised a resurrection of the dead; I just thought he had something a little different in mind.

Herschel is saying that the post-apocalyptic zombie earth is now the post-rapture Tribulation prophesied in the Bible, when mass resurrection of dead persons will crawl out of their graves as Jesus did and walk through Jerusalem.

I had the pleasure of interviewing Mr. Morehead about his thoughts.

Mr. Morehead, a pleasure to have a chance to ask you your thoughts on zombies!

John T. Morehead: Thank you for the invitation and the opportunity to discuss this interesting topic. And thanks for addressing it in your book as well.

First off, what inspires you to write on the subject of horror in general, and zombies, in particular?

John T. Morehead: I have been fascinated by horror, as well as science fiction and fantasy for most of my life. I was bitten by the bug when I first saw THE CREATURE FROM THE BLACK LAGOON as a young child, when I was about eight. I found these things both frightening, and yet also strangely drawn to them. I

Victorian iron cage over grave. *Photo courtesy Library of Congress.*

re-approached them as an adult and have been able to probe them more deeply. While the frightening aspect has diminished greatly, nevertheless, I am still drawn to the various expressions of these things. They help me wrestle with my own mortality, the dark side of life that must be embraced as well as the light; they expand my imagination and help me keep my sense of youthful wonder, and in many ways they also provide windows into the sacred.

As to zombies, they have been one of my favorite monstrous icons since I first saw *NIGHT OF THE LIVING DEAD* in the early 1970s. I found them more frightening than other monsters I was used to previously. There is something about the shuffling living dead that you may have known in life reduced to a cannibalistic urge that has the potential to not only kill me, but turn me into one of their flesh-eating kind that I, and obviously many others, find particularly horrifying. But another part of the appeal of the zombie is that it is so flexible in terms of the types of things it can be used to address in terms of personal, social, and cultural issues.

I notice not only are you the author of a book on the subject yourself, but you write quite a bit about religion and the aspects of horror, especially in this genre. Do you find it unsettling in the religious community to mix the two subjects, or is there a growing element such as _THE WALKING DEAD'S_ Christian doctor (named Hershel) who mentions the "walkers" as being part of the Resurrection?

John T. Morehead:
The book you mention is a new one that I was fortunate to coedit with Kim Paffenroth, and contribute a chapter to that looks at some meanings behind the zombie walk phenomenon, particularly where Zombie Jesus may be present, hinting at possible "End Times" ideas in relation to Christian concepts of resurrection of the body. I also write on related topics on my blog, _TheoFantastique.com,_ and for other places when I get the opportunity, such as _Cinefantastique Online_, and a few contributions to some additional books.

I work in the area of religious, cultural, and theological studies, and was pleasantly surprised after graduating from seminary to find that when I applied my academic background to my appreciation for horror and other fantastic

genres, that this provided some interesting insights. Of course, one has to be careful to allow any cultural artifact speak for itself, and resist the temptation to read into it to discover your presuppositions coming back at you, but accounting for my own biases, I have found some interesting elements, including those that touch on the religious, the spiritual, the sacred or the transcendent.

This may strike some people as odd, particularly religious conservatives, but some scholars, like Rudolf Otto, have noted the experience of awe and repulsion found in religious encounters with the divine that parallel the experience of horror. In addition, monsters are found in all religions, including the Judeo-Christian tradition with its Behemoth, Leviathan, the dragon, and Satan. Some have argued that God himself in the Old Testament operates in monstrous fashion, with some texts seemingly condoning violence with divine command, which opens up the possibility that portions of the Bible may be classified as horror in terms of genre. When you add to this that religious people can often cast those they don't like as monsters

18

because of their actions or beliefs, such as Witches, Pagans, and Muslims, then it is easy to see that monsters have a strong and intimate connection to religion, even if many don't acknowledge it and argue to the contrary, as even my brief sketch has demonstrated.

I don't find this connection between religion and horror unsettling. I take it for what it is, and as a person with religious convictions myself, I find this intriguing and must work to come to grips with all of this as I work to understand what it means and to oppose human monstrousness. However, many religious people do find this unsettling. In fact, they frequently state that there is an incompatibility between conservative religious traditions, particularly Christianity, and horror, and decry those who readily combine them with apparent ease.

I don't know that Hershel's character in THE WALKING DEAD signals an increasing Christian ease with horror so much as an opportunity to address religious ideas, particularly Christian ones, that are raised by an apocalyptic scenario. The fact that it provides a postmodern twist on the Christian resurrection idea confirms this in my view. I do know that a small number of Christians have begun to produce so-called "Christian horror," but there is surely a small number of Christians comfortable with this, and it is sanitized so much that it really doesn't resemble more mainstream horror much, and it is surely miles away from the religious elements contained in past Gothic horror.

If, as some speculate, such apocalyptic fiction works are only allegoric tales reflecting our real world issues, (such as racism in the 1960s, and mindless consumers of the 1980s) where is the next step in what the zombie represents in your opinion?

John T. Morehead: It has long been recognized that our monsters reflect us, and they do so in many ways. Zombies are one of the most pliable in terms of how we shape them to address certain issues. Not every zombie represents metaphor, but when they do in the present, there are a number of interpretive possibilities. During the Occupy movement many dressed as zombies, so a critique of economic disparity is evident there. We have also seen in films like SHAUN OF THE DEAD and FIDO something related to this in terms of the exploitation of the worker, wherein we are already dead and becoming living dead merely completes and amplifies a pre-existent form in terms of *SHAUN OF THE DEAD*, and questions are raised about those in various service industries in *FIDO*.

The zombie also seems to increasingly reflect our growing sense of nihilism [meaning (from the *Free Merriam-Webster Dictionary):* a viewpoint that traditional values and beliefs are unfounded and that existence is senseless and useless]. If we are nothing more than fleshly eating machines destined for death and decay, and if we are not connected to any kind of transcendence, do we have meaning and purpose? These kinds of questions are wrestled within *THE WALKING DEAD*, and can also be found in other depictions of the zombie. The postmodern critique of all overarching stories, including secular and religious ones, leaves many wondering whether life is worth living, and this leads us back to the idea that we are already zombies.

I know it is a source for amusement for most of us, but what major life's lessons can be gleaned from these films and televisions shows beyond mindless gore and nihilism of despair—is there hope for us, fictionally speaking or otherwise?

John T. Morehead: I've alluded to some of this previously in terms of our tendency to create monstrous others, and therefore we can hopefully be more aware of this and work individually and collectively not to do this. It is too easy to conceive of others as monsters and us as monster slayers, and when that happens, genocide becomes much easier.

We can also learn much from our hopes and fears. While contemporary horror does have much by way of nihilism and despair, I think this needs to be acknowledged. This reflects our current mindset, but is that all there is? Is there a possibility of hope?

In an episode of *THE WALKING DEAD*, in Season 2, part of the group of survivors went into a church and this provided an opportunity for character Rick Grimes, the group leader, to share his sense of frustration through prayer directed to God through a large crucifix. This scene reflected both the human desire for God, and yet skepticism in the face of apocalypse as to divine reality. In the final episode of Season 3, another element is added where Hershel refers to his belief in the resurrection based on the Bible, but he adds that he thought God would do it differently than through zombie "resurrection."

In my chapter in the book *The Undead and Theology,* I pick up on our contemporary angst depicted via horror, and suggest that it also includes both a hope for and skepticism of survival of death, including in bodily form, which reflects a postmodern understanding of the Judeo-Christian idea of resurrection. In the conclusion of my chapter, I offer suggestions to theologians who want to interact with this aspect of popular culture, and I suggest, among other things, that they try to interject a theology of hope. The great sociologist of religion, Peter Berger, referred to "signals of transcendence," sociological and anthropological insights on theology wherein certain aspects of human activity may at times be interpreted as providing windows into the sacred. It may be that our current fascination with zombies, particularly with zombie walks, where thousands dress up and shuffle about as the living dead, represents not just entertainment and performance art, but also a skeptical acknowledgement of our desire for bodily survival of death, however warped and visceral. Theologians might positively engage the zombie as the monster of the moment and argue that nihilism need not necessarily be the only response to horror, and that hope might be considered as a possibility by way of consideration of "zombie Jesus" that takes postmodern skepticism and concerns into account.

Thank you for taking the time to share your thoughts with my readers!

John T. Morehead:
Again, I appreciate the opportunity and the invitation.

Zombie stories do indeed seem to greatly contend with religious themes, such as the apocalypse and resurrection. As religious writer Chad Brooks says:

> ...zombies provide the perfect postmodern secular eschatological narrative.... To mainstream it, zombies tell the best "end of the world" story for folks living in current western society. Zombies interact well with the base level religious past we have in America and are a perfect product of postmodernity.

Brooks believes, as many others do, that:

> The examples of faith are a perfect mirror for our culture. Faith and religion are major threads in our history and cannot be denied. They influence western society at every place. Even in a completely secular framework, it must be dealt with because of how it has formed us. In that way, it will always be relevant, but the context will be the plumb line to how it is viewed.

If indeed zombies did exist, how and why, asks the Devil's advocate, is it that good people (such as the God-fearing Hershel character) are left behind? Atheists point to the overtly religious overtones, and make the case that the Rapture is a lie—and even some of the people in THE WALKING DEAD state similar views. This is no doubt influenced by George Romero's similarly nihilistic viewpoints of an apocalypse with no hope for those left on Earth.

The Bible

The Bible is full of stories of the dead coming to life, the end of days, and numerous tales of the undead coming back to life. Many theology and mythological scholars who compare religions of the past, Christ's resurrection was borrowed from the god of ancient Egypt, Osiris. Farrell Till, the editor of the *Skeptical Review* writes:

> Osiris's evil brother Set plotted with others to kill Osiris. This was accomplished by tricking Osiris during a banquet to lie down in a chest that had been especially prepared for him. When Osiris was inside the chest, Set and his cohorts closed it immediately and took it to the Nile and put it into the river. When Isis, the sister-wife of Osiris heard what had happened, she set out to find the chest. The legend is detailed, but to make a long story short, Isis learned that the chest had

drifted out to sea and landed on the coast of Byblos. She went there, found the chest, recovered the body, embraced it, and wailed inconsolably. She hid the body in a secret place, which Set discovered, after which he severed the body into fourteen different pieces and scattered them throughout Egypt. The myth then continues as Isis searched Egypt, found the body parts, put them back together, and then hovered over Osiris and fanned the breath of life back into his body.

Many biblical passages allude to a plague that is reminiscent of a *28 Weeks*-styled zombie pandemic:

Zechariah 14:12: And the LORD will send a plague on all the nations that fought against Jerusalem. Their people will become like walking corpses, their flesh rotting away. Their eyes will rot in their sockets, and their tongues will rot in their mouths.

Zechariah 14:13: On that day they will be terrified, stricken by the LORD with great panic. They will fight their neighbors hand to hand.

Revelation 11:11: But after the three and a half days a breath of life from God entered them, and they stood on their feet, and terror struck those who saw them.

Ezekiel 37:10: So I prophesied as he commanded me, and breath entered them; they came to life and stood up on their feet–a vast army.

Zombie Jesus

Zombie Jesus; that's right. I recall the first use of this phrase from the *Futurama* cartoon show, created by *The Simpsons'* Matt Groening in the episode "When Aliens Attack" on November 7, 1999. In it, Professor Hubert J. Farnsworth has been known to shout out, "Sweet Zombie Jesus."

As John Morehead mentioned it earlier, I discovered there was even a website about Zombie Jesus, who made an appearance at the Philly Zombie Crawl (in Philadelphia, Pennsylvania), an annual event, kicked off at Easter. Zombie Jesus is an important part of this gathering.

Although shocking as it may be to fundamentalist Christians, some religious writers think Christians should appreciate the Biblical influence, overt or not, that their faith causes people to pause for thought. Zombie Jesus has become a widespread pop-culture phenomenon, becoming a common sight on items such as shirts and bumper stickers—Zombie Jesus even has an appearance in the *Dead Meat Walking: A Zombie Walk Documentary*, and an entire film called *Zombie Jesus*, directed by Steve Miller, the writer/director of skits on *Saturday Night Live*. The film won multiple awards, including Best Film by the HSBC Canada Filmmakers Awards, and Best Short at the After Dark Film Festival. In 2009, comedian Jamie Kilstein came out with a comedy album entitled *Zombie Jesus*.

The *Zombie Jesus Day* website defends its creation, saying:

> Everything that rises from
> the dead is a zombie.
> Easter is touted as the
> death and resurrection of
> Jesus Christ. So let's call a
> spade a spade, eat lots of
> chocolate, and celebrate
> Zombie Jesus Day.

Jesus's resurrection, like Osiris mentioned earlier, predates Christianity—who also came back from the dead—and is pointed at by Christian zombie fans in humor. Equally, atheist fans cite the Biblical passage of John 6:53:

> Jesus said to them, "I tell
> you the truth, unless you
> eat the flesh of the Son of
> Man and drink his blood,
> you have no life in you."

The Black Death

Europe's most prolific period for myths and legends about the walking dead was during the Middle Ages, when it was commonly believed that the souls of the dead could return to earth and haunt the living. The belief in revenants (someone who has returned from the dead) has been interchangeably used for both zombies and early vampires and are well documented by contemporary European writers of the time. According to the *Encyclopedia of Things that Never Were*, by Michael Page and Robert Ingpen (1987), particularly in France during the Middle Ages, the revenant rises from the dead usually to avenge some crime committed against the entity, most likely a murder. The revenant most often took on the form of an emaciated corpse or skeletal human figure and wandered around graveyards at night.

Bubonic plague, or as it is called "The Black Death," struck back in Central Asia in 1338, eventually reaching India by 1346. This disease began when rats and the fleas they carried on them were regular passengers on merchant vessels. It spread throughout the Mediterranean and nearly wiped out a full half of Europe's population, bringing the known world population down to 350 million in the 14th century. If ever there was a pandemic of biblical proportions, this was it.

It started many stories of the walking dead when people who had recently died came back home with stains of blood on their shirts. This is one of the origins of many folklore tales of both zombies and vampires. One of the symptoms of the bubonic plague happened to be that the victim would pass out, falling into a brief comatose state, then wake vomiting blood.

24

"Danse Macabre" from the *Dance of Death* by Michael Wolgemut (1493).

Islamic Zombies

Yes, as surprising as it is, even the Islamic countries have their ancient version of the zombie, better known as a ghoul, a being who would haunt the cemeteries at night and would survive off the dead. The belief in ghouls comes from the Middle East region, around the bedrock of civilization's birthplace in the Mesopotamian dessert. I discovered they were thought to be a punishment for people who died after living an immoral life, usually a fallen woman—typically a prostitute—that called out to men like a siren to eat them. Romero even used the name siren originally instead of zombie!

My college friend, Rosemary Ellen Guiley, author of *The Vengeful Djinn*, wrote about it and I cite her as a reference in my work, *Satan's Minions: A Guide to Fallen Angels, Demons and other Dark Creatures.* I wrote:

> Ghouls are mythological creatures in the far Islamic folklore that dwell in burial grounds and other uninhabited places. The English word comes from the Arabic name meaning *demon*, and is a type of jinn believed to be sired by Iblis, the Muslim Devil.

Illustration of the Black Death from the Toggenburg Bible (1411).

The ghoul is a shape-shifting demon that can assume the guise of an animal, especially a hyena. It lures unwary travelers into the desert and eats them. It robs graves, and eats the dead (necrophagia) taking on the form of the one they previously ate.

Ghouls were thought to have been flesh-eating demons, says Rosemary, and were a lower form of the Islamic Djinn, being both malicious and ravenous and preferring the taste of human flesh, either rotting or living.

This powerful being perhaps influenced one of the early fiction stories of the dead returning in a more modern time frame. The story "The Monkey's Paw," by W.W. Jacobs, was published in England in 1902, taken from the old legend where wishes were granted by a Djinn/Genie, but with outcomes not as the person requesting them really wanted. In this account, the paw of a dead monkey is a powerful talisman that grants its possessor three wishes; however, the results are twisted and come at an enormous price for the asker interfering with fate.

The story involves a certain couple, a Mr. and Mrs. White and their adult son, Herbert. An old friend of the couple, Sergeant-Major Morris, a member of the British Armed Forces in India, comes to visit. During his time there, he gifts them the monkey's paw and informs them that it has the mysterious power to grant three wishes. Ominously, he mentions the former owner was an old fakir or holy man, who used his third and final wish to request his own death.

As the story progresses, Mr. White wishes for £200, which will pay off his home debt. Suddenly, they get the news that Herbert (the son) is killed by machinery at work, and the family is given the exact amount of £200 as his death benefit.

After the funeral, Mrs. White, who is sick with grief, begs her husband to wish Herbert back to life with the paw. Reluctantly, he does so. Later on, there is a knock at the door. Mrs. White fumbles at the locks in an attempt to open it, knowing that her deceased son is on the otherside—brought back to life by the paw. Mr. White stops her, though, because he knows their son was horribly mutilated by the accident and that it was this disfigured being that would be behind the door. So he uses the third wish asking that Herbert stay dead. As abruptly as the knocking started, it stops.

The moral here is explained in the story itself. "It [the paw] had a spell put on it by an old fakir," said the sergeant-major, "a very holy man. He wanted to show that fate ruled people's lives, and that those who interfered with it did so to their sorrow."

Viking Legends

In old Nordic legends, a *draugr, draug*, or *draugen*, and from the Norwegian, Swedish, and Danish, *draug*, also known as *aptrgangr,* translates as "again-walker," or "one who walks after death." The draugar were

believed to live in the graves of the dead, and the draugr was the animated body of the dead, who was very nearly indestructible, like our modern version of zombies that are nearly indestructible—except by decapitation or immolation (fire). They possessed superhuman strength, had a foul and unmistakable stench of decay, and had immense and nearly insatiable appetites. They were undead Vikings that retained some semblance of intelligence, and had the ability to rise from the grave to devour their victims' flesh, and drink their blood. The creation of a draugr was not exactly clear, but in one old story, it spoke of a shepherd killed by a draugr and rising the next night as one himself. The draugar were said to be *nár-fölr*, which meant corpse-pale. The only thing that could stop it was a hero who was capable of forcing it back into its grave.

The draugr has made its presence known in modern gaming. In *The Morganville Vampires*, draugr are the ancient enemies of the vampire, and in *The Elder Scrolls V: Skyrim*, there are hordes of draugr in ancient Nordic tombs.

Voodoo

As almost everyone loving zombies knows, the word *zombie* means "spirit of the dead," a reanimated corpse brought back to life by mystical means. The word originally came from the Caribbean Creole, from either Kikongo, zonbi or zumbi which means "fetish," or the North Mbundu region of the people called Kimbundu that speak of it as nzambi, or "god."

Vodun (a.k.a. Vodoun, Voudou, Voodoo, Sevi Lwa) is commonly called Voodoo (vû'dû) by the public. The name of this religion was derived some time back, almost 6,000 years ago in Africa, from the god Vodun of the West African Yoruba people who lived in 18th and 19th century Dahomey. Its roots may go back a thousand years in Africa's history to an old god from nzambi, which means "god" in the Congo. That country occupied parts of today's Togo, Benin, and Nigeria. Slaves brought their religion with them when they were forcibly shipped to Haiti and other islands in the West Indies.

The rituals of West Africa and Haiti present an even more familiar form of the zombie. According to the West African Vodun tenets of Vodou, a dead person can be revived by a bokor, which translates to "sorcerer." These zombies remain under the control of the bokor as they have no will of their own. In an old Vodou legend, feeding a zombie salt would make it return to the grave.

Vodun was actively suppressed during colonial times. Many Vodun priests were executed and their items destroyed because of the threat they posed to Euro-Christians. So those who were left created underground societies in order to continue the veneration, or worship of their ancestors.

Vodun has been freely practiced in Benin since a democratic government was installed there in 1989; about 60% of the population follows this religion. Vodun is recognized as the non-official religion in Haiti, as most of the population are nominally Roman Catholic; similarly, it is practiced in cities in America, particularly in the southern states.

Today over 60 million people practice Vodun worldwide. Religions similar to Vodun can be found in South America where they are called Umbanda, Quimbanda, or Candomble.

History of Vodun in the West

Slaves were baptized into the Roman Catholic Church upon their arrival in Haiti and other West Indian islands. However, there was little Christian infrastructure present during the early 19th century to maintain the faith. The result was that the slaves largely followed their original native faith, which they practiced in secret, even while attending Mass regularly.

The inaccurate and sensational book, *St. John, Haiti or the Black Republic* was written in 1884. It described Vodun as a profoundly evil religion, and included lurid descriptions of human sacrifice and cannibalism, the details of which had been extracted from the Vodun priests by torture, rendering the confessions quite invalid from the truth, as people will admit to anything to stop suffering. This book caught the imagination of people outside the West Indies, and was responsible for much of the misunderstanding and fear that is present today. Hollywood found this a rich source for Voodoo screenplays, and thus, horror movies like *WHITE ZOMBIE* began in the 1930s and continue to today to misrepresent this faith. It is only since the late 1950s that accurate studies by anthropologists have been published.

Other religions (Macumba, Candomble, Umbanda, and Santeria) bear many similarities to Vodun. Vodun beliefs contain many traditions and have several different spiritual paths with the worship of a different pantheon of spirits, called *Loa*, which means "mystery." There are in fact hundreds of minor Loa:

- **Agwe:** spirit of the sea
- **Aida Wedo:** rainbow spirit
- **Ayza:** protector
- **Baka:** an evil spirit who takes the form of an animal
- **Baron Samedi:** guardian of the grave
- **Dambala (or Damballah-wedo):** serpent spirit
- **Erinle:** spirit of the forests
- **Ezili (or Erzulie):** female spirit of love
- **Mawu Lisa:** spirit of creation
- **Ogou Balanjo:** spirit of healing
- **Ogun (or Ogu Bodagris):** spirit of war
- **Osun:** spirit of healing streams
- **Sango (or Shango):** spirit of storms
- **Yemanja:** female spirit of waters
- **Zaka (or Oko):** spirit of agriculture

As surprising as it might seem initially, there are a number of points of similarity between Roman Catholicism and Vodun: Both believe in a supreme being, the existence of invisible evil spirits or demons, and an afterlife. The Loa are much like Catholic Saints, and often certain candles are used as a representation of them.

The purpose of rituals is to make contact with a spirit, to gain their favor by offering them animal sacrifices and gifts, to obtain help in the form of more abundant food, or improved health. Human and Loa depend upon each other: Humans provide food and other materials and the Loa provide health, protection from evil spirits, and good fortune. Rituals are held to celebrate lucky events, to attempt to escape a run of bad fortune, to celebrate a seasonal day of celebration associated with a Loa, for healing, at birth, marriage, and death.

Vodun priests can be male (houngan or hungan), or female (mambo). A Vodun temple is called a hounfour (or humfort). At its center is a poteau-mitan, a pole where the God and spirits communicate with the people. An altar will be elaborately decorated with candles and pictures of Christian saints, and believers hold a feast before the main ceremony.

The origin of the concept of zombies stems from Haitian Voodoo folklore that contends that bokors supposedly had an ability to resurrect the deceased through the administration of coup padre—a powder made up from tetrodoxin, the deadly substance of the notoriously poisonous fou-fou, which is more commonly referred to as a porcupine fish. The victim, or willing participant, then appears to die, as the heart rate slows almost to nothing, and the body temperature decreases. The people watching would bury the victim, fooled into thinking that the person was dead. The person would then be exhumed, still alive, of course, by the bokor, who would "revive" the dead and command the victim to do his bidding, under the influence of powerful drugs administered by the sorcerer—a great con, if there ever was one, to retain a position of power within a culture!

Some people still believe that witches create zombies by killing and possessing the victims in order to obtain slave labor. Stories are handed down about "witch trains." After rail roads were built to transport migrant workers, nighttime runs (witch trains) were controlled by the vudan and operated by zombi slaves.

LaLaurie Mansion

LaLaurie Mansion was owned by Madame Delphine LaLaurie and her husband, Dr. Louis LaLaurie, socialites of great wealth and prominence in the city of New Orleans in the 1830s. They would host elaborate parties at the house. But late one night, a fire broke out in the mansion. When help arrived, they witnessed a horrific scene in a hidden room. They discovered tortured and abused slaves who worked in the house, as reported in *Real Zombies, the Living Dead, and Creatures of the Apocalypse,* by Brad Steiger, which describes in detail the horrendous experiments conducted on living people. Some were kept in cages or bound to operating tables in various stages of dissection or unneeded surgery. Delphine fled, never to be seen again.

The home has undergone many changes and owners over the years, with the most recent owner being actor Nicolas Cage. Cage said of the LaLaurie house:

> You know, other people
> have beach-front property;
> I have ghost-front property.

Unfortunately, Cage lost the property in a foreclosure auction.

New Orleans' Voodoo Cemetery Gates Of Guinee, The Portal To The Afterworld.

Also known by locals as "The Portal To The Afterworld," this cemetery is named after Ghede, the wise man, for his familiarity and accumulation of the knowledge of all the deceased. He stands on the center of all roads that lead to "Guinee," or the Afterworld. The New Orleans tour guides and haunted cemetery or ghost tours will skirt around the issue; the older people who know about voodoo say only that someone pure of heart with only one burning question to be answered by the dead is ever told the whole truth. An unnamed New Orleans Voodoo priestess says quite bluntly:

> Search and you shall find
> them rusted shut, or worse
> they will certainly find you
> and be wide and opened.

Lafayette Cemetery No. 1 (2008). *Photo courtesy of Judi Bottoni.*

However, you may just find someone in the local occult shops who would be willing to help you!

City of the Dead, Lafayette Cemetery No. 1

Lafayette No. 1 is the cemetery most often used in films made in New Orleans. The oldest city burial site since 1833, Lafayette Cemetery No. 1 is placed on the National Register of Historic Places by virtue of its significant history, location, and architectural importance. Built in 1833, by the year 1852, the cemetery was filled to capacity when almost 2,000 yellow fever victims were buried there. Today, many tombs are still sinking into the ground, swallowed up forever.

Many say this is the most haunted cemetery; indeed, this decaying grandeur location stirred the imagination of local author Anne Rice, who has used the place in many of her books. She even staged a mock funeral here, to launch the publication of *Memnoch the Devil*, with Anne herself as a corpse wearing an antique wedding dress in an open coffin carried by pall bearers. Her most known title turned into film was INTERVIEW WITH A VAMPIRE, filmed throughout the French Quarter, and starring Tom Cruise, Brad Pitt, and Kirsten Dunst.

Legions of Voodoo practitioners make their way through the "City of the Dead" to visit the grave of voodoo high priestess Marie Laveau, who was buried here; and for generations, the devoted and the curious have been visiting this site, conducting rituals, and leaving all kinds of gris-gris, which is, according to my friend and Voodan priest, Andrieh Vitimus, a voodoo amulet originating in Africa, used to protect the wearer from evil—

consisting of a small cloth bag, with a ritual item inside, typically worn by the owner. Marie Laveau, born to a wealthy French planter and a mother (who sources indicate) could have been a mulatto slave, was a Caribbean Voodoo practitioner, and she used theatrics and wealth to rise to the top of the city's most colorful and sought-out celebrity by using creative staging to put on performances—her general voodoo practice became highly lucrative.

In Haunted Places: The National Directory (1996), by Dennis Hauck, writes of Marie:

> Her ghost and those of
> her followers are said to
> practice wild voodoo rituals
> in her old house.

Voodoo Museum

The New Orleans Historic Voodoo Museum, which lies in the heart of the New Orleans French Quarter, is one of the most unique, and interesting, small museums in the country. It exists to preserve the legacy of New Orleans' Voodoo history and culture, while educating and entertaining the visitor all about the secrets, the history, and folklore of rituals, zombies, and gris-gris. It has been a fixture in New Orleans since 1972.

Lafayette Cemetery No. 1 is located in the Garden District, Washington Avenue and Prytania section of New Orleans and accessible by the St. Charles Avenue Streetcar, between Bourbon Street and Royal Street located at 724 Dumaine Street, New Orleans, Louisiana.

French Quarter, New Orleans. Cigar shop and Rev. Zombie's Voodoo Shop. *Courtesy of Beth Dolgner, author of* Everyday Voodoo.

CHAPTER TWO

Zombies and Science

Hazardous materials released at Institute for
Genomic Biology. Escape area if safe to do so.
Otherwise seek shelter.

~Tweet from a lab, May 28, 2013

At one time or another, those of us who love zombie movies have
pondered the possibility of a full-out George Romero-styled zombie
attack; it truly is happening in the real world. Even the Max Brooks
tongue-in-cheek book, *The Zombie Survival Guide*, has become a best
seller. As far back as *The Mask of the Red Death*, in 1842 by Edgar Allen
Poe, the story of Prince Prospero's and his wealthy friends' callous
disregard to the sufferings of the commoners outside, as they lived in
the safety of an abbey, is similar to the remake of *The Land of the Dead*.
In this film, the wealthy attempt to avoid an epidemic called The Red
Death (in Romero's work, zombies) in their own safe luxurious palace
(a state-of-the-art high-rise condo). The story is an allegory, and a
mysterious figure enters the fortress revealed as the personification of
Death—all the guests succumb to the disease.

Zombie walk Vancouver (2008).
Photo courtesy David Defreno.

H.P. Lovecraft

Back in the year 1985, Staurt Gordon was inspired to remake H.P. Lovecraft's *Re-Animator*, based on the writer's short story, *Herbert West—Reanimator*. This cult film tells the tale of Herbert West, who brings his dead professor, Dr. Hans Gruber (Al Berry), back to life at the Zurich University Institute of Medicine in Switzerland.

Herbert West arrives as a student at the Miskatonic University, and while there, sets up a hidden laboratory in the building's basement and makes it his own personal laboratory. This is where West has re-animated his dead cat, while searching for a way to defeat death. Herbert and a friend break into the morgue to test his formula on a cadaver. The revived corpse goes on a rampage, attacking them and killing Herbert's friend, the scientist—who promptly kills the attacker, and he then injects his friend who returns to life as a zombie. More carnage and reanimation follows in this bloody cult classic.

The director wished to do the *Re-Animator* film because he felt that there were too many *Dracula* movies. Browsing the Chicago Public Library, he found H.P. Lovecraft's *Reanimator*. Gordon and the special effects crew used a book on forensic pathology to research exactly how a corpse looked once the blood settled in the body, to reproduce the decay and skin tones. The film required twenty-four gallons of fake blood!

People Eating People

It can be said that the Apostolic Creed is the Niceno-Constantinopolitan message of the death, resurrection, and return of Christ. This is a part of a church service which looks forward to the return of the dead, the symbolic and positive "bringer of life," unlike the zombie, which clearly is quite the opposite. As a joke, some people refer to the mention in the previous chapter of "eating the body of Christ" as more than mere symbolism; but in seriousness, could it not be said the sin of cannibalism is hypothetically the reason for zombies as a damnation and punishment? Man has almost always had a taboo against eating people, including the Greek mythology stories of Titans eating their children. The Donner Party of eighty-five travelers in the West headed for the state of California, surviving by eating half of their party who had died of exposure to the cold.

This is even depicted in the Wendigo legend by Native Americans, where sometimes there is a creature referred to as Windigo, Wiindigoo, Windago, or Windiga (also thought to be the origin of the modern Bigfoot or Sasquatch stories). This legend portrays the Wendigo as a large bipedal creature with glowing eyes, long yellowish canine teeth, and who was a warrior, once glorious, on the battlefield. Having saved his people, he ate his enemies and became cursed, forever having a taste for human flesh.

The first accounts of the Wendigo myth by explorers and missionaries date back to the 17th century.

In the winter of 1878, a Native named Swift Runner butchered and ate his wife and five children. Swift Runner was an example of what is called Wendigo psychosis, a culture-bound disorder which involves an intense craving for human flesh. Swift Runner confessed to the murders and was executed.

As of this writing, there has been a rash of news stories being labeled the beginning of "the zombie apocalypse," where crazed people have attacked and eaten other people. The first incident, a major story that lit up the Internet, involved a naked man, Rudy Eugene, who climbed on top of Roland Poppo, a 65-year-old sleeping homeless man, and then dragged, stripped, and beat him before eating what was originally said to be eighty percent of his face. Later, it was corrected to be the upper half and one eye. Those first responding to the trauma said Poppo was nearly unrecognizable as a human being. A passerby summoned the police, who told the attacker to back away. Eugene looked up with pieces of human flesh hanging from his mouth and growled at the police, then went back to eating the victim's face.

The police shot Eugene multiple times before he went down. The victim not only lived through the ordeal, but is recovering and watching sports with his good eye. He seems optimistic.

Bath Salts
The New
Tetrodoxin?

These tales have spread many wild ideas concerning why and how Rudy Eugene turned into a zombie, or more correctly, a mad cannibal. Speculated to be the cause of the psychotic attack is that he was high on a dangerous street drug called "Bath Salts," but before we go pulling Epsom salts from the first-aid aisles, this is merely the street name and has nothing in common with harmless bath salts.

Some people "...go completely insane and become very violent," said Armando Aguilar, president of the Miami Fraternal Order of Police in an interview with CNN. Known by street names like "Ivory Wave,"

Zombie walk Vancouver (2008).
Photo courtesy David Defreno,

"Vanilla Sky," "Bliss," "Dynamite," and "Purple Rain," these highly dangerous drugs made headlines in 2011 after thousands of calls to poison control centers, ER visits, and many deaths grew at an alarming rate.

The synthetic, designer drug is deemed an "imminent threat to public safety" by the US Drug Enforcement Administration, which has issued a one-year ban on the possession and sale of the ingredients, which include mephedrone and methylone, amphetamine-like chemicals that have uniquely hazardous effects on the brain, and are put into the body by being swallowed, snorted, or injected. "If you take the worst attributes of meth, coke, PCP, LSD, and Ecstasy, and put them together, that's what we're seeing sometimes," Mark Ryan, director of the Louisiana Poison Center, told *The New York Times*.

The effects producing feelings in the drug user, according to a CNN report, are of "...euphoria, sensory awareness, and hallucinations. Other reported effects include rapid heart rate, high blood pressure, and sweating. According to the DEA, "MDPV, which stands for the drug Methylenedioxypyrovalerone, is a psychoactive drug with stimulant properties used as a norepinephrine-dopamine reuptake inhibitor, and was developed in 1969. It has been reported to cause intense panic attacks, psychosis, and a strong desire to use the drug again."

The CDC advises people against the usage of these "Bath Salts" abusers: Users risk both psychological side effects and physical side effects that include high blood pressure and increased heart rate. According to a *Huffington Post* report, ninety-one percent of users had neurological damage and half of them had psychological difficulties associated with taking the drug, as many attempted to commit suicide.

Originally, the Rudy Eugene case in Miami was thought to involve "Bath Salts"; however, the toxicology tests performed on Eugene found marijuana in his system, but no other drugs or alcohol. Bruce Goldberger, professor and director of toxicology at the University of Florida, says:

> There is an almost infinite
> number of chemical
> substances out there
> that can trigger unusual
> behavior. There are many
> of these synthetic drugs
> that we currently don't
> have the methodology to
> test on, and that is not
> the fault of the toxicology
> lab. The challenge today
> for the toxicology lab is to
> stay on top of these new
> chemicals and develop
> methodologies for them,
> but it's very difficult and
> very expensive. There is no
> one test or combination of
> tests that can detect every
> possible substance
> out there.

According to the American Association of Poison Control Centers, the use of "Bath Salts" appears to be on the rise, poison control centers getting twenty times the calls related to the drug in 2011 in comparison to calls in 2010.

The Eugene incident is yet one of many cases of "zombie" attacks in the news.

Wayne Carter, a 43-year-old from Hackensack, New Jersey, was hospitalized in critical condition after officers responded to reports of a man barricaded in a room who was threatening to harm himself.

Police Lt. John Heinemann said that two officers kicked in the door and saw Carter in a corner, holding a knife in his hand. Carter, ignoring the officers' repeated orders to drop the weapon, stood up and stabbed himself in the abdomen, legs, and neck, according to the reports.

Carter yelled at the officers and took an aggressive stance, and the officers used pepper spray in an attempt to subdue him, but it had no effect, Heinemann said. His wounds were so deep that his intestines poured out of his cut abdomen. "He didn't seem to feel the pain as he ripped pieces of his intestines and flesh and threw them at the police."

"The officers decided to retreat and call in the Bergen County SWAT team," Heinemann said, adding that he believes drug use or mental illness may have contributed to Carter's behavior. Finally the SWAT team was able to subdue him, and then went to get decontaminated. The man was finally restrained and was taken to a hospital just before midnight. Carter had been arrested in the past for both aggravated assault and resisting arrest.

Another victim was a 22-year-old man named Tim McLean who was murdered, beheaded, and partially eaten by a psychotic fellow passenger on a Greyhound bus. The victim was, witnesses say, asleep when Vince Weiguang Li, a 40-year-old former church worker, attacked McLean with a knife, and ate some of his victim's flesh. From a police scanner recording, the attack was described as the event happened:

> "[Li is] at the back of the bus, hacking off pieces and eating them..." [Li, who earlier begged police to kill him, denies murder on the grounds of mental illness.]

> "A voice from God told him Mr. McLean was the force of evil and was about to execute him," said the 40-year-old's psychiatrist, Dr. Stanley Yaren, "...he ate to stop him from coming back to life." Prior to the killing, Li left his wife a note which said, "I'm gone. Don't look for me. I wish you were happy."

Another incident was that of Jarrod Wyatt, a cage fighter from California who attacked his training partner in his apartment after drinking a mushroom tea. Hallucinating that the man was possessed by a demon, Wyatt killed him, ripped out his heart, cut out his tongue, and tore off his face. He began to burn the body parts to get rid of the demon. Wyatt was found by a friend, naked and covered in blood, with the victim's body parts scattered around the room.

In Baltimore, Maryland, Alexander Kinyua, a 21-year-old student, admitted to killing his roommate and eating his heart and brain. His brother found a human head and hands in a basement sink of their home and called police.

A headless, limbless torso was discovered in a suitcase in the garbage in a Montreal neighborhood. The same day, an employee of the Conservative Party of Canada headquarters in Ottawa opened a package that contained a severed foot.

Montreal police issued a warrant for Luka Rocco Magnotta for murder after obtaining a disturbing video of Magnotta stabbing a man repeatedly on a bed that was circulating online and was sent to the *Montreal Gazette*. Police also confirmed that the suspect at large in the gruesome murder and dismemberment once dated Karla Homolka, a notorious sex killer.

Magnotta was later arrested in an Internet cafe in Berlin, according to Germany's *Bild* newspaper. German police spokesperson Stefan Rieldich said someone at the cafe recognized Magnotta and called the authorities. Magnotta is now denying he is the killer shown in the video.

No Need for Panic

The Twitter "tweet" from the University of Illinois at Urbana-Champaign about a leak of hazardous materials from the Institute of Genomic Biology, coupled with the multiple crazed attacks previously mentioned, are certainly seen as fragments of a zombie film such as *28 WEEKS*, but The Center for Disease Control says we really have no need for panic.

An email to the *Huffington Post*, a news organization who evidently asked The Center for Disease Control this question, reported this response in an official statement to the public by agency spokesman David Daigle:

> CDC does not know of
> a virus or condition that
> would reanimate the dead.

But as you will discover at the end of this chapter, the CDC is apparently ignorant of science projects conducted back in the 1800s that were perfected by a research team here in the United States!

A writer from the *Huffington Post* says:

> So, why we got all worked
> up about zombies when
> all we were dealing with
> was cannibals is the
> real mystery, you guys.
> Seriously, nothing to worry
> about! It's just cannibals!

These cases are mounting evidence for those who believe that this is a start of the "zombie apocalypse." One truly has to wonder if it is scientifically possible or whether these incidents are just a few isolated acts of random insanity.

Back in 2009, Robert J. Smith, a mathematician at University of Ottawa, published a paper in a book about infectious disease modeling, entitled *"When Zombies Attack! Math-*

Risen. Artwork by the author.

ematical Modelling of an Outbreak of Zombie Infection," that originally started as a class project, when some students suggested they model zombies. Smith said:

> I think they thought
> I'd shoot it down, but
> actually, I said go for it.
> That sounds really great.
> And it was just a fun way
> of really illustrating some
> of the process that you
> might have in modeling an
> infectious disease.

The group used mathematical equations to show that only by quickly and aggressively attacking the zombie population could normal humans hope to prevent the complete collapse of society. This sparked more studies, such as the book *Mathematical Modelling of Zombies*, conducted by an epidemiologist and a mathematician at Australian National University that concluded that:

> ...only when human skill
> levels are very low do the
> zombies have a chance
> of winning, while only
> high human skill levels
> ensure a human victory.
> For the in-between state of
> moderate skill a substantial
> proportion of humans
> tend to survive, albeit in
> packs that are being forever
> chased by zombies.

One has to wonder, if not for drugs like "Bath Salts" or tetrodoxin, how would an outbreak of zombies be possible? There are some interesting theories on how this could happen that have been around since the 1930s.

The Serpent
and the Rainbow

While researching Haitian folklore back in the year 1937, Zora Neale Hurston came across the case of a woman who appeared in a village, whose family claimed she was Felicia Felix-Mentor, a relative who had not only died, but had been buried back in the year 1907. She mysteriously reappeared in the village years later. Hurston attempted to track down the facts of the case, and surmised that the affected victim was given a powerful psychoactive drug, but she was unable to locate individuals willing to offer much information. Zora wrote on the incident, saying:

> What is more, if science
> ever gets to the bottom of
> Voodoo in Haiti and Africa,
> it will be found that some
> important medical secrets,
> still unknown to medical
> science, give it its power,
> rather than gestures
> of ceremony.

This is hardly an isolated case study. Clairvius Narcisse was another. In Haiti, in 1962, a gentleman was declared dead by two doctors and then buried. Villagers found

The Zombies of Mora Tau. *Photo courtesy public commons.*

him wandering around the village eighteen years later. Local voodoo priests had been using natural chemicals to enslave people, putting them to work on the sugar plantations—a very old method of getting cheap labor.

Harvard ethnobotanist Wade Davis traveled to Haiti in 1982 and based his research there. He presented a pharmacological case for zombies in two books, *The Serpent and the Rainbow* (1985) and *Passage of Darkness: The Ethnobiology of the Haitian Zombie* (1988). Davis informed readers that a living person could be turned into a zombie by two special powders being introduced into the blood stream. The first one (mentioned earlier) was a substance known as tetrodotoxin (TTX), a powerful neurotoxin found in the flesh of the puffer fish, and the other drug was a dissociative (such as datura). Combined, they induced a zombified state where individuals

could be controlled by a voodoo doctor. Davis went on to detail that the victim, after a lapse into suspended animation, was then revived after being buried. Typically, the person went into a psychotic state due to psychological trauma. Davis hypothesized that it was in part due to cultural belief that caused the individual to "... reconstruct their identity as that of a zombie," as they believed they were truly dead and they simply behaved as they felt they needed to—automatically.

There are other types of poisons that slow bodily functions in a similar manner, inducing a trance-like state without memory, but still allowing the individual to perform simple tasks. Neurotoxins, such as the poison from fugu, a Japanese blowfish, can do this. Steven Schlozman, an assistant professor of psychiatry at Harvard University and author of *The Zombie Autopsies: Secret Notebooks from the Apocalypse,* blames an airborne contagion for the zombie phenomenon in his work of fiction. He says:

> An effective agent would target, and shut down, specific parts of the brain.... The walking dead have some of their motor skills intact—walking, of course, but also the ripping and tearing necessary to devour human flesh. The frontal lobe, which is responsible for morality, planning, and inhibiting impulsive actions is nonexistent. The cerebellum, which controls coordination, is probably still there, but not fully functional. This makes sense, since zombies in movies are usually easy to outrun or club with a baseball bat....

The brain eventually deteriorates, believes Schlozman, but before that, a metabolic change would occur, which he says causes "seizures, twitching, and just look awful like a zombie."

Jay Fishman, director of Transplant Infectious Diseases at Massachusetts General Hospital in Boston, proposes that using a virus that causes encephalitis, which is an inflammation of the brain's casing, might be part of the sickness, saying:

> After infection, we need to stop the prion takeover so that our zombies don't go completely comatose, their minds rendered entirely useless.

Scottish psychiatrist R.D. Laing suggests that mental illness, like schizophrenia, combined with cultural expectations, would make some behave as if they were zombies. Brain disorders can cause zombie-like symptoms, such as Mad Cow Disease—the medical term is Creutzfeldt-Jakob disease. For example, Mad Cow changes someone's manner of walking (they lurch about); it can cause hallucinations, muscle twitching, and lack of coordination or seizures, as well as delirium and dementia.

Parasites and Fungi

Zombies in the Animal Kingdom

There are parasites that can turn victims into mindless, zombie-like slaves in nature—this process being called toxoplasmosis. Oxford scientists discovered that the minds of infected rats became altered, as they demonstrated that healthy rats would avoid areas that have been doused with cat urine, this almost always inducing a neurochemical panic. However, toxoplasma-ridden rats displayed no such reaction; some of the infected rats actually sought out the cat urine-marked areas repeatedly.

Associate Director for Laboratory Research at the Stanley Medical Research Institute, Dr. E. Fuller Torrey cites links between toxoplasma and schizophrenia in human beings; approximately three billion, nearly half the human population on Earth, are infected with "toxoplasmosa gondii." Pregnant women with high levels of toxoplasma are much more likely to give birth to children who will develop the disorder of schizophrenia, as mentioned previously in this chapter; it makes one speculate that combined with illegal drug use, a condition may result in flesh-eating attacks—if we combine Dr. Fuller and Mr. Laing's hypothesis.

Parasites can manipulate the behavior of host organisms, as in that of the parasite known as a lancet fluke (Dicrocoelium dendriticum) that forces an ant to attach to the tips of grass blades, the easier to be eaten. The fluke needs to get into the entrails of any animal to complete its life cycle.

Deep within the Brazilian jungle lives another parasite attacking ants in the rainforest, infecting them with a fungus where spores collect on them. The spores use enzymes to get inside the insect's body, and within a week, release chemicals that cause the ant to wander off and bite onto some sort of vegetation, moments before it dies. (Researchers found that one infected zombie ant had bitten the neck of one of its dead fellows, mistaking it for a leaf.) After that, the fungus slowly sprouts from the ant's head and grows a pod of spores, which are released into the jungle after dark to begin the cycle again.

Studies also reveal that some of the fungi produce spores that rest on the ground, slowly growing a secondary spore, which juts upright from the forest floor, so it can attach itself to ants as they walk by, thus having a second chance to procreate their species. Scientists have found six more species of the fungus that infect ants, taking over their bodies and eventually killing them in a place that is just right for the organism to grow inside them. These parasites are so destructive they can wipe out entire colonies and leave enormous ant graveyards.

Records of this phenomenon were made as far back in history as 1859 by Alfred Russel Wallace, a naturalist who found two specimens in Sulawesi in Indonesia, and collected specimens while in the Amazon to bring back to London. But he lost them when his ship caught fire and sank on its return voyage.

David Hughes from Penn State University commented on the fungus after working in the Atlantic rainforest in Minas Gerais, southeastern Brazil. Hughes says:

> It's a fabulously complex organism. There is a beauty to the whole thing, whether it is the chemicals at work that take over the ant, or the spores which try one strategy and then another to find a host on the forest floor.

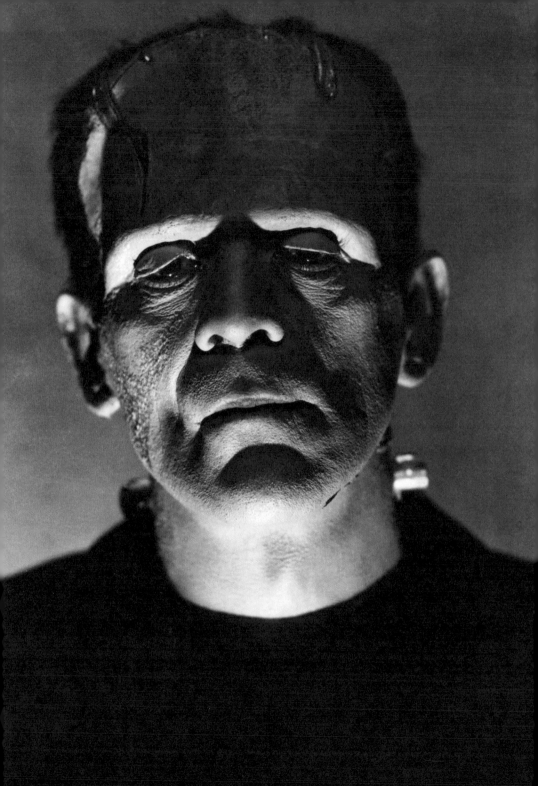

Boris Karloff's **FRANKENSTEIN, Universal Pictures, (1931).**
Photo courtesy of public commons.

Mary Shelley's
Frankenstein

Humans as a species have almost instinctively had a great fear of the dead returning. We fear that the dead want revenge on those who still live, out of a hideous and jealous rage. Archeologists often discover bricks inserted into the mouths of the dead at many digs, and in some cultures the word *maschalismos* (meaning "to mutilate") is performed. This ritual comes from the Greek and Roman practice of physically rendering the dead incapable of rising/returning or haunting the living in undead form, and can be as simple as removing organs or cutting off the feet. The Chinese bound the body in the coffin itself. The Nordic people moved a body from the home feet first to confuse the corpse, and this ritual continued into the 20th century in America—to avoid having the dead beckon the family to join them. This is also why we fasten coffins shut when there is no real need to do so.

However, humanity has also been drawn to that which it fears, our Pandora's Box if you will, and do just the opposite to test fate as in the fictional story *Frankenstein: The Modern Prometheus*, written by Mary Shelley, about a massive man produced by a depraved doctor in a lengthy, yet successful, scientific experiment. Originally published in France in 1823, Mary had traveled the region in which the story takes place, where the topics of galvanism and occult subjects were themes of conversation among her group of companions, particularly her future husband, Percy Shelley; the libertine poet, Lord Byron; and John Polidori. It was during one of these dark and gloomy gatherings that they all decided to have a competition to see who could write the best horror story. Mary had a dream about a scientist who had created life and was horrified by what he had done, thus she created one of the oldest Gothic horror stories.

Frankenstein is infused with some elements of the Gothic novel and one of the earliest stories one might consider science fiction. The story is based off of Giovanni Aldini's electrical experiments on both dead and living animals, as well as a few others we will find out about, all the inspiration behind Dr. Frankenstein. The tale was also a warning against the lack of morality in man playing God with science during the period of the Industrial Revolution, as one can tell by its subtitle, *The Modern Prometheus*. The monster refers to himself speaking to Dr. Frankenstein as "the Adam of your labors," and also as "your fallen angel." The monster called Frankenstein actually had no given name in the original story. As horrific as creating a living person from dead body parts might be in fiction, it pales in comparison to the deeds committed by the real mad scientists Mary Shelly had read about.

Johann Konrad Dippel

Johann Konrad Dippel was a 1670s alchemist who was trying to find ways to extend life. He lived in the real castle of Frankenstein in Darmstadt, Germany. Similar to the black-and-white horror films that came from Hollywood decades later, once the villagers discovered that corpses from the Frankenstein cemetery began to disappear, he was chased out of town. History shows he was reputed to have done other experiments, like boiling the flesh off corpses and animals to create elixirs. He was an ardent vivisectionist, that is to say, he loved to operate on live subjects.

Giovanni Aldini

Giovanni Aldini was the nephew of Luigi Galvani, the man who discovered the concept of galvanism, a method of stimulating muscles with electric current, and who experimented with said currents on frogs' legs. Aldini took this experiment to the next level, conducting his own experiments on corpses.

Italian scientist Giovanni Aldini conducted an experiment on the fresh corpse of George Forster, the subject of a death sentence. Forster was hanged on January 18, 1803, shortly before which he made a full confession to the murder of his wife and child by drowning them in Paddington Canal, London.

He was sentenced not only to death, but also to dissection right after. This was done to provide doc-tors with corpses upon which to examine and experiment, and also to ensure that the condemned could not rise at Judgment Day, their bodies having been dissected and disposed of. A BBC documentary called REAL HORROR: FRANKENSTEIN RISES details the trial and proceedings afterward.

During my research on this case, an old record of executions called *The Newgate Calendar* mentions there was no reason to believe Forster was alive:

> Some of the uninformed bystanders thought that the wretched man was on the eve of being restored to life. This, however, was impossible, as several of his friends, who were under the scaffold, had violently pulled his legs, in order to put a more speedy termination to his sufferings. The experiment, in fact, was of a better use and tendency. Its object was to show the excitability of the human frame when this animal electricity was duly applied. In cases of drowning or suffocation it promised to be of the utmost use, by reviving the action of the lungs, and thereby rekindling the expiring spark of vitality. In cases of apoplexy, or disorders of the head, it offered also most encouraging prospects for the benefit of mankind.

The hanged man was void of blood and his spinal cord severed after the execution. It was then reported that:

> On the first application
> of the process to the face,
> the jaws of the deceased
> criminal began to quiver,
> and the adjoining muscles
> were horribly contorted,
> and one eye was actually
> opened. In the subsequent
> part of the process the
> right hand was raised and
> clenched, and the legs and
> thighs were set in motion.

Several of those present believed that Forster was being brought back to life, and one man, Mr. Pass, of the Surgeons' Company, was so shocked that he died shortly after leaving.

Andrew Ure

Andrew Ure, a Scottish doctor, was famous for many experiments on fresh corpses. At one time he gathered a group of people and required them to observe his newest finding. Andrew took the body of a freshly hung murderer, named Matthew Clydesdale, and to the growing horror of his audience, he proceeded to insert metal conducting rods to the man's rectum, whereby the dead man began to flinch and flail about. Still more attachments with electric current running through it were applied to the dead man's face, and when the scientist finished his efforts, he was able to make it move, including the opening of his left eye.

The first experiment involved an incision in the nape of the neck. Part of the vertebra was removed. An incision was then made in the left hip. Then a cut was made in the heel. Two rods connected to a battery were placed in the neck and hip, which caused great, uncontrollable convulsions. The second rod was then placed into the heel, whereby the left leg kicked with such force, that it nearly knocked over an assistant. The 2nd experiment made the diaphragm of Clydesdale's chest rise and lower, as if he were breathing.

Ure claimed that, by stimulating the phrenic nerve, life could be restored in cases of suffocation, drowning, or hanging. He wrote about the experiment in 1819:

> Every muscle of the body
> was immediately agitated
> with convulsive movements
> resembling a violent
> shuddering from cold....
> On moving the second
> rod from hip to heel, the
> knee being previously
> bent, the leg was thrown
> out with such violence as
> nearly to overturn one
> of the assistants, who in
> vain tried to prevent its
> extension. The body was
> also made to perform the
> movements of breathing
> by stimulating the phrenic
> nerve and the diaphragm.

When the supraorbital nerve was excited, every muscle in his countenance was simultaneously thrown into fearful action; rage, horror, despair, anguish, and ghastly smiles, united their hideous expressions in the murderer's face, surpassing far the wildest representations of Fuseli or a Kean. At this period several of the spectators were forced to leave the apartment from terror or sickness, and one gentleman fainted.

Vladimir Demikhov

Vladimir Demikhov was a pioneer in organ transplantation, who did many transplants in animals. He was most notoriously known for creating what people described as a "cruel monstrosity" in 1954. He surgically attached the head, shoulders, and front legs of a puppy onto a mature dog. Over the next fifteen years, he created almost two dozen such animal reconstructions, but with no long-term success, as most died due to tissue rejection or infections within a month.

Nazis, the CIA, and Zombie Super Soldiers

If you think *Call of Duty Black Ops* video game with the zombie section is only the fantasy of people watching too many movies and making a quick buck off of fans, think again. Nazis actually worked very hard on the science of zombies in order to create the perfect super soldier, a stupefied populace who would not fight back, mind-altering chemicals, and transplantations similar to those described previously.

In the book *Hitler, Zombich, und die Häagan-Dazs*, Mark Walker and German author Michael Schaaf describe the efforts of Nazi scientists to create a zombie army to be used against allied forces in Europe. Known as "the ghoul research effort," conducted by the Kaiser Wilhelm Institute and led by the physicist Werner Heisenberg, along with a military team under the scientific leadership of Professor Kurt Diebner, the program was originally funded through the German Post Office, under the Reich Research Council.

Dr. Paul Harteck helped to develop the zombie virus invented by Dr. Erich Bagge, in 1942, also known as a synapse sluice, but usually referred to as the "Harteck Virus." Dr. Harteck, in particular, had worked with Dr. Fritz Houtermans on the problem of active brain cell reanimation using corpses. Harteck led a team at Hamburg in his at-

48

tempt to create a zombie operated U-boat, and later, Dr. Otto Haxel took over scientific leadership of the Oberkommando der Marine ghoul project. In 1944, Harteck gained Nazi funding for industrial scale zombification of Jews. Orders were placed for production of Jew and gypsy corpses.

According to Walker and Schaaf, Heisenberg's team intended to build an undead army for Hitler. Heisenberg tried to identify the average cross section of brain cell release during his experiments in reanimation. In 1942, a reanimated chimpanzee was sustained by using two chimpanzees' brains separated by heavy water. However, Heisenberg failed in controlling the reanimation. Another heavy water zombie test reactor in Haigerloch was built in a cave and used cubes of brains suspended by chains, but this too failed to work.

Communist Russian scientists in the 1930s experimented with re-animating, reviving, and sustaining clinically dead animals, using severed dogs heads, as well as attaching multiple heads to single bodies in a March 1940 film of the reanimation experiment that was smuggled into Germany and shown to the Nazi Himmler. Soviet scientists also sent this film to the United States, showing their experiment using a device called the Autojektor in the black-and-white film: *EXPERIMENTS IN THE REVIVAL OF ORGANISM*. British scientist J.B.S. Haldane is in the film's introduction and narrates the film, which contains Russian text with English and Russian subtitles.

Haldane was a highly respected experimental biologist, most famous for research in genetics, physiology, blood oxygen levels, and the use of decompression chambers. The operations are credited to Doctor Sergei S. Bryukhonenko. The film depicts a series of medical experiments, such as a canine heart which is shown having four tubes attached, and a lung in a tray, operated by bellows, which then oxygenated the blood.

This primitive heart and lung machine, the autojektor, was composed of a pair of diaphragm pumps and a supply of oxygenated blood going to a dog's head. The head of the animal responded to material dipped in a strong scent and the sound of a hammer being banged near it.

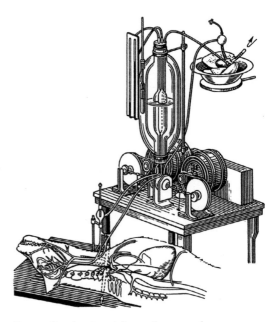

Patent for the Autojektor photograph.
Photo courtesy Library of Congress.

Another dog was brought to life from its clinical death once they drained all blood from it, left for ten minutes, and then connected to the heart-lung machine. After several minutes, they fibrillated the heart, and it resumed its normal rhythm. Once the dog's breathing resumed, the machine was removed and the animal continued living as normal. Bryukhonenko developed a new version of the autojektor for use on people, which can be seen today at the Museum of Cardiovascular Surgery at the Scientific Center of Cardiovascular Surgery in Russia. Metallica used part of the film in their ALL NIGHTMARE LONG video, in 2009. (If you are interested, I saw this clip in the public domain online, from the Prelinger Archives. Real video footage—ghastly stuff: http://archive.org/details/Experime1940, of "successful experiments in the resuscitation of life to dead animals (dogs), as conducted by Dr. S.S. Bryukhonenko at the Institute of Experimental Physiology and Therapy)

The original facts released to American scientists and detailed to the public in *Time Magazine*, Monday, November 22, 1943 say:

The autojector, a relatively simple machine, has a vessel (the "lung") in which blood is supplied with oxygen, a pump that circulates the oxygenated blood through the arteries, another pump that takes blood from the veins back to the "lung" for more oxygen. Two other dogs on which the experiment was

performed in 1939 (were still alive four years later). The autojector can also keep a dog's heart beating outside its body, has kept a decapitated dog's head alive for hours—the head cocked its ears at a noise and licked its chops when citric acid was smeared on them. But the machine is incapable of reviving a whole dog for more than about 15 minutes after its blood is drained—body cells then begin to disintegrate.

The CIA even sought to conduct investigations into creating zombies that would be the perfect assassins for quick covert operations, through the use of drugs, where victims would need to be totally void of any memories of their actions— perfect "fall guys." The United States Government used similar ideas to the Nazi's use of fluoride as a subtle experiment to make obedient servants to the cause, but found it had little to no major results for their mind control projects. However, its use has continued to this day in many countries' water treatment facilities. Recently, many scientists and workers at these places have objected to the use of fluoride in drinking water. It has no health benefits; this is propaganda by dentists who grew up on the indoctrination of our 1950s mentality that the government would never take actions to harm the public good. Although fluoride naturally occurs in water as calcium fluoride, it is toxic when it is added to water supplies in the form of fluorosilicic acid, a waste product of the phosphate fertilizer industry full of arsenic, lead, and radioactive materials, all widely used to fluoridate public water supplies.

Adverse effects of fluoride include hyperactivity, lowered IQ, Alzheimer's disease, and other forms of dementia, genetic mutations—and quite the opposite of the claims made by public health campaigns—a condition known as dental fluorosis. Early (pre-fluoridation) editions of the American Dental Association's (ADA) own professional journals were critical of the practice and even justified it through research, proving that instead of preventing cavities, fluoride merely delayed their appearance for a few years. This is why we get white or brown spots on the teeth, the result of weakened enamel! Large doses of this chemical interfere with basic vital functions; it severely inhibits enzyme activity, as well as oxygen use by cells, and accelerates the breakdown of our body's major structural proteins. This finding prompted 1,500 Environmental Protection Agency professionals to voice opposition to fluoridation in 1999, noting that there were many shocking aspects to fluoride as a hazard, including even very low levels of ingestion common to drinking water.

Modern Medical Zombies

It would seem that scientists at The Safar Center medical labs in Pittsburgh, Pennsylvania, are picking up right where the grizzly animal experiments left off sixty years ago.

Currently, medical experiments are being conducted on dogs; yet again, over resuscitation bears a frightening similarity to The Safar Center for Resuscitation Research defends their study, citing the "benefits of prolonging death" for saving the living. The center calls it "resuscitation medicine," with programs studying traumatic brain injury, cardiopulmonary arrest, hemorrhagic shock, and emergency resuscitation.

Safar was reported by *The New York Times* writer Stephen Mihm, who wrote an article entitled "Zombie Dogs," published December 11, 2005.

> Just as dogs preceded
> humans in making the
> first risky voyages into
> space, a new generation
> of canines has now made
> an equally path-breaking
> trip—from life to death
> and back again....Doctors
> at the Safar Center for
> Resuscitation Research at
> the University of Pittsburgh
> managed to plunge several
> dogs into a state of total,
> clinical death before
> bringing them back to the
> land of the living. The feat,
> the researchers say, points

the way toward a time when human beings will make a similar trip, not as a matter of ghoulish curiosity but as a means of preserving life in the face of otherwise fatal injuries.

In the experiments, The Safar Center team flushed the live dogs' bodies of blood and replaced it with a solution of saline, oxygen, and glucose. The dogs almost immediately went into cardiac arrest and died. Patrick Kochanek, the director, prefers to call this process a state of suspended animation. After waiting three hours, the steps were reversed and the saline solution drained, the blood replaced, and the dogs' hearts were restarted with a small electric shock. A few of them suffered permanent damage, but overall, the experiment was a success.

Normally, doctors cannot save patients with huge amounts of blood loss or tissue damage that a soldier might sustain. The Safar Center's next step is to use human patients who have suffered cardiac arrest due to massive blood loss. This was shown in the 1992 film UNIVERSAL SOLDIER with Jean-Claude Van Damme and Dolph Lundgren. UNIVERSAL SOLDIER was about a secret group of programmed reanimated soldiers who had died in Vietnam and were brought back in the year 1992 to be used by the government for covert missions.

Dr. Steven Schlozman is an Assistant Professor at Harvard Medical School and a psychologist at Massachusetts General. He has lectured on neurobiology, with his explanations involving the science behind zombie movies—specifically, George Romero's NIGHT OF THE LIVING DEAD. In a lab dedicated to reanimation research, scientists have been able to re-grow the brains of comatose head trauma patients until they woke up and walked around again. Reanimating a person does seem to be problematic: This method can cause the brain to die off, since it has not yet been perfected.

This chilling aspect of modern reanimation is hardly the stuff of Tim Burton's FRANKENWEENIE. Maybe, just maybe, RESIDENT EVIL isn't so far from our distant future at all.

CHAPTER THREE

The Zombies of Fiction and Film

The figure of the zombie has made its presence known, lurking back into our minds from time to time, often when we are most fearful of real issues in the world. Issues of everything from race, the questioning of religion's end of times, xenophobia, disease, and mass consumerism is under the thin guise of fiction when we seek to understand the morality contained in these horror stories. Recall, in the beginning of this book, I mentioned *SHAUN OF THE DEAD* being a clear reenactment of the mindless drones we notice plodding through their daily existence.

Tumultuous times seem to be the catalyst for the zombie craze. If we look back in history to when *NIGHT OF THE LIVING DEAD* came out in 1968, George Romero's zombie film reached its peak. It became an international sensation. People then, as they are now, were scared of the future, with the Vietnam War and racism a huge issue at the time. Zombies, on the other hand, didn't care about who they devoured in their path, just that they could.

DAWN OF THE DEAD movie poster.
George Romero (1979).

Max Brooks, author of *The Zombie Survivors Guide*, echoes my thoughts when he says:

Romero's work was total
social commentary,
from that tradition of
Rod Serling and Gene
Roddenberry where you
can't talk about the real
problem directly.

THE NIGHT OF THE LIVING DEAD sequels were just as compelling in their commentary of the world: DAWN OF THE DEAD, as a satire on consumerism; DAY OF THE DEAD, as a study of the conflict between science and the military, and LAND OF THE DEAD, as an examination of d class conflict.

Braaaaains! Zombie Anthology (2012). Photo courtesy Dark Moon Press.

Today, we live with the fear of our deaths caused by terrorism, and we can point to the fact that there are ongoing fears of national debt all over the world. Movies such as *28 DAYS LATER* and a remake of *DAWN OF THE DEAD* are good examples; we need look no further to see how social conditions affect our interests in fantasy escapism than the simple fact that *THE WALKING DEAD* television show has ratings of more than ten million viewers each week.

Brooks says, "It's not the zombies that are cyclical, it's the anxiety." Dr. Robert Thompson, director of the Bleier Center for Television and Popular Culture at Syracuse, believes zombies can thrive in both good and bad times. He says:

The most important
variable is that they are
appropriate stories for
modern life. Right now
we really are in a rich
zombie period, but five
years from now, regardless
of the economy, there will
probably be many zombie
manifestations out there.
They keep rearing their
heads. Zombie and vampire
stories are like real zombies
and vampires. They keep
coming back.

Back in 1929, *Time* magazine claimed that the novel *The Magic Island*, by William Seabrook, "introduced 'zombi' into US speech." The prototype for early zombie movies was *WHITE ZOMBIE* (1932), where director Victor Halperin filmed the horror master Bela Lu-

WHITE ZOMBIE movie poster. United Artists (1932).

Still from the movie *WHITE ZOMBIE*. United Artists (1932).

gosi in a classic film that utilized the Voodoo zombie theme used in *THE MAGIC ISLAND*. Like that book, the film took a great deal of its story elements directly from the Haitian zombie stories (discussed in Chapter Two). *WHITE ZOMBIE* depicted Lugosi's character as a rich Haitian businessman who wanted to steal away a woman by turning her husband into a zombie.

Other zombie movies of the '30s and '40s followed the Haitian theme, such as *THE VOODOO MAN* (1944) and *I WALKED WITH A ZOMBIE* (1943), as did *REVOLT OF THE ZOMBIES* (1936) and *ZOMBIES ON BROADWAY* (1945), but with varying geographic location. *REVOLT OF THE ZOMBIES* is in the public domain, and can be copied or distributed without regard to copyright law. This horror

film was directed and produced by the Halperin Brothers starring Dean Jagger and Dorothy Stone. Originally created as a loose sequel to Victor Halperin's moderately successful *WHITE ZOMBIE*, actor Bela Lugosi's eyes appear in the film when "zombifying-powers are

KING OF THE ZOMBIES (1941). Horror Mantan Moreland.

Lucio Fulci's *Zombie*.

used" taken from *White Zombie*. The storyline: During World War I, a chaplain of a French colonial regiment is condemned to life imprisonment due to the fact that he possessed the power to turn men into zombies. While incarcerated, the priest prepares to burn a paper containing the location of his formula. Colonel Mazovia kills the chaplain and takes the remains of the paper. After the war, an expedition of representatives from the Allied countries with colonial interests, are sent to Cambodia in order to locate and destroy forever the so-called "Secret of the Zombies."

In the 1950s and 1960s, zombies began to adopt a more sinister air. Films that depicted zombies as mindless cannibals that were forced to maintain their existence by actually consuming the flesh of people began in movies such as *I Eat Your Skin* (1961) and *The Plague of the Zombies* (1965).

George Romero

George Andrew Romero was born February 4, 1940, and has been hailed as the godfather of all modern zombies.

Zombies were featured prominently back in horror comics in the early 1950s. A company called EC Comics eventually gave birth to the television show *Tales from the Crypt*, which featured more than a few scary episodes with zombies.

Romero was reported as having said the classic comic-books were an influence. The comics incorporated adaptations of Lovecraft's stories, which included "In the Vault," and the previously mentioned "Reanimator."

After his graduation in 1960 from Pittsburgh's Carnegie Mellon University, Romero began his career shooting short films and commercials. Along with nine friends, he formed Image Ten Productions in the late 1960s, and produced *Night*

57

From the film, *Night of the Living Dead*. George Romero (1968).

of the Living Dead (1968). The movie, the first one ever directed by Romero, was co-written with John A. Russo. This gruesome horror film was destined to become a cult classic involving a zombie apocalypse.

In 1978, Romero returned to the zombie genre with *Dawn of the Dead* (released in 1978). On a budget of a mere half million dollars, the film's return was over $55 million worldwide and was named one of the top cult films by *Entertainment Weekly* in the year 2003. The filmmaker updated his original screenplay and then produced the remake of *Night of the Living Dead*, directed by Tom Savini in 1990. A year later, in 1991, Romero had a cameo appearance in *The Silence of the Lambs*, where he

played the part of one of Hannibal Lecter's jailers.

In 1998, he directed the live-action commercial promoting the video game *Resident Evil*, fighting with a horde of zombies; however, a contract dispute prevented the commercial from being shown outside of Japan. Universal Studios produced and released a remake of *Dawn of the Dead* in 2004, though Romero was not involved. He eventually filmed a fourth film in the set entitled *Land of the Dead*. The movie's working title was *Dead Reckoning*, the name of the battle wagon taken by the character played by John Leguizamo in the film. It was released in the summer of 2005 by Universal Pictures, the same company that released the

DAWN OF THE DEAD remake. Both are must-see films, if you haven't already watched them!

Romero wrote and directed GEORGE A. ROMERO'S DIARY OF THE DEAD, which follows a group of college students making a horror movie in the woods, when they stumble on a real zombie uprising. This movie was independently financed and the first one of its type that the producer had filmed in many years.

In 2008, Romero's newest zombie film, SURVIVAL OF THE DEAD, was originally meant to be a direct sequel to DIARY OF THE DEAD, but this follow up had a new cast of characters.

As of this writing, the last work where Romero appears is in the downloadable map expansion pack called Escalation in the video game Call of Duty: Black Ops, featured alongside actors Sarah Michelle Gellar, Danny Trejo, and Robert Englund. At the end of it, he himself appears as a zombie! Romero says he has plans for two more DEAD movies, both linked to DIARY OF THE DEAD.

The Crazies

(1973)

THE CRAZIES, also known as CODE NAME: TRIXIE, was a 1973 sci-fi horror and action film about an accidental release of a military biological weapon upon the people of the small American town of Evans City, Pennsylvania. Written and directed by George A. Romero, the film depicts civilians who attempt to stay alive during the course of the movie, and fight both zombies and soldiers alike. Will McMillan plays the starring role as a firefighter, and his girlfriend, Lane Caroll, plays Judy, the nurse. Harold Wayne Jones plays Clank, also a firefighter. Both male characters served in Vietnam.

Heavily armed US troops clad in white hazmat suits and gas masks arrive in the city, led by Major Ryder (Harry Spillman), who takes over the doctor's office. It is revealed that an Army plane carrying an untested bioweapon recently crash-landed in the hills near the town, infecting the water supply with a top-secret virus code named Trixie, either killing victims or causing them to become homicidal.

The authorities in Washington decide to send out airborne bombers, armed with nuclear weapons, to destroy the infected town, if necessary. The Army blocks off the town and starts shooting anyone who tries to escape. At this point of the movie, nearly all of the townspeople have been infected, including Clank, who stays behind and kills several soldiers before he is shot in the head. Judy gets killed and the furious and frightened David surrenders to the government.

Dr. Watts finally develops a cure, but he is mistaken for one of the infected as he attempts to deliver the vaccine. He is forced into a quarantined area by soldiers. The test tubes containing the vaccine are then shattered when the doctor falls to his death, pushed down a flight of stairs by a mad horde of the infected.

Wes Craven's
The Serpent and the Rainbow
(1988)

Directed by Wes Craven and staring Bill Pullman, THE SERPENT AND THE RAINBOW (1988) is a heavily fictionalized account of Wade Davis' book. The film depicts ethnobotanist Wade Davis recounting his experiences in Haiti, investigating the story of Clairvius Narcisse (see Chapter Two on the science of zombies), who was allegedly poisoned and buried alive, only to return later from the grave as a zombie.

Anthropologist Dennis Alan, while visiting the Amazon jungle, receives a potion connecting him to his protective totem (a jaguar) through a series of spiritual visions, and is led by a jaguar from the rainforest itself. After his return to Boston, he is sent to Haiti by a pharmaceutical corporation looking to investigate a drug used by the Haitians as an anesthetic.

Alan searches throughout Haiti to find the drug, assisted by Dr. Marielle, and draws the attention of the authorities. The commander of the Tonton Macoute, the Haitian paramilitary force, warns Alan to leave Haiti. Alan refuses, and continues to investigate until he meets a local witch doctor, Mozart, who can produce the drug he seeks. Alan eventually returns to Boston to study the components and effects of the drug. Alan receives a warning that he faces imminent death. He returns to Haiti, where he is buried alive. Having emerged from the grave, he returns to the Tonton Macoute headquarters looking for Marielle. Alan and his jaguar spirit defeat Captain Dargent Peytraud, commander of the Tonton Macoute goon squad. Afterwards, Marielle says, "The nightmare is over."

STAY ALIVE!

Watch out for the witch doctor – he may put a spell on you and make you work his plantation fields! The military and police are crooked and not to be trusted, so if you travel to the islands, bring your own magic charms of protection!

Actually, this movie is based more on the original traditional zombie more than any other for many years to come, and was inspired by the nonfiction book exploring the truth behind the legends.

Resident Evil

(1998)

RESIDENT EVIL, known as *BIOHAZARD* in Japan, is a media franchise owned by the video game company Capcom. It started as a survival horror game series in 1996. Since then, the *RESIDENT EVIL* media franchise has been expanded to comic books, novels and novelizations, films, and collectibles. In total, five live-action films were all written and produced by Paul W.S. Anderson. The film's main hero is Alice, an infected yet immune agent who leads the fight against the evil Umbrella Corporation. The film series has made over $600 million worldwide. This series holds the record for the "Most Live-Action Film Adaptations of a Video game" in 2012 by the *Guinness World Records: Gamer's Edition*. In 1997, Marvel Comics published a comic based on the original *RESIDENT EVIL*, as a promotional giveaway alongside the original PlayStation game.

STAY ALIVE!

Beware your ex-lovers; they may not be who you think they are! And holographic children may be bribed just as easily as real children, but this one in *RESIDENT EVIL* was more deadly than a two-year-old on a sugar high with a machine gun!

To this day, this is the highest respected game-to-film movie on zombies that fans could hope for. It has spurred multiple movies, games, and merchandise, as well as "zombie walks" and costumes—more than any other film on zombies!

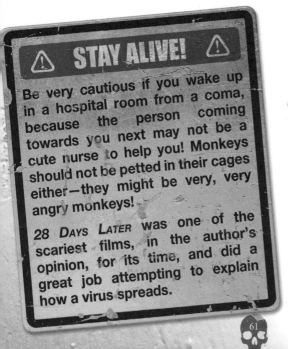

STAY ALIVE!

Be very cautious if you wake up in a hospital room from a coma, because the person coming towards you next may not be a cute nurse to help you! Monkeys should not be petted in their cages either—they might be very, very angry monkeys!

28 DAYS LATER was one of the scariest films, in the author's opinion, for its time, and did a great job attempting to explain how a virus spreads.

28 Days Later

(2002)

This British horror film was directed by Danny Boyle and was a huge commercial success. It was followed by a 2007 sequel, *28 WEEKS LATER*, a graphic novel titled *28 DAYS LATER: THE AFTERMATH*, which expands on the timeline of the outbreak, and a 2009 comic book series. The screenplay was written by Alex Garland, and the film stars Cillian Murphy, Naomie Harris, Brendan Gleeson, Megan Burns, and Christopher Eccleston. The film depicts the breakdown of society following the accidental release of a highly contagious virus called "rage," and follows four characters who manage to survive.

A flashback begins with animal liberation activists who break into a laboratory in Cambridge and are caught by a scientist while trying to free some chimpanzees being used for medical research. Despite the warnings of the scientists, the activists open the cages and release the chimpanzees. A chimp attacks one of the activists and immediately infects her. She, in turn, infects the other members of the group. Twenty-eight days later, a bicycle courier named Jim, played by actor Cillian Murphy, awakens from a coma in a deserted hospital. Bewildered by an abandoned London, he is soon chased through the streets by psychotic people before being rescued by two survivors, Selena (Naomie Harris) and Mark (Noah Huntley), who kill the zombies chasing him. After they reach safety, they explain to him that the pandemic has spread from London to Paris and New York City. They discover two more survivors, Frank (Brendan Gleeson) and his teenage daughter, Hannah (Megan Burns), holed up in a block of flats, and they all stay together for the rest of the night.

Frank plays them a pre-recorded radio broadcast transmitted by an Army blockade near Manchester, that claims to have "the answer to infection" and telling survivors to try to reach them. The survivors decide to leave the city to search for the military. When the four reach the deserted blockade, Frank is infected when a drop of blood from a dead body falls into his eye. As he succumbs, he is killed by the soldiers, who take the rest of the group to a fortified mansion. Jim, however, discovers that a commander, thinking to defeat the infected, is planning to wait them out and starve them to death, and that the radio broadcast was made to attract female survivors in order for them to become sex slaves—to rebuild the population with his men. Jim attempts to escape with Selena and Hannah, and they notice a jet flying high overhead, as they drive away after a vicious fight with the platoon. Jim is shot, so Selena and Hannah rush him into a deserted hospital where Selena manages to save him. Twenty-eight days later, Jim is shown waking up in recovery again, this time at a remote cottage. As another fighter jet flies overhead, infected people are shown dying of starvation along a road. The jet flies past the survivors, and their distress sign. As it flies away, Selena asks, "Do you think he saw us this time?"

The film originally had several alternative endings (most of which are included as DVD extras), all of which conclude with Jim dying.

On the DVD commentary, it is explained that this was the original ending of the film's first cut, which was tested with preview audiences. Ultimately, it was rejected for seeming too bleak, yet creators felt Jim waking in the hospital and ending there would have brought the movie full circle, as he starts and finishes the story in bed in a deserted hospital.

Resident Evil

(2002)

The first in the series of films starring Milla Jovovich, Michelle Rodriguez, Eric Mabius, and James Purefoy, borrows many elements from the video games *Resident Evil* and *Resident Evil 2*. The film follows Alice and a band of Umbrella Corporation commandos as they attempt to contain the outbreak of the T-Virus in one of the secret underground mega complexes, called the Hive. A computer holographic projected young girl first tries to kill all of the commandos, but Alice stops it in time and uses it in her own escape.

STAY ALIVE!

Don't pet a burning dog—or, in this case, a mutated zombie dog.

This movie followed the mega successful original; and at the end, it has Alice standing, with a shotgun and a newspaper blowing by with the headline: "The Dead Walk!" a tribute to Romero's works.

Alice slowly regains her memories, and finds she is a secret agent, and that her "husband" Spence is also an agent and not truly married to her. He becomes infected at the end of the movie onboard a train as the remainder of the group fights to freedom. The Umbrella Corporation commandos seize both of them and separate them. Alice wakes in a hospital bed and slowly makes her way to the city street, only to find a wrecked, silent city.

Dawn of the Dead

(2004)

This remake of George A. Romero's 1978 film was my very first zombie movie—from then on, I was hooked! It stars Sarah Polley, Ving Rhames, and Jake Weber. The film is about a handful of human survivors who try to make a new life in a Wisconsin shopping mall surrounded by swarms of zombies. Released by Universal Pictures, there were cameos from original *LIVING DEAD* cast members Ken Foree, Scott Reiniger, and Tom Savini.

STAY ALIVE!

Rosie and other celebrities look out! A survivor at the gun store might have you in his sights!

DAWN OF THE DEAD grossed $102,356,381 worldwide and is still one of the most popular zombie films of all time.

The nurse, Ana (Sarah Polley), returns to her suburban neighborhood and to her husband, Luis (Louis Ferreira). In the morning, Vivian, their neighbor's daughter, enters their bedroom and kills Luis, who almost immediately comes back as a zombie and attacks Ana. She flees in her car, but eventually crashes. A montage of news depicts zombies overwhelming people all around the world. Upon coming around from the blow to the head, Ana meets police sergeant and former marine Kenneth Hall (Ving Rhames), as well as a motley group of survivors. The group breaks into a nearby mall where security guards make them surrender their weapons in exchange for shelter. The group eventually makes it to the roof of the mall where they see another survivor, Andy (Bruce Bohne)—my favorite character, but sadly, he didn't have much of a role—who is stranded alone in his gun store across the parking lot. The next day, a delivery truck carrying more survivors is rescued by the mall defenders, including a severely bloated woman who cannot walk; she is wheeled inside via wheelbarrow. Soon after, she dies only to come back as a zombie; she tries to bite the people in the group, but is killed, and the group realizes now how the disease is spread.

We discover that a pregnant group member has been bitten in an attack by one of the zombies; she dies shortly after going into labor, coming back as a zombie herself—as does the infant. When an older lady, Norma, goes to check on them, she discovers this horrifying little family. The father of the family has tied his zombie

Zombie walk Vancouver (2010). *Photo courtesy David Defreo.*

girlfriend down and is protecting her and the child. He has lost his mind and shouts at Norma, then shoots her to death, but not before she returns fire, killing him and his zombie girlfriend. The rest of the group arrives to find a zombie baby, and they kill it. The survivors decide to make a run for the Milwaukee marina, and use a group member's yacht to make a break for an island in Lake Michigan. They begin reinforcing two buses from the parking garage to escape.

Andy (from the gun shop across the street) is dying from lack of food, so the group sends in both food and a walkie-talkie via a dog named Chips. As Andy calls for Chips, one of the zombies in the streets gets in through the door of the store before he can close it. Another character down. Nicole, another group member, takes a delivery truck and crashes it into the gun store, where she is attacked by a now-zombie Andy. A portion of the group makes a run for the gun store, killing Andy, saving Nicole. They rapidly load up on guns and ammunition and head back to the mall through the sewers.

Eventually, everyone piles into the reinforced buses, and on their way through the city, they are overrun by hordes of zombies in the streets. Glen loses control of his chainsaw, killing himself and Monica; the driver loses control of the bus. (The special effects are very well done when the chainsaw cuts Glen and Monica and blood splatters on the windshield.) They take the remaining bus to the marina, where a bitten C.J. blows up the bus so that the rest of the group can escape the swarm of zombies that are closing in on them. By this time Ana, Kenneth, Nicole, Terry, and Chips the dog are the only survivors.

A camcorder left on the boat shows the group running out of supplies before they arrive at the island. They are attacked by a group of zombies as they arrive, and the movie ends as we see dozens of zombies chasing them through the lens of the dropped camcorder, leaving us to speculate their fate.

Shaun of the Dead

(2004)

SHAUN OF THE DEAD was a critical and commercial success in the UK and the US. This is a 2004 British zombie comedy directed and co-written by Edgar Wright, and co-written and starring Simon Pegg. Pegg plays the main character, Shaun—a man attempting to makes sense of his (former) and current mess of a life: He deals with his girlfriend, his mother, and stepfather, all while attempting to cope with a zombie apocalypse!

This is one of my favorite zombie films, as it not only finds humor in odd moments, but the very beginning makes a strong case for how the non-zombie city inhabitants act as mindless as they later are as zombies.

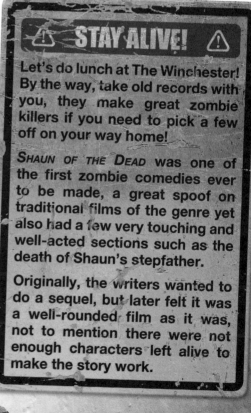

STAY ALIVE!

Let's do lunch at The Winchester! By the way, take old records with you, they make great zombie killers if you need to pick a few off on your way home!

SHAUN OF THE DEAD was one of the first zombie comedies ever to be made, a great spoof on traditional films of the genre yet also had a few very touching and well-acted sections such as the death of Shaun's stepfather.

Originally, the writers wanted to do a sequel, but later felt it was a well-rounded film as it was, not to mention there were not enough characters left alive to make the story work.

65

The movie begins with Shaun and Liz, his girlfriend, sitting in a local pub known as the Winchester Tavern, which is named for the rifle which hangs above the bar.

Liz wants them to spend more time away from Shaun's immature roommate, Ed, who crashed at Shaun's place five years ago and never moved out. Shaun promises her that things will be different, and that he'll book them a table at a fancy restaurant for their anniversary.

The next day, while at work at an electronics store, Shaun's step-father, Phillip, stops by to see him and he reminds Shaun that it's time for his bi-monthly visit. He asks him to bring the flowers to his mother that Shaun forgot on Mother's Day. Later, Shaun tries to get a last-minute reservation, but the restaurant is full. Liz calls and Shaun admits that he forgot to make the reservations. He suggests that they go to the Winchester but an exasperated Liz hangs up on him. In order to make it up to her, Shaun takes the flowers he bought for his mom with him, but he forgets the tag, which says "For a Wonderful Mom."

Liz is fed up with him and dumps him. Shaun walks through the rain to the Winchester, where he drowns his sorrows in beer, crying to Ed who tries to cheer him up. Ed and Shaun leave, and in a drunken stupor, make fun of a staggering figure down the street, who is actually a zombie. Back at their apartment, Shaun's other roommate is yelling at them for being losers and that he is trying to sleep. When asked about his bloodied hand, Pete answers that he was bitten by what he thought was a mugger. Pete goes to bed, and Ed says to Shaun, "The next time I see him, he's dead."

Shaun decides to turn his life around by getting his ex-girlfriend Liz to take him back.

The next morning, Shaun is half asleep and heads out to the convenience store, and doesn't notice the zombies around him or other signs, like bloody handprints. Back at the apartment, the television is showing reports about sickness spreading throughout the city, but Shaun doesn't pay any attention, as he is interrupted by Ed, who tells him that there's a girl in the back yard. When they go outside, a zombie girl lunges at Shaun, and he pushes her backwards. She falls, impaling herself on a pipe sticking out of the ground. More zombies come into the backyard, and Ed and Shaun run inside. When they try to call for help, they discover lines are busy. Another zombie comes into their home, and Ed hits it in the head with an ashtray. The news reports drone on and the two friends finally understand they are in danger. They go outside in a weak attempt to kill the two other zombies by throwing things at them. Ed grabs an album and throws it at a zombie. They go into the tool shed and grab a cricket bat and shovel.

Shaun tries to call Liz, but the line is still busy. His mother calls and tells Shaun that some men tried to get into the house. Shaun is relieved to learn that she is unharmed, but not so happy to know that Phillip has been bitten.

Shaun and Ed immediately make plans to kill Phillip, and Shaun tells his mom that they are coming over. Ed yells to her, "We're coming to get you, Barbara!" (a nod to the classic line from NIGHT OF THE LIVING DEAD).

They run through several scenarios on how to rescue Liz and Barbara, and kill Phillip. Arriving at Shaun's mother's house, they get his mother and Philip outside. More zombies are in the driveway, and Phillip is attacked yet again. They jump in Philip's Jaguar and head to Liz's apartment. Shaun climbs up onto the balcony, and talks Liz and her friends, David and Dianne, into going to the Winchester. Phillip, by now deathly sick, apologizes to Shaun for being hard on him as a boy, saying he just wanted him to be strong and that he loves him. Then he dies, quickly changing into a zombie. The group flees the car, only to find that they are surrounded by zombies. They finally reach the Winchester, but the street outside is crawling with undead. To avoid them, they decide to pretend to be zombies.

That night, we find the group sitting in the dark, surviving on peanuts and drinking beer. The zombie bar owner attacks the group. Ed grabs the Winchester hanging over the bar and throws it to Shaun. He uses it to smashes the zombie's head through the jukebox glass. Outside the door, the zombies begin to break through the barricade. Barbara starts convulsing and dies. After a fight with his friends, Shaun fires the rifle and kills his mother. Soon, the bar is overrun by zombies, and one of them comes up from behind Ed and bites him. They run down into the cellar but can't get the door open—it appears that they are trapped. Shaun and Liz prepare to share one last cigarette; the flame from the lighter reveals a lever that opens the doors. They get to the street, and Ed tells them to go on without him. At that moment a convoy of soldiers arrives and blows away all the zombies.

Six months afterwards, back at Shaun's home, we see that zombies are on a television game show. Shaun tells Liz that he's going out to the tool shed for a few minutes, and once inside, we find the zombie Ed chained up playing a video game. Shaun sits down and joins in the game, as if nothing has ever changed. The screen goes black.

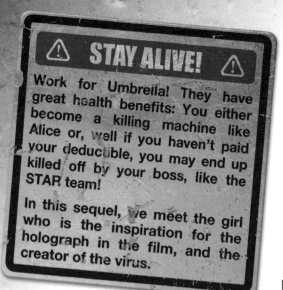

Resident Evil: Apocalypse

(2004)

The second installment in the *RESIDENT EVIL* film series picks up thirteen hours after the initial T-virus outbreak in The Hive. The infamous Umbrella Corporation sends a research team to the complex, but they are slaughtered by zombies.

Alice was recovered by Umbrella, and now discovers she has superhuman strength and speed. She wakes up in an empty hospital and wanders outside the facility to find the virus has infected the city, which by now is almost completely abandoned. An Umbrella supervisor seals the exit and orders his soldiers to fire over the crowd of people's heads, sending them back into the city. Carlos Olivera (Oded Fehr) of the Special Tactics and Rescue Squad (STARS) sends units to defend the city against the wave of zombies. Umbrella dispatches their Nemesis program, which is an enhanced zombie, also called the Pursuer or Chaser, to kill all remaining STARS operatives, as they plan to wipe out the city with a nuclear weapon. When Nemesis encounters members of STARS, they open fire.

Dr. Charles Ashford is the Umbrella scientist and creator of the T-virus. It was made in order to save his daughter from a disease, but it mutated into a bioweapon. Ashford refuses to leave during an evacuation of the city until his daughter is found. He asks Alice to rescue his daughter, Angela, and in exchange, he will take the group with him to safety. Nemesis shows up and kills Peyton Wells, one of the sergeants of the commandos. Alice saves the group of fighters and friends, and again finds Angela in the school. Dr. Ashford gives Alice the location of the extraction point at City Hall where the helicopter waits, but Major Cain commands Alice to fight Nemesis. Alice refuses, but when Dr. Ashford is shot, she has no choice. Defeating Nemesis, she realizes he is Spence, her "husband" when they were covert ops. Alice snaps him out of their control; they join forces and attack the Umbrella troops. Nemesis is killed when an attacking helicopter crashes on top of him. Alice and her group escape in another helicopter, and as Major Cain tries to jump on board with them, Alice throws him out of the helicopter. The Major is helpless as the infected move in for him, until a nuclear missile explodes over the city. The helicopter crashes deep in the mountains. Umbrella employees locate the helicopter's crash site and take Alice's body to another research facility, where she awakens in a water tank.

At first, she appears to have no memory, but eventually Alice fights her way out of the facility. Once outside, she finds that she is surrounded by more Umbrella guards at gunpoint. Jill, Carlos, and the others of her group, disguised as Umbrella employees, show the guards a written order placing Alice in their custody, and they drive away.

Dr. Isaacs, however, had allowed them to leave and then initiates "Program Alice." We see a close-up of her eye that has a flashing Umbrella logo embedded.

28 Weeks Later

(2007)

I remember this one very well, as I went to see it for my birthday that year. *28 WEEKS LATER* is a 2007 sequel to the 2002 film *28 DAYS LATER*, that opens with Don and his wife Alice in an English cottage sheltering from the Rage virus that has overtaken Great Britain. A boy starts shouting and banging on the door and Don opens it, letting the frightened child in, who tells them he managed to escape the zombies. The infected have followed him, and the survivors all try to flee. Don waits impatiently while Alice grabs the boy, but the zombies break in and trap Alice and the child. Alice screams for help, but Don slams the door shut and runs, leaving them to be killed. Don climbs out the window and escapes by boat just as Jacob finishes untying it. He kicks Jacob (one of the survivors hiding with the family) off, who dies, mangled by the boat's propeller.

The outbreak of infection has spread so swiftly that Britain is now under quarantine, but as the last of the infected are dying from starvation, the small band of people are waiting on the arrival of American-led NATO troops, the government's planning of repopulating, and finally 28 weeks later the outbreak is in high gear.

US Army Medical Officer Scarlet Levy watches as a plane lands in London; inside is Tammy and her younger brother, Andy. Two Americans, Doyle, a wisecracking sniper, and Flynn, a helicopter pilot, show up. After being checked at a medical facility, Andy and Tammy are moved into District 1, a safe modern part of the city via the helicopter pilots. The children are reunited with their father,

STAY ALIVE! Join the military! Go to foreign lands, meet people, and shoot the walking dead!

Filming locations for this movie included the famous Aldwych Underground Station, parts of London, and other places in the United Kingdom.

who turns out to be Don from the beginning of the movie. He explains that their mother was killed and that he could not save her. The next morning, the children sneak out to go home to collect a picture of their mother. At the house, they discover that their mother, Alice, is still alive and has been hiding in the attic. The reunited family is found by the army and they are brought back. Scarlet conducts a blood test on Alice that reveals she is infected, but is somehow immune to the virus; however, she is still a carrier.

Don finds out where his wife is, and confronting her, he begs for forgiveness and she accepts with a kiss—that rapidly infects him. Enraged, he kills her by sticking his thumbs into her eyes in his "rage" and breaks out of the area and into District 1, attacking the soldiers; a *code red* is sounded. Scarlet rescues Tammy and Andy and they flee, but Andy becomes separated in the pandemonium. Doyle is given the order to kill anybody and everybody, including the uninfected.

Andy escapes the crowd and is reunited with Tammy and Scarlet. Doyle joins the group of survivors and tells them he will take them out of the district safely. Flynn tells Doyle that in minutes the district will be firebombed, so they hide in a tunnel while most of London is destroyed by napalm, killing both zombies and civilians. Scarlet tells Doyle that the key to curing the infection lies with the kids. They plan an escape; a group of infected chase them. Flynn chops down the horde of zombies with his helicopter blades and flies away, telling Doyle to meet him alone at Wembley Stadium as the pick-up spot.

As army troops carrying flame-throwers battle zombies, Doyle tries to jump-start a car, but is killed when he is set on fire. Scarlet drives the car away but crashes it soon and flees with the kids through the London Underground. She makes her way through the dark with the night vision scope on Doyle's rifle. The group becomes separated, and as Scarlet tries to find the kids, she is attacked and brutally beaten to death by Don, who continues to attack and bite his own son, Andy. Tammy kills her infected father with the rifle. Andy, despite being bitten, remains without symptoms, just like his mother. The two escape and walk to Wembley Stadium, where they are picked up by Flynn, who takes them to France.

Twenty-eight days later, the remains of the helicopter are shown; in the final scene, zombies are heading towards the Eiffel Tower.

⚠ ZOMBIE FLASH! ⚠

23 Months Later (2013)

The director of 28 DAYS LATER and producer of the sequel, 28 WEEKS LATER, Danny Boyle is vaguely talking about the possibility of yet another outbreak of the Rage virus. Talking to MTV, Boyle hinted at the possibility of making a third installment to his 28 franchise.

Diary of the Dead

(2007)

⚠ STAY ALIVE! ⚠

The dead walk the Earth! It must be a sign the end is near—hurry, get a camera; let's make a movie!

Actually, this is one of the first zombie movies to be shot as if it were really happening to people, to be documented for anyone who survived to put the pieces back together to understand. One of Romero's best movies.

Independently produced by Romero, *Diary of the Dead* is the fifth film in Romero's *Dead* series, but not a direct sequel. It was distributed theatrically by Dimension Films and was released in 2007. A group of film students are making a horror film at the onset of a disease outbreak, and the characters (Debra, Mary, Gordo, Tracy, Tony, Jason, Eliot, Ridley, and Maxwell) then decide to record the epidemic in a documentary-style home movie. Debra, the story narrator, cannot contact her family, so the group uses an RV to try to make it to her house. When the fuel line of the RV breaks, they receive help from a deaf Amish man named Samuel. They hide in his barn, which is surrounded by zombies, while Tracy repairs the RV. Before Samuel can escape with them, he is bitten—but in defiance, he kills himself and the zombie biting him by impaling himself with a scythe through both of their heads (one of the most shocking scenes of the film).

By this time, the only way they can get any news is via the Internet from bloggers, which is important, as it seems to be the only form of communication available to the survivors. The group finally makes it to Debra's house, only to discover that her mother and brother are now zombies, and her father is being eaten. They escape the house, make a run for Ridley's mansion, and find it abandoned. (Ridley is one of the original members of the group who had left in the beginning, after the first attack.) Behind a bookcase is a panic room where Ridley has been hiding. He tells the group that his parents and the staff were all killed by zombies. He invites Debra and Tony to follow him outside to where the family and the servants are lying dead, but in truth, Ridley had just dumped them in the pool.

Ridley is going crazy, the others soon find, and he starts to hunt the group, beginning by killing Eliot, electrocuting him in a bathtub, and proceeding to attack Tracy and Jason at the RV—but Tracy knocks him out. She drives away, angry at Jason for filming what was happening instead of helping. The survivors decide to hold out in the panic room, except for Jason, who believes that it is not worth surviving in the zombie-infested world; he stays behind in order to continue filming the events for "whoever remains." Ridley returns and Jason distracts him long enough for Tracy to escape before Ridley bites him. Maxwell kills Ridley and Debra kills Jason. Debra decides to continue the video, and as they hide in the panic room from more zombies, Debra watches the last thing Jason filmed: a group of rednecks shooting humans who are still alive and tied up, who are then reanimating as zombies. They then use them as zombie shooting targets. As the movie ends, Debra wonders aloud if humanity is worth saving.

Resident Evil: Extinction

(2007)

This is the third RESIDENT EVIL film, where Alice, along with a group of survivors, tries to travel across the Mojave Desert to Alaska to escape zombies.

Dr. Sam Isaacs maintains Alice's capture as the corporation's top priority and tries to persuade the Umbrella board that he can use her blood to develop a permanent cure. But the new Umbrella chairman, Albert Wesker, refuses the idea and orders Isaacs to use the clones of Alice to create a cure instead.

Meanwhile, Claire Redfield's convoy nears a deserted town, and while searching a motel for supplies, L.J. is bitten. The convoy is attacked by infected crows that were feeding on infected flesh. Alice appears and saves them by using her newly discovered psionic powers, given to her by the Umbrella Corporation in the Alice Program. Alice meets Claire, and gives her a diary that talks about a safe place in Alaska. Umbrella, in the meanwhile, is able to triangulate Alice's location by tracking her use of her psionic abilities. Dr. Isaacs drops off a crate filled with his "new" zombies as an ambush on the convoy. Carlos gets infected by L.J. and sacrifices himself by plowing his truck into the zombie horde, blowing them all up, and giving Alice and Claire time to get the rest of the group to a helicopter. Alice and "K-Mart" (a rescued friend of Alice) use Isaacs' computer to locate Umbrella's underground facility.

Isaacs kills all the facility employees. Alice enters the facility, where she is greeted by the Red Queen's sister, AI, the White Queen, who informs Alice that her blood is the cure for the T-Virus. (For those of you not familiar with the films, the Red and White Queens are holograph projections of Issac's daughter, programmed to protect the system in each Hive.) Alice finds a clone of herself, but it dies. During the final battle between Isaacs and Alice, they are trapped in a laser corridor. The grid activates and slices Isaacs into cubes, but another Alice clone shuts it off before Alice is caught by the lasers. Alice's hologram shows up in front of Wesker, who says she is coming for him and all of Umbrella Corporation. Standing beside her clone, Alice looks out onto the hundreds of pods containing her developing clones, and the movie ends. An army of Alice.

Zombie Strippers

(2008)

ZOMBIE STRIPPERS is a comedy film written and directed by Jay Lee, starring Robert Englund, Jenna Jameson, and Tito Ortiz, and is loosely based on Eugene Ionesco's classic play *Rhinoceros*.

This film opens with a news montage explaining that The U. S. Congress has been disbanded and that the United States is involved in many wars all at once, as there are not enough soldiers left in the world to fight zombies.

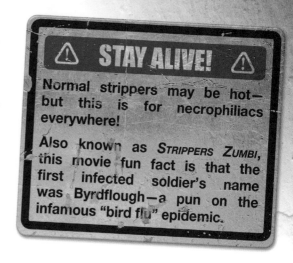

STAY ALIVE!

Normal strippers may be hot—but this is for necrophiliacs everywhere!

Also known as *STRIPPERS ZUMBI*, this movie fun fact is that the first infected soldier's name was Byrdflough—a pun on the infamous "bird flu" epidemic.

This low budget film stars porn star Jenna Jameson and actor Robert Englund. It is not a adult film, but more of a spoof on the zombie genre.

To solve the situation, a secret laboratory run by Dr. Chushfeld has a virus to re-animate dead Marines and send them back to war. However, it has infected test subjects and scientists, and they are at risk of escaping the lab. A team of Marines only known as "Z" Squad is sent in to kill the zombies. One of the Marines is bitten but escapes, and ends up in an alley outside an underground strip club named Rhino. The Marine becomes a zombie and then goes into the strip club. The club is owned by Ian Essko (Robert Englund). When his star dancer, Kat (Jenna Jameson), is attacked by the Marine, she becomes an even more popular dancer as a zombie than she was as a human.

One at a time, the human strippers become zombies, and during private dances, the zombie strippers bite their customers. Essko tries to keep the zombies in a cage in the basement, but eventually, as the zombies escape, the "Z" Squad bursts in to shoot them. We then discover that the zombies were allowed to escape in the first place by the Bush Administration (serving another term), in the hopes that the ensuing zombie plague would distract the public over the failed war effort and the worsening economy. Additionally, one reviewer mentioned on the finale, "...necro-erotic parade of absurdity that culminates in a predictable film-ending anti-zombie raid by the Z-Squad, an elite group of undead-killing military folk–many of whom are inexplicably scantly clad." With plenty of nods to famous zombie films and titillation, the movie also takes jabs at stereotypes—like strippers are not (quite) as dumb as people think by having Jameson's character reading a book of Nietzsche when we first see her.

I am Legend

(2008)

This modernized remake from Warner Brothers, starring Will Smith, is a retelling of the classic story *I am Legend* (equally as good, but of course greatly updated) and its remake called OMEGA MAN by Peter Matheson. The inhuman creatures that military virologist Dr. Robert Neville examines are chemically altered humans who attack other people and have metamorphosed into a mixture of vampire and zombie.

Victims of a genetically-engineered variant of the measles (originally meant as a cure for cancer) mutated into a lethal strain. It spread throughout the world, wiping out ninety percent of humanity. Neville, immune to the virus, strives to find the cure while scouring the city with his dog. One of the most intense scenes in the movie is when Smith's character follows his dog into a dark building and finds himself totally surrounded by the mutated people. Another section in the movie, shot at the Brooklyn Bridge, cost the studio five million dollars, the most expensive scene ever filmed in New York City.

Neville spends his off time working out, hunting for food in thousands of empty apartments, and playing golf off the deck of a ship. He has fortified his condo/lab, and as he stumbles across what he thinks is the cure, he captures a young specimen and injects her with it, only to be surrounded by her family. The movie provides an alternative ending on CD, which offers a bit more hope for the future. The cinematic release was much bleaker—depending on which point of view you take regarding the people in the film.

THE LAST MAN ON EARTH (1964 film), an Italian science fiction by Ubaldo Ragona and Sidney Salkow.

Zombieland

(2009)

In this comedy/action film, zombies have taken over America. A college student, Columbus, leaves Texas. He tells the audience he has survived by following his thirty rules, like always "look in the back seat," "do cardio," and "avoid public restrooms." He tries to travel to Ohio to see if his parents are alive, and gets a ride with a Tallahassee man who is a gun-toting lunatic, bound and determined to get the last Twinkie on the planet. They are soon joined by a pair of girls, Wichita and Little Rock, who are heading to a Los Angeles amusement park they claim is zombie free.

The movie has excessive, but tongue-in-cheek, violence with computer-generated effects of blood splatters. Bill Murray guest stars, playing himself, as the group crashes his home and kills him when he pretends to be a zombie to scare them, ruefully admitting it was not a well thought-out gag. Leaving the Murray Manor after a few nights, and of course giving a four-gun salute to their "host," the girls leave together and are followed by Columbus and Tallahassee. Our motley little band of zombie killers are off to the park, to ride the various amusements while blasting away at hordes of the undead that follow them inside. As if fate rewards them for their valiant last stand, a room full of Twinkies ends up being at the park.

⚠ ZOMBIE FLASH! ⚠

Zombieland 2 (2013, US)

Soon after ZOMBIELAND's release, a 3-D sequel was confirmed by director Ruben Fleischer; but two years later, ZOMBIELAND 2 has yet to arrive, with Fleischer saying in July 2012 that the sequel was stuck in the "not-happening-process." It may yet succeed as a TV show.

The Crazies

(2010)

This is a very well-done remake of the 1973 film by the same name. It was this movie that sprang to my mind when I first heard about the Miami cannibal attack (discussed in Chapter Two), as the "infected" are more like real "mad" people than traditional zombies. This great film stars Radha Mitchell, Timothy Olyphant, and Danielle Panabaker, and was produced by Lionsgate film company. Its opening weekend brought in $16.1 million in the US. The make-up for the film was designed by Almost Human Studios, which provided make-up for other horror films (like QUARANTINE).

Like the original, this movie is about a small town's water supply and its accidental infection with the "Trixie" virus. After an incubation period of 48 hours, this virus gradually transformed the mental state of the infected into that of cold and mindless killers, no matter who the victim was.

The story changed somewhat beyond the initial premise. The local sheriff, David (played by Timothy Olyphant), is at a baseball game and all is normal until a local farmer, Rory Hamill, enters the field with a shotgun. David is forced to shoot Rory. David, and his wife Judy, the town doctor (Radha Mitchell), begin to notice other town residents exhibiting bizarre behavior, especially when a neighboring farmer burns his house down with his wife and son trapped inside, killing them both.

David and his deputy, Russell, investigate the discovery of a pilot hanging dead in the swamp; they discover a military aircraft submerged under the water. Soon after, communication services are cut off when soldiers arrive to take the residents to quarantine at the high school. Everyone is examined for symptoms of infection. Judy is separated from David, as she tries to explain that her fever is due to her pregnancy, but they ignore her. The building is breached by the infected and the military personnel evacuate, abandoning Judy and anyone else left in the examination area (strapped to tables and unable to escape). David escapes with Russell, and they rescue Judy and her hospital assistant, Becca. The four make their way out of town and encounter Becca's boyfriend, Scotty, who tells them that the soldiers have been ordered to shoot anyone who may have been exposed. The group is attacked by a group of infected and Becca dies.

Russell stops a government SUV with a police spike strip, and the driver, who is a government agent, reveals that the cargo plane contained "Trixie," a prototype biological weapon. Enraged, Russell shoots the driver, then threatens both Judy and David. Russell realizes he is infected, and later dies while distracting soldiers at a blockade so that his friends can sneak past them.

David and Judy arrive at a truck stop and escape in a semi-truck. Their town, Ogden Marsh, is destroyed in a massive explosion, and their truck crashes from the resulting shockwave. As the couple walk towards Cedar Rapids, a view from a military satellite highlights first the couple, then pulls back to show the city, and we see on a screen, "Initiate containment protocol."

Resident Evil: Afterlife

(2010)

AFTERLIFE was the fourth film in the *RESIDENT EVIL* saga, and the first to be shot in 3D. The film broke even its opening weekend, making back its budget of $60 million in the U. S. and Canada, and made $236 million overall. Like the others, it again surpassed the previous film's total in the second week of release, earning a worldwide total of $296 million.

This installment of the franchise depicts Alice searching and rescuing the remaining survivors in Los Angeles as they set out to battle against Albert Wesker, the head of the Umbrella Corporation. Chris Redfield, a main villain from the video games, is featured for the first time in this film, as well as a few other key aspects from the video game *RESIDENT EVIL 5* that came out in 2009.

This film opens about five years after the outbreak of the T-virus, and hits the viewer's fast and furious as "Alice clones" break into one of the Umbrella Corporation's headquarters in Tokyo, in a bold attempt to kill Albert Wesker (Shawn Roberts). Wesker escapes and destroys the base, killing all of the clones. The real Alice is aboard his getaway craft, and in a fight, he stabs her with a device that removes her powers—just as the aircraft crashes. However, Alice manages to survive.

Six months later, Alice is in America flying an airplane while listening to an emergency broadcast from someplace called *Arcadia* in Alaska. Alice is attacked by Claire (Alice's best friend from the previous films), who has lost her memory. Alice removes a device stuck on Claire's chest that has driven her mad. They travel to the ruins of Los Angeles, where they find a group of survivors living in a prison surrounded by swarms of zombies. With their help, Alice later comes to find that *Arcadia* is not a city, as they'd previously thought, but a cargo tanker off the coast. Alice and the survivors decide to find an alternate means to make it to the *Arcadia*.

As zombies tunnel into the prison through the sewers, Alice, accompanied by others, goes deeper into the prison to retrieve additional guns from the arsenal. Zombies swarm and break down the gate, allowing the zombies outside to enter the facility. Alice and her group use a boat and board the *Arcadia*, finding it abandoned, until they discover K-Mart and more of her friends under the floor in stasis. As Alice explores more of the vessel, she stumbles across Wesker, who is much stronger now, but the T-virus is in control of him. He believes that by eating Alice he will overcome it, since she was the only one who successfully bonded with the T-virus.

Alice defeats Wesker with help from K-Mart; Wesker then flees. He activates a bomb that he'd left onboard the *Arcadia*; however, Alice had already discovered said bomb earlier and had placed it on Wesker's plane. In the distance, we see a parachute in the sky. And as they start to feel safe, Umbrella assault helicopter squadrons suddenly appear.

STAY ALIVE!

Don't eat the green glowing ice cream, no matter how fantastic you think it might taste!

The author found this film to be great, if only for the reason it was told from such a unique point of view—from the eyes of a zombie, a suffering anti-hero that only wanted to survive.

Aaah! Zombies!!

(2010)

The movie *Aaah! Zombies!!* has also been released with the title *Wasting Away,* as a zombie comedy. When a ragtag group of friends add a gooey green fluid from a barrel they found to their ice cream, they become infected with a zombie virus. Oblivious that they have become infected, they are puzzled by why people run screaming from them. Of course, the military shows up, and a reject from the military who befriends the group reveals what they all are. He valiantly tries to lead them to a safe utopia where they can exist peacefully.

What is unique about this film is the method in which the viewer sees the action. Added also is the fact that the story is told primarily from the zombies' points of view, this accomplished in high speed (almost cartoon-like) voices, confusing the central characters. Color footage shows the action from the zombie point of view in which they see themselves as still normal. Other segments of the movie will suddenly switch to black and white footage, showing the points of view of *normal* people, and the zombies look decayed and slow moving.

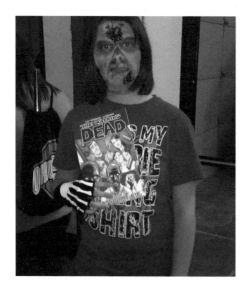

A fan wearing a *Walking Dead* t-shirt.

The Walking Dead

(2010)

The Walking Dead mega popular AMC television series premiered in October of 2010. Six million viewers caught the second season finale of the television show in 2012. The series is based on a comic book by the publisher, Image Comics. The comic was created by writer Robert Kirkman and artists Tony Moore and Charlie Adlard. Robert Kirkman, an admirer of Romero, has contributed to the recent popularity of the genre in comics, first by launching his self-published comic book *The Walking Dead*, beginning in 2003, chronicling the story of survivors in a world overrun by zombies; then by writing *Marvel Zombies* in 2006 and its sequels: *Marvel Zombies: Dead Days*, *Marvel Zombies vs. The Army of Darkness*, *Marvel Zombies 2*, and *Marvel Zombies 3*.

The gritty black-and-white comic book series, *The Walking Dead*, began in October of 2003, and, like the television show, chronicled the life and struggles of former sheriff Rick Grimes, his family, and other survivors who joined him along the way during a zombie apocalypse. *The Walking Dead* received the 2010 Eisner Award for Best Continuing Series at San Diego Comic-Con International.

Though we all love to watch the zombies meet their ends, the television show is not primarily about zombie death; it is about the trials of life and how humanity faces adversity and triumphs under disastrous circumstances—how we face death, keep moving forward, and encourage one another to live are the issues tackled by writer Robert Kirkman. Creator Robert Kirkman and Charles H. Eglee, who are currently writers and executive producers of the TV show, say escapism is essential. Kirkman says:

> At a time when everyone
> is worried about whether
> or not they are going to be
> able to pay their mortgage
> or afford their groceries,
> it's oddly comforting to
> be able to sit down at the

end of the day and watch a television show where they can say, "My life kinda sucks, but at least I'm not getting chased by zombies."

The television show is so popular it has been translated into both Portuguese and Spanish. Kirkman approved the use of the story and name for a video game by Telltale Games on April 24, 2012. *The Walking Dead* has won the Emmy® award for Outstanding Prosthetic Makeup for a Series, Miniseries, Movie, or a Special.

Also, it is interesting to note that there is an infantry battalion of the United States Marine Corps (1st Battalion 9th Marines) nicknamed "The Walking Dead."

Actor Chandler Riggs

I had the pleasure of meeting one of the cast members of *The Walking Dead* just a few weeks before the third season aired. Chandler Riggs, the young boy growing up in the apocalyptic series, is a brilliant actor who plays the part of Carl Grimes.

Chandler was pleasant to talk to, but unfortunately wasn't allowed to be interviewed as the series and its actors are kept closely guarded so as not to spoil future plot details. He did sign a photo and posed for a picture with me. For a youth who had spent the prior day filming and then flying in to meet fans Saturday morning at Scarefest in Kentucky, he was full of energy, bouncing and smiling all day while greeting a long line of fans. He admits to being a

Actor Chandler Riggs with author at Scarefest (2012). Note the photo held by the author showing the characters Carl and Rick Grimes from the television show. *Photo courtesy of author.*

lot like his character, saying, "…a lot like Carl—his personality, and of course I look like him!"

THE WALKING DEAD is not his first acting role, nor first experience with zombies. In 2006, he was in JESUS H. ZOMBIE as part of the zombie ensemble. He is pretty nonchalant about the gore and other scary parts. When asked if it bothers him he said, "As long as you know that it's fake and you see them do all the make-up, it's not that scary." Right before the television series, in 2010, he was in the film THE WRONGED MAN. Chandler was nominated for his performance as a Lead Actor in THE WALKING DEAD at the 33rd Young Artist Awards. One of the moments he loved most, however, was celebrating his last birthday on set after filming, complete with cake, cast, and crew. When asked about what he would miss most in the event of a real zombie apocalypse, he says, "video games. I love video games!"

For more *behind the scenes* features for the show, I suggest people visit the official website at http://www.amctv.com/shows/the-walking-dead.

WALKING DEAD tattoo art by Art on You.
Photo courtesy Storm Anderson.

World War Z

and

The Zombie Survival Guide

Max Brooks, who wrote *The Zombie Survival Guide* and *World War Z: An Oral History of the Zombie War*, points out that zombies are:

> ...the only American monster we have....
> They are to monsters as jazz is to music.

"In my misanthropic paranoid worst, my biggest nightmare is that other people will become the monsters I've always suspected and feared they have been," he told the *Wall Street Journal;* but not everyone agrees. "Zombies are a big threat," Brooks says. "They're not a small threat. Werewolves are a small threat. You go to a town, there's a dude who walks around late at night, and you wake up in the morning and your chickens are dead. But zombies are apocalyptic. They're an existential threat."

Fantasy Crosses Reality

Zombie fiction is now a sizeable sub-genre of horror, usually describing a breakdown of civilization that occurs when most of the population becomes flesh-eating zombies—a zombie apocalypse.

CHAPTER FOUR

How to Survive a Zombie Attack instruction. *Photo by Acey Duecy.*

Zombies
as a Warning

La Salle University philosophy professor Stephen Joel Garver says zombies resonate with so many people because of the Great Recession:

> We live in a time where we talk about "zombie banks" and "zombie corporations"—the economic equivalent of the walking dead points to a bigger anxiety about an "apocalypse" in which the familiar secure structures of our lives fall apart—in the face of economic collapse...

There are others who largely voice the zombie apocalypse has a fictional warning to people about the very real possibility of a rapidly spreading pandemic disease, such as H1N1 and AIDS. This is shown in *RESIDENT EVIL*, *28 WEEKS*, and *THE WALKING DEAD*, as well as the Max Brooks' novel *World War Z*. The situations presented have had such an impact in the minds of people, far beyond pop culture. The idea of zombies as a metaphor for the outbreak of pandemic disease has even been the subject of a Canadian medical researcher who published a chapter about zombie epidemiology in a serious 2009 academic book on disease modeling (as mentioned earlier), titled *When Zombies Attack!: Mathematical Modelling of an Outbreak of Zombie Infection*. Max Brooks says every time we turn on a TV, everything we see can be disas-

Zombie Uncle Sam. Artwork by author.

trous. The looming and real threat of devastation on the world is more present to the people of the world, and paranoia is a social contagion in and of itself.

As modern society has conveniences, such as widespread international travel, it means that disease can spread in days and can adapt and become immune to cures more and more rapidly; pandemic viruses are among the worst. Imagine for a moment just how quickly an infected person can travel by jet from one point on the planet to another, then by subway or bus to any location. They might then cough on or touch more people in a day than the average person in the time of the worst pandemic in history—Black Plague—saw during their lifetime. The 1918 Spanish Flu, for example, killed 500 million people, which was over one-quarter of the entire Earth's population.

Emergency preparedness is something I personally believe people should be proactive with. Even if you laugh at the symbolic silliness of a zombie outbreak causing the end of the world as we know it, consider real events outside of H1N1, like Hurricane Katrina and Tropical Storm Sandy. Quoting the *Preparedness 101: Zombie Apocalypse* blog written by Assistant Surgeon General Ali Khan of the CDC, he says:

Melbourne Zombie Shuffle. (June 14, 2008.) *Photo by Andrew Braithwaite.*

There are all kinds of emergencies out there that we can prepare for. Take a zombie apocalypse for example. That's right, I said z-o-m-b-i-e a-p-o-c-a-l-y-p-s-e. You may laugh now, but when it happens you'll be happy you read this, and hey, maybe you'll even learn a thing or two about how to prepare for a *real* emergency…. The rise of zombies in pop culture has given credence to the idea that a zombie apocalypse could happen. In such a scenario, zombies would take over entire countries, roaming city streets eating anything living that got in their way. The proliferation of this idea has led many people to wonder "How do I prepare for a zombie apocalypse?"

Well, we're here to answer that question for you, and hopefully share a few tips about preparing for *real* emergencies too!"

The Zombie Apocalypse page on the CDC website (which has a link to the CDC's Emergency Preparedness and Response page: http://www.cdc.gov/phpr/zombies.htm) was posted around the debut of THE WALKING DEAD. (They even have a couple episodes where the CDC shows up—including the finale of season one). As I mentioned in the Introduction, this is linked to the television show

Night of the Living Dead **scene.**

The author's membership card for The Zombie Squad. *Photo courtesy of author.*

by Nat Geo, (National Geographic) *Doomsday Preppers* in extreme sense, as the "prepper community" builds bunkers, stockpiles food, water, and personal arsenals in case of legitimate emergencies of any sort, such as economic collapse, food shortages, or the grid going down. This obsession has gained momentum from thousands of people who are preparing for a doomsday of any type or reason— zombie or not.

Imagine if large groups of people, especially those who previously had vague morals to begin with, were to band together in gangs, roving the streets looking for survival because they did not plan for the disaster— and others did. Does that scenario not echo the likes of *The Walking Dead*? However, the point is not to simply cause widespread panic over the possibility of a devastating pandemic disease, or other disaster; it is a wake-up call for people to be prepared for such emergencies. Hence, The Zombie Squad!

Zombie Squad

Internet fans, myself included, are part of an increasingly growing international group that make up an online forum whose mission statement is:

> Our mission is to make sure you are prepared for any crisis situation that might come along in your daily life, which may include

your home being invaded by the undead menace... to educate the public about the importance of personal preparedness and community service, to increase its readiness to respond to disasters such as earthquakes, floods, or zombie outbreaks.

www.zombiehunters.org

Zombie Squad is a disaster preparation community focusing its efforts towards:

...promoting the importance of emergency preparation awareness and working with local communities around the globe to teach them what is needed to survive whatever crisis may come along, like natural disasters or man-made disasters.

Zombie Squad supports local and international disaster relief organizations and charities, while holding fast to the belief that:

...if you are prepared for a scenario where the walking corpses of your family and neighbors are trying to eat you alive, you will be prepared for almost anything.

Zombie Squad is very serious about encouraging public awareness of the need for survival preparation and contingency planning—and is *not* an overzealous militia group.

The founders respond to this allegation by saying:

[The] Zombie Squad respects and adheres to all local, State, Federal and International laws that we fall under. We require anyone who is involved with the ZS organization to follow all the laws of their land.... The organization is apolitical in nature. We don't support one party or political ideology over another. We have members from all walks of life that come together for one purpose, and that is to survive.

For the record, the Zombie Squad stresses the importance of obeying *all* laws, especially when it comes to weapons. It is the burden of all citizens who decide to arm themselves to be aware of what is legal. Even in a disastrous scenario, law enforcement will be out, indeed, even more so if zombies do show up! As a gun owner well versed in firearms, I am a strong advocate in plenty of range time practice, being responsible, and well educated on safety and first aid.

Zombie Max

Zombie Max Ammunition is an innovative bullet and shotgun ammunition line from the manufacturer Hornady. "BE PREPARED – supply yourself for the Zombie Apocalypse with Zombie Max™ ammunition" is the

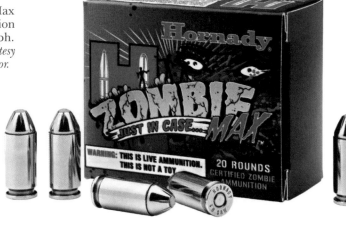

Zombie Max Ammunition photograph. *Photo courtesy of the author.*

company motto. They encourage *prepper*-minded folks to be sure their "bug-out bag" is ready with "nothing but the best!"

I had a call back from Everett Deger, marketing communications manager at Hornady who was delighted by my interest in the company line. He told me that Steve Hornady (the founder) is a fan of THE WALKING DEAD and of the zombie genre in general. He approached the board and marketing department, who took the challenge of designing the product line. Originally made along the lines of "zombie match shooting," such as Cowboy Action Shooting, also known as Western Action Shooting or Single Action Shooting. Western Action Shooting or Single Action Shooting is the same: People dress up in garb and weapons of the time period or style they are enacting. In this case, people dress up as if they are really going to face off a horde of enemies and use the real weapons against zombie targets. Both types of scenarios are, of course, conduct-

ed with the safety of your standard DNR officer handy (Department of Natural Resources, a law enforcement branch in nearly every state).

This cartridge is clearly not a toy, despite its novelty. Deger tells me it is like their "Varmint calibers, not for personal protection like our Critical Mass line, but as is very clearly marked on the packaging, it is not a toy."

DISCLAIMER FROM COMPANY:
Hornady® Zombie Max™ ammunition is NOT a toy (IT IS LIVE AMMUNITION), but is intended only to be used on... ZOMBIES, also known as the living dead, undead, etc. No human being, plant, animal, vegetable, or mineral should ever be shot with Hornady® Zombie Max™ ammunition. Again, we repeat, Hornady® Zombie Max™ ammunition is for use on ZOMBIES ONLY, and that's not a nickname, phrase, or cute way of referring to any body, place, or thing. **When we say Zombies, we mean...ZOMBIES!**

Hornady introduced a zombie bullet last fall with a green painted tip and it was one of their most successful product launches ever, according to Everett Deger.

The *preppers*, and zombie fans and manufacturers, are far from wrong in their proportion of all things zombie being carried over into our real world. Many gun owners crowd around displays of lifelike zombie shooting targets at the National Rifle Association's "Guns and Gear" exhibits at gun shows, with dozens of vendors displaying zombie targets, zombie bullets, zombie paint job services for guns, as well as zombie patches for shooting jackets. Brad Ross, a division manager for Law Enforcement Targets, Inc., a maker of zombie targets, says:

> Firing ranges across the country are offering zombie-themed shooting events, some held as daylight fades for atmosphere.

People get bored with shooting cans or simple store-bought targets, and those offered by Brad Ross and Zombie Industries keep people from being tired of using the same old things. Sales of zombie targets are booming with almost a million targets sold this year, Ross said.

The zombie-themed paint coatings for guns are among the ten most popular camouflage designs offered by DuraCoat Firearm Finishes, said Operations Manager Amy Lauer-Potaczek. Gun stock makers themselves such as ATI (Advanced Technology Industries)

have an aftermarket stock for a Mossberg 12 gauge shot gun called "Zombie Stalker Adjustable Stock," and a matching forend package has a zombie painted on it.

Zombie Targets

Ever wanted to pick up a gun and shoot a zombie to watch its head explode into a gooey mist? Well, now you can. Zombie Industries has made it a reality.

> Each Patent Pending Zombie is cloned in our San Diego, California facility and is hand painted to accurately resemble an infected human that just finished gnawing your neighbor Zed's leg, to give you that realistic look so you really feel the hate. What makes our Zombies so special? They're filled with biodegradable matter, which makes clean up a wee-bit easier…(are you happy, Mom?)…and, oh yeah, let's not forget, they bleed and burst into little pieces of blood-soaked Zombie matter when you shoot them!

The website also includes information regarding their being featured on the Discovery Channel show SONS OF GUNS season finale, in season 3, called "Zombie Gun!"

In this finale episode, Max Brooks, author of *The Zombie Survival Guide*, paid a visit to the show, which first aired on April 18th,

A Zombie Target from Zombie Industries. *Photo courtesy of the author.*

Zombie and friend from Zombie Industries. *Photo courtesy of the author.*

2012. Brooks challenged the geniuses at Red Jacket Firearms to see who could create and build the ultimate zombie-killing gun. The shop divided into Team Max and Team Will; they built two guns, and then later met up in the woods for a nighttime zombie apocalypse shootout. Zombie Industries' targets were used in the show.

DISCLAIMER FROM ZOMBIE INDUSTRIES: With our perfected chemical composition, Zombie Industries is able to offer you the best Exploding Rifle Target on the market today and has proven to be legal in courts throughout the United States. By mixing the oxidizers and fuels in our ZOMBOOM! Exploding Rifle Targets, you are making "black powder," an act that is legal in every state, if it is used in conjunction with small arms for sporting purposes. To comply with law, you may not sell or transfer the ZOMBOOM! to any other person AFTER it is mixed, or use for any commercial reason. Please use common sense when handling any explosive; this product is not a toy, and it can and will cause injury if used inappropriately.

Remember, the use of Zombie Industries' ZOMBOOM! Exploding Rifle Targets are permitted by law but only if used as described in the Simple, Legal, Instructions area below [see the website]. Although targets are lawful, this will not acquit you of any legal ramifications if manipulating any explosive device or product in a negligent or reckless manner. Customers have been charged with "Disturbing the Peace" as well as other crimes when using compositions of this nature, as anything other than a shot indicator. Do NOT augment or make any changes to the chemical structure, as this could generate an unstable product. We assume no liability regarding any use of this product. Use at your own risk. Consider yourself warned!! Zombie Industries' ZOMBOOM! Exploding Targets are safe, legal, and fun.

Zombie Apocalypse Store. *Photo courtesy of the author.*

Zombie Apocalypse Store

"**DO YOU HAVE WHAT IT TAKES TO SURVIVE?!!**" asks the Zombie Apocalypse Store. They have everything from guns, ammunition, freeze-dried foods, to the zombie targets, T-shirts, bumper stickers, Zombie Max ammunition and survival weapons and swords—all of which have been flying off the shelves, as customers are flocking to the store for zombie-killing weapons. Max Brooks even did a book signing there.

Mike Monko opened up the Zombie Apocalypse Store at Polaris and Spring Mountain in Las Vegas, Nevada, following the motto of the Zombie Squad. Despite the fun involved behind the décor and name, this store provides a lot of practical supplies that would be good for any emergency, things from freeze-dried food rations to water filters, to canned meat and first-aid kits.

In case of a small or large scale emergency. Monko says:

> Most people recognize that *zombie* is just a metaphor, and it's a metaphor for many different things: It could be natural disaster, it could be things like earthquakes…. Once you're prepared for a zombie apocalypse, though, you're prepared for pretty much anything.

The Zombie Apocalypse Store
3420 Spring Mountain Road
Las Vegas, Nevada
1- 866-784-7882

The store is open Monday through Saturday, 9 a.m. to 7 p.m., and on Sunday from 9 a.m. to 5 p.m.

Zombie Fiction

As with any other genre of horror, there exists a slew of fiction books on zombies. One of the best is written by a man I had the pleasure of getting to know at Scarefest in Lexington, Kentucky's convention after talking to Chandler Riggs of THE WALKING DEAD.

Jack Wallen

Jack Wallen is the author of several series, like the *I Zombie* trilogy, the *Fringe Killer* series, *Shero*, and the upcoming *The Book of Jacob* series.

Jack Wallen, zombie author.
Photo supplied by Jack Wallen

Mr. Wallen, please tell my readers a bit about yourself and how you first became fascinated by the zombie.

Jack Wallen: Since I was a child, I have been passionate about horror. There is a catharsis within the genre that doesn't exist within any other. I love to scare and be scared. But when Romero brought to life the dead in his classic film, everything changed and the zombie grew into a metaphor for the evolution of the consumer, corporate America, the (un)life of the nine-to-fiver, and the dumbing down of society. To a writer, this is the stuff of magic.

What was it that inspired your work most? Do you have a favorite film?

Jack Wallen: Music inspires me more than anything. But while in graduate school I learned that the artist finds inspiration in all things. Staying true to that, I live life with eyes wide open. I am a watcher and try very hard to not let anything pass me by.

As far as film is concerned, my favorite would be Clive Barker's *HELLRAISER*. Not only is Barker an idol of mine, that film has done more to inspire the horror genre than any other in the last few decades.

What other projects are you involved in?

Jack Wallen: Quite a lot actually. At the moment I am writing a one-off horror novel (I mostly do series), called *Hell's Muse*. Once that book is finished I go back to the *I Zombie* series with *Cry Zombie Cry*. I am very excited about that

book as I have managed
to pull off something no
other author has done (to
my knowledge). I have an
internationally recorded
metal band (Unsun)
recording the title song
for the book and will also
appear in the book as
themselves. I wrote the
lyrics of the song as an
homage to the heroine of
the series.

Once I complete that book,
I will go back to my *Fringe
Killer* series and then I
might be writing a script
for a film.

**Where do you see the future of
zombies leading us?**

Jack Wallen: Straight
to the end of the world.
Seriously—the apocalypse
will come and it will be
brought to you by the
human race. I'd like to
say it won't happen in our
lifetime, but based on our
current trajectory with
madness.... I'm afraid it
will.

Thank you sir for your time!

You may find Jacks books on his
website at www.monkeypantz.net.

Zombie Art

I have had the pleasure of
meeting quite a few talented and
unusual people in my line of work.
Over the years, I used to produce
a magazine (now a compiled book
called *Into the Inferno: The Ninth
Gate Magazine*), and a few years ago,
I interviewed a man who is called
Buzz by his fans and friends. Buzz
is a master of zombie art.

Buzzworks

**Welcome Buzz! Please tell our
readers a bit about yourself, and
how you started Buzzworks.**

Buzz: I am based in
Cleveland, which whether
people know it or not, is
a hotbed for many very
talented Dark Artists.
My interests have always
been on the Darker side,
horror movies and haunted

houses, and the macabre. I am a Wood Patternmaker by trade, and in my spare time, I sculpt spooky art for friends.

I notice quite a bit of your works are inspired by artist Joseph Vargo. Can you relate how you began working together, and are there any other artists you've collaborated with?

Buzz: Joseph Vargo is the main reason Buzz-works. com exists; I was going to events with some of my sculptures and seeing what reaction I got. Joseph and Christine Filipak were at a horror movie con—I

believe it was '98—and we met. He really liked my art and we decided to work together. They have been my greatest supporters and some of my best friends ever since. Christine Filipak even designed my website and various other projects for Buzz-works.com. Now I vend at conventions and feature all of our works. One of the things I wanted to do with my website was promote the many artists in Cleveland. Rich Klink is an amazingly talented sculptor who has produced several exclusive pieces for Buzz-works. They include the zombie bust and graveyard zombie, amongst others. Steve Direggirio is a special FX man who is a huge fan of the Misfits and has had many of his works sold through the band's website and catalog. His "Crimson Ghost" models, "Cyclops," and other great sculptures are available on my site. I have promoted several other skilled artists by getting their work out there.

What do you think is the appeal of various creatures, such as zombies and gargoyles, to fans of horror?

Buzz: Many of my products are Decor, so my customers are decorating their homes with it. It creates a mood. I think this stuff is a universal draw to people who enjoy spooky things. I can't say it is just one type of people—my clientele is so diverse, it is quite interesting to see.

Do you ever do custom work for clients?

Buzz: Absolutely, in many forms. Every Halloween I make full-size props for a local tavern and setup their courtyard. I have a lot of fun with it. My favorite was the "Crypt" I made last year. I have also produced special orders for various things. My custom skull boxes have gone over very well.

Any future plans for Buzzworks looming on the horizon?

Buzz: Several different projects are in the initial planning stages. Joseph Vargo is a constant inspiration to keep moving forward; he never rests on his laurels. We constantly look at new things to get going, I cannot thank him enough!

Thank you for joining us, and keep creating those awesome sculptures!

Buzz: I appreciate the opportunity to speak with you and your readers!

Back in September of 2009 Buzz released a zombie-themed music score called *Zombie Influx*; the debut CD features performances by musicians Nox Arcana, who also co-wrote and produced the CD. Joseph Vargo is a master of ambient haunted house music and co-wrote and produced the tracks along with fellow musician William Piotrowski. As the buzz-works website reveals:

> ...nightmare soundscape creates the horror and panic of a zombie invasion with eerie sound effects, emergency news bulletins, and cinematic music.

With tracks such as "Creeping Death," "Echoes of the Living," "The Pain of Dying," "Flesh Eaters" and "Ravenous," it certainly captures the full range of a Romero style horror flick.

Find out about this and more at www.buzz-works.com.

Corvis Nocturnum (E.R. Vernor)

The author/artist says of his zombie art: "To me, horror art—like zombies—has a few colors in particular associated with it. Color helps trigger feelings, and browns, grays, and blacks are what I think of when it comes to these creatures; red and black for blood and shadows. The red/black colors are especially a tribute to the original horror comics that inspired *TALES FROM THE CRYPT*. These shades symbolize the decay and dirt as

Author's rendition of aspiring zombie actress Angela Tallent before and after.

they rise up from the ground, making me imagine the rot of flesh. This work was inspired while writing the book *Zombie Nation: From Folklore to Modern Frenzy*. I became a fan of *RESIDENT EVIL*, *THE CRAZIES*, and of course George Romero's works, like *DAWN OF THE DEAD*."

So You Want
to be a Zombie?

THE WALKING DEAD'S Special FX Make-Up Designer Greg Nicotero and his KNB EFX Make-Up Artist Andy Schoneberg have laid out a step-by-step video to show you exactly how to do up your own zombie make-up for any Halloween party or Zombie Walk. Visit the AMC official website (http://www.amctv.com/shows/the-walking-dead/make-up-tips) and you will see not only a list of what's needed, but a video link to see the experts demonstrate techniques. The list is made up of mainly common household items and easy-to-find makeup, like:

- Liquid latex
- Uncooked oatmeal
- Liquid food coloring
- Cosmetic sponge
- Tissue
- A hair dryer
- Face powder
- Some type of base foundation makeup
- A grey, black, or greenish eye shadow
- Corn syrup
- Popsicle stick
- Inexpensive paintbrush

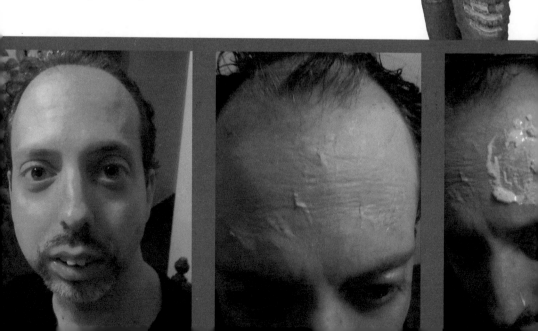

01 Latex stipples the skin and is hardened with the hair dryer and then powder is applied immediately after. This is done by stretching the skin while dabbing the latex on, so when you let it go, it wrinkles.

02 Rotting skin is created by putting the oatmeal on top of the latex, smoothing it out with the popsicle stick and powdered. Dry again.

03 Mix a pack of gelatin with 1/3 cup water or less, cut into cubes, then microwave for ten seconds. Add food coloring, then apply to the bony parts of the face.

04 As it sets, work it with the stick again and rough up the edges for wounds.

05 A sponge around the edges creates texture.

06 By tearing up the facial tissues and adding more latex to the torn flesh area—wrinkle the edges—to make it appear as though it was eaten flesh.

07 Next blow it dry (but do not melt the gelatin).

08 The pale dead skin is completed by adding another layer of latex to the entire face, but avoid the open wounds.

09 Once dry, add the face powder.

10 Add color— mix a base foundation with a little mineral oil and apply with a sponge. Using the darker colors creates depth in the shadow areas and using the green powder makes the wounds look sickly.

11 The last step is to combine corn syrup and red food coloring (or buy fake blood) to splatter the face using the paint brush, and then blow dry.

Note: Take care: Latex hurts when you peel it off!

YOU NOW SHOULD NOW HAVE A ZOMBIE MASTERPIECE!

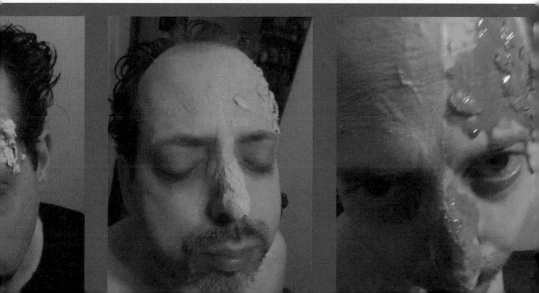

More Zombie Makeup at Scarefest

Scarefest was an intense and fun-filled, long three-day weekend. I set up thinking it would be just like any other horror convention I normally attend to promote my works from Schiffer Publishing and from Dark Moon Press, but even *I* was in for a rare treat. So many people attending got into the fun and excitement of zombies during this event and dressed up like them. A few even stopped at the booth where the winner of Sci-Fy's show *FACE OFF* set up and asked the winning make-up artist to do a real Hollywood-style job on them. I met the friendly young man, Rayce Bird, and having watched the entire show leading up to his winning the contest, it was awesome to shake his hand. He was very down to earth and thanked me and his other fans who came to see him. I watched him airbrush someone's face afterward.

The fans I saw walking by stopped to pose for me and my helpers, hamming it up and truly adding to the experience for all of us.

I am sure over the next few years people reading this book will no doubt see me in Kentucky or at other Zombie events again, and if they bring this book with them, I will be delighted to talk to them and sign their copy! (Zombie make-up required!)

(But Before the End...)

The zombie has been a part of us, fighting to survive beyond the decay of its once-living body, and relentless over time as it mindlessly pursues us—refusing to ever truly die off in either fiction or as a social icon. Other creatures and fads have sprung forth from the creative individuals in Hollywood, but the zombie, despite being relatively new in our world, spin off entertainment in books and film and seem to be a reoccurring idea in more ways than one.

As everything from Max Brooks' books and film, to Colson Whitehead's *Zone One,* with his own post-apocalyptic vision of New York, we are taken along a much more intellectual route than with previous zombies in pop culture that were more low budget and predictable.

The mythos and movies of the current zombie craze echo our inner fears, fears that we hide from by making jokes like: "When the zombies come, I will be ready." But, indeed, it makes you think to yourself, at least on some level—what if? My own research on the science of zombies may not be a defining indication that we are on the verge of a George Romero pandemic tomorrow, but one of these days, a freak accident may well be the cause of something like it. One thing I do know: Those who are ready for any natural or man-made catastrophe stand a better chance of living another day under such circumstances. Until that happens, join me in the dark theatre, and enjoy the adrenaline rush you get from seeing them on the screen!

David Denofreo

I've been fascinated with photography ever since I bought one of the first digital cameras to come on the market. My experience with portrait photography began over ten years ago at private parties and local events. Later on, I started taking photos at burlesque shows, learning to work with limited light and moving subjects, and then moved into the studio where I like to experiment with different angles and setups. Being at a zombie walk is about as close as I'm ever going to get to actually witnessing a zombie apocalypse, and since I'm mainly a portrait photographer, I focus in on the faces. People put a lot of work into creating their zombie personas, and I'm always happy to be there with my camera to capture them. www.blackopalimages.com.

Bob Jagendort

Bob originally comes from New Jersey. He travels extensively and never leaves home without his Sony NEX or Nikon D7000 cCamera. His photos have been published in many other books, the *New York Times*, calendars, and for websites and magazines. He especially enjoys going to the Zombie Walk held in Asbury Park, New Jersey, and the New York City Halloween Parade. Please visit his Flicker site to see more of his work or to contact him directly: http://www.flickr.com/photos/bobjagendorf/.

SELECTED BIBLIOGRAPHY and Further Reading

Ackermann, Hans-W. and Jeanine Gauthier (1991). "The Ways and Nature of the Zombi." The Journal of American Folklore 104 (414): 466–494. doi:10.2307/541551. JSTOR 541551

Bishop, Kyle William (2010). *American Zombie Gothic: The Rise and Fall (and Rise) of The Walking Dead in Popular Culture.* McFarland, Jefferson, North Carolina, ISBN 978-0-7864-4806-7

Black, J. Anderson (2000). *The Dead Walk.* Noir Publishing, Hereford, Herefordshire, ISBN 0-9536564-2-X

Curran, Bob (2006). *Encyclopedia of the Undead: A Field Guide to Creatures That Cannot Rest in Peace.* New Page Books, Franklin Lakes, New Jersey, ISBN 1-56414-841-6

Davis, E. Wade (1983). "The Ethnobiology of the Haitian Zombi." Journal of Ethnopharmacology 9 (1): 85–104. doi:10.1016/0378-8741(83)90029-6. PMID 6668953

Davis, Wade (1988). *Passage of Darkness: The Ethnobiology of the Haitian Zombie.* University of North Carolina Press, Chapel Hill, North Carolina, ISBN 0-8078-1776-7

Dendle, Peter (2001). *The Zombie Movie Encyclopedia.* McFarland, Jefferson, North Carolina, ISBN 0-7864-0859-6

Flint, David (2008). *Zombie Holocaust: How the Living Dead Devoured Pop Culture.* Plexus, London, ISBN 978-0-85965-397-8

Forget, Thomas (2007). *Introducing Zombies*. Rosen Publishing, New York, ISBN 1-4042- 0852-6 (juvenile)

Graves, Zachary (2010). *Zombies: The Complete Guide to the World of the Living Dead*. Sphere, London, ISBN 978-1-84744-415-8

Littlewood, Roland and Chavannes Douyon (1997). "Clinical Findings in Three Cases of Zombification." The Lancet 350: 1094–6. doi:10.1016/S0140-6736(97)04449-8

McIntosh, Shawn and Marc Leverette (editors) (2008). *Zombie Culture: Autopsies of the Living Dead*. Scarecrow Press, Lanham, Maryland, ISBN 0-8108-6043-0

Moreman, Christopher M. *A Modern Meditation on Death: Identifying Buddhist Teachings in George A. Romero's Night of the Living Dead, Contemporary Buddhism*, Volume 9, (No. 2, 2008), 151-165.

Moreman, Christopher M., and Cory James Rushton (editors) (2011). *Race, Oppression and the Zombie: Essays on Cross-Cultural Appropriations of the Caribbean Tradition*. McFarland, ISBN 978-0-7864-5911-7

Moreman, Christopher M. and Cory James Rushton (2011). *Zombies Are Us: Essays on the Humanity of the Walking Dead*. McFarland, ISBN 978-0-7864-5912-4

Morehead, John T. *The Undead and Theology*. (Forthcoming as of this publication)

Newman, Kim. *Nightmare Movies: A Critical History of the Horror Film 1968–1988* (1988), ISBN 978-1408805039

Russell, Jamie (2005). *Book of the Dead: The Complete History of Zombie Cinema*. FAB, Godalming, England, ISBN 1-903254-33-7

Savini, Tom (1984). *Bizarro!* Harmony, First edition, ISBN 978-0517553190

Skipp, John. *Book of the Dead* (1989). Mark V Ziesing; First hardcover edition, ISBN-13: 978-0929480084

Vuckovic, Jovanka *ZOMBIES! An Illustrated History of the Undead. Foreword written by George A. Romero,* St. Martin's Griffin, Original edition (2011), ISBN 978-0312656508

Waller, Gregory A. (2010). *Living and the Undead: Slaying Vampires, Exterminating Zombies.* University of Illinois Press, Urbana, Indiana, ISBN 978-0-252-07772-2

Williams, Tony. *Knight of the Living Dead: The Cinema of George A. Romero.* (2003) London: Wallflower Press, ISBN 978-1903364734

ABOUT THE AUTHOR

Occult, vampire, and paranormal researcher Eric R. Vernor, best known to his fans under the pen name Corvis Nocturnum, has been an invited speaker at the 2006 World Religions Seminar at Indiana-Purdue University, Fort Wayne, a consultant in 2010 for A&E's *PARANORMAL STATES* episode "Satan's Soldier," and a guest panelist at Dragon Con 2011 in Atlanta, Georgia, alongside paranormal and vampire authors such as Michelle Belanger and Rosemary Ellen Guiley. As an official media representative for The Church of Satan, Vernor has appeared on The BET Channels' *THE LEXI SHOW* on The Word Network, detailing the difference between Satanism as a religion versus Devil worship. The author is an artist who lectures on other subjects as well, such as vampires, zombies, secret societies, and Goth culture, debunking the many myths and stereotypes prevalent about dark subcultures at conventions and universities. Vernor has appeared in magazines such as the October 2009 *Penthouse Magazine* article interview on sex and Satanism, *Philadelphia Weekly* as an artist at Germ Gallery (2009), and he occasionally writes for *Dark Gothic Resurrected Magazine*. He is the founder and publisher of Dark Moon Press. Corvis Nocturnum/E. R. Vernor has dual associates' degrees in Business Management and a Bachelor in Criminal Justice. He is currently working on a sequel to *Eerie America: Travel Guide of the Macabre* and a book of myths on vampires, *Vampire Evolution: Myth to Modern Day.*

BOOKS BY
Corvis Nocturnum
INCLUDE:

Embracing the Darkness:
Understanding Dark
Subcultures.
(Dark Moon Press, 2005)

A Mirror Darkly.
(Dark Moon Press, 2006)

Promethean Flame.
(Dark Moon Press, 2008)

Allure of the Vampire:
Our Sexual Attraction
to the Undead.
(Dark Moon Press, 2009)

Cemetery Gates: Death and
Mourning through the Ages.
(Schiffer Publishing, 2011)

I. Lucifer: Exploring
the Archetype and
Origins of the Devil.
(Schiffer Publishing, 2011)

Satan's Minions:
Fallen Angels, Demons
and Other Dark Creatures.
(Dark Moon Press, 2011)

Walking the Path of
the Ancient Ways:
Pagans in Their Own Words.
With Andrieh Vitimus.
(Dark Moon Press, 2012)

Haunted Asylums.
(Schiffer Publishing, 2012)

Most Haunted:
Scariest Places on Earth.
(Dark Moon Press, 2012)

The E.R. Vernor:
Into the Inferno.
(Dark Moon Press, 2012)

Goth Girls, Vampire Vixens
and Satan's Sirens.
Introduction by Gavin Baddeley,
Corvis Nocturnum, and *Old Nick*
Magazine.
(Dark Moon Press, 2012)

Eerie America:
Travel Guide of the Macabre.
With Kevin Eads.
(Schiffer Publishing, 2013)

Zombie Nation:
from Folklore to Modern Frenzy.
(Schiffer Publishing, 2013)

Dark Visions:
The Art of Corvis Nocturnum.
Introduction by Joseph Vargo,
Corvis Nocturnum.
(Dark Moon Press, 2013)

PRAISE FOR E.R. Vernor's WORKS

Haunted Asylums

Corvis Nocturnum's book *Haunted Asylums* is a glimpse into these historic asylums, and reminds us that the patients housed within were real people and not just faceless figures in a horror story.
~Eilfie Music, Paranormal Research Society

Satan's Minions: A Guide to Fallen Angels, Demons and Other Dark Creatures

Take a walk if you dare on the shadow side in this devilishly delightful collection of entities who have mischief and malevolence on their minds. Packed with information and lore, *Satan's Minions* educates as well as entertains; a winning combination that makes for a guaranteed page-turner!
~Rosemary Ellen Guiley
The Encyclopedia of Demons & Demonology

I. Lucifer: Exploring the Archetype and Origins of the Devil

Corvis Nocturnum has done an admirable job tracing the genealogy of the devil from pre-Christian mythologies, through the witch-hunts of early modern Europe, and into the Satanic Panic of the modern era. *I. Lucifer* is a truly ambitious project.

~Joseph Laycock, PhD
Boston University, Religion and Society
Vampires Today: The Truth about Modern Vampirism

Corvis Nocturnum has, with this book, given the reader a whole new way of looking at the Devil. *I. Lucifer: Exploring the Archetype and Origins of the Devil* is, in my opinion, the most comprehensive look at the creation and evolution of this key demonic figure, who has for so many generations frightened and captivated mankind's imagination, to date. This is no small statement on my part. I too am one who has, with my own writings, spent much time visiting with and studying this character or characters that is Satan, Belial, Lucifer, etc. However, this book taught even me a thing or two new about the Devil.

~Hydra M. Star
Fiction writer and columnist
Belialian Woman for *Horrotica Magazine*

Promethean Flame

Promethean Flame traces varied threads of free thinking as practiced by rampant individualists, sorcerers, rogues, and creators, as well as secret societies, also touching upon how their inextinguishable sparks continue to impact our contemporary culture in both cinema and music. It will kindle your desire to delve even more deeply into these fascinating people.

~Magus Peter H. Gilmore
High Priest, Church of Satan

Cemetery Gates: Death and Mourning Through the Ages

Dying is no longer a part of our politically and socially correct society. The Rites of Death, once known by the entire tribe, have become hidden secrets that today fill the hearts of man with dread. As with his previous works, Corvis Nocturnum not only rips the lid off of dark subjects, but lays them at our feet in a comprehensive manner to be observed and understood. *Cemetery Gates: Death and Mourning Through the Ages* is a fascinating book that sheds light upon our final inevitable Rite of Passage and our quest for the proof of an afterlife. Utterly fascinating!

~Rev. Tim Shaw
Host of the *Black Cat Lounge Radio Hour*

It's not easy to take a subject like DEATH and turn it into a book that is actually enjoyable and hard to put down. *Cemetery Gates: Death and Mourning Through the Ages* does just that. It is a fascinating look into all aspects of death from crossing over, to burial rites and customs, the afterlife—and everything in between. If death were a color, most would see it as black, but author Corvis Nocturnum paints death in a colorful spectrum that is pleasing to the eye and the soul.

~Marla Brooks
Workplace Spells and *Animal Spells and Magick*

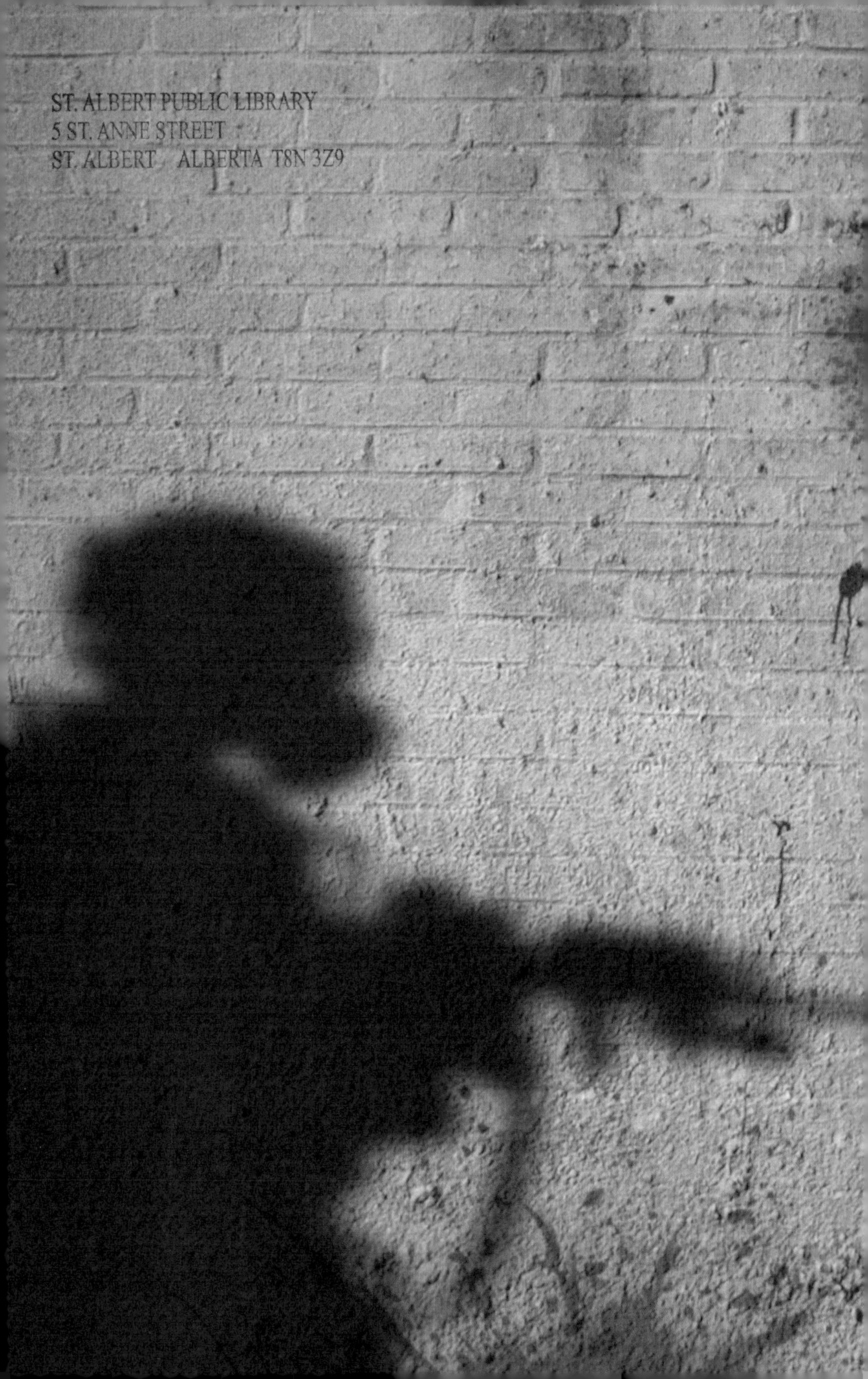